My Sister, My Love

by
Lucille Iremonger

WILLIAM MORROW AND COMPANY, INC.

New York   1981

Library of Congress Cataloging in Publication Data

Iremonger, Lucille.
My sister, my love.

1. Byron, George Gordon Noël Byron, Baron, 1788-1824, in fiction, drama, poetry, etc. 2. Leigh, Augusta, 1784-1851—Fiction. I. Title.
PR6017.R45M9   1981   823'.914   80-21357
ISBN 0-688-00055-X

Printed in the United States of America

First Edition

1 2 3 4 5 6 7 8 9 10

BOOK DESIGN BY MICHAEL MAUCERI

My dearest love, I have never ceased, nor can cease to feel for a moment, that perfect and boundless attachment which bound and binds me to you, which renders me utterly incapable of *real* love for any other human being —for what could they be to me *after you*? . . . I can never be other than I have been; and whenever I love anything it is because it reminds me in some way or other of yourself.

—*Lord Byron to the*
Hon. Augusta Leigh,
May 17, 1819

❧ PREFACE ❧

I have had much kind help in my researches for this book, and am glad to have an opportunity to express my gratitude in these pages.

Senator Premote of Venice was most helpful to me in my efforts to establish the precise, and still disputed, situation of the Palazzo Mocenigo, which Byron inhabited in that enchanting city; as was Professor Montuori, Director of the Istituto Italiano di Cultura in Belgrave Square, London, after Mrs. Emilio Sanna had kindly introduced me to him.

In Pisa my husband and I were most courteously received by the public officials now in occupation of the Palazzo Lanfranchi, and were allowed to range at will through the finely decorated rooms of this charming little palace and see Byron's favourite room, in which he worked on *Don Juan.*

Mr. Brian Loughbrough, Arts Director, City of Nottingham Leisure Services, was helpful in arranging for our visit to Newstead Abbey to refresh old memories, and Miss Pamela Wood, Keeper in charge of the Abbey, was most knowledgeable and cooperative in showing us round.

The County Archivist of the Suffolk County Council, Mr. William Serjeant, also helped me in my efforts to establish whether any trace remained of Augusta Leigh's house at Six Mile Bottom in Cambridgeshire, as did the Assistant County Librarian in the County of Cambridgeshire, Mr. Andrew J. Armour, F.L.A.

June, Marchioness of Aberdeen and Temair, M.B.E., and the late fourth Marquess took us on a memorable visit to

Gight Castle, famous in Scottish legend and once owned by Byron's mother.

Dr. J. C. Macaulay, M.D., F.R.C.P., was, as ever, most generous in giving me the benefit of his great knowledge with regard to the possible cause of the fits from which Lady Caroline Lamb's son suffered, and which may have been the result of an extremely rare medical condition.

I also owe warm thanks to the Reverend F. W. H. White of St. Mary's Vicarage, Harrow-on-the-Hill, who not only responded most kindly to my inquiries as to the whereabouts of the grave of little Allegra, Byron's illegitimate daughter, but sent me a photocopy of the entry giving the date of her burial as September 10, 1822, and, interestingly, an erroneous statement as to her age at her death. Then the Reverend Canon D. H. Williams, M.A., Rural Dean of Bulwell and Rector of Hucknall, helped me with information as to the person whose initials B.B. appear on the memorial plaque to Allegra Byron in Hucknall Parish Church—a lady not connected with the Byron family, but named Blanche Byron.

My warm thanks go to John Murray's, the publishers, and especially to Mr. John R. Murray for showing me and my husband Byron treasures at 50 Albemarle Street, London, including the shirt, once owned by King George II, which he wore at his wedding. I must also thank John Murray's for permission to quote extracts still in copyright from unpublished manuscripts, including John Cam Hobhouse's diary; an original letter in Augusta Leigh's hand; a letter from Douglas Kinnaird, the banker; the manuscript diary of Dr. Bruno, Byron's deathbed physician; a letter from George Finlay; and a letter written by Prince Mavrocordatos. I also owe John Murray's thanks for permitting me to make brief quotations from Leslie A. Marchand's invaluable three-volume biography, *Byron*; from the Marchesa Iris Origo's remarkable work, *The Last Attachment*; and from *Byron—A Self-Portrait*, edited by Peter Quennell. I am grateful, too, to

8

the Oxford University Press for permission to make brief quotations from *The Letters of Percy Bysshe Shelley*, edited by F. L. Jones and published by them.

It also gives me great pleasure to thank my editor, Hillel Black, of William Morrow, New York, my American publishers, for his percipient comments and suggestions, and my agent, Bruce Hunter, of David Higham Associates Ltd., for his unfailing encouragement and understanding.

I am particularly happy to give my thanks to my daughter Pennant, Mrs. Nicholas Huskinson, for her help in many, and imaginative, ways. My husband, as always, gave his unique and priceless support and help at every stage of the work, and it is impossible for words to express my gratitude to him.

—LUCILLE IREMONGER

34 Cheyne Row
Chelsea
London SW3 5HL

CHAPTER

❦ 1 ❦

Lord Byron was on his way to bury his mother; and he could feel nothing but hatred for her.

Byron sprawled in his carriage as it lumbered from London to Newstead Abbey in Nottinghamshire. He had taken even more care of his appearance than usual that morning, and was pleased with it. His dark coat set off the pallor of his skin, already too pale from the purgatives he used so excessively and from an almost exclusive diet of potatoes and vegetables. He had arranged his reddish, dark-brown hair, fresh from its curlpapers, before the mirror so that it clustered round his forehead, and admired his finely cut straight nose, his full, loose mouth, which turned sulkily down at the corners, his large, bright eyes, with lashes as long as a woman's, under the well-marked brows, and his strong chin with a cleft in it. One eye was smaller than the other, and his ears had no lobes—a pity, but few people noticed, he was sure. Now he sat scowling; biting the nails of his very small, very white, bejewelled hands.

It was August 1811, and the sixth Lord Byron, aged twenty-three, had just returned from a two years' tour of the Near East, which he had begun as soon as he had reached twenty-one, and taken his seat in the House of Lords. In spite of already frighteningly large debts, he had managed to lay his hands on the money for the expedition. Hanson, the solicitor who managed his estate and answered to his guardian, Lord Carlisle, had been so slow about producing any cash that he had been obliged to borrow from Scrope Davies. Dashing and reckless as ever, Scrope had signed a bond for him for four thousand eight hundred pounds.

Byron had gone abroad, he thought, as much to get away from his hated mother as for enjoyment. Oh, he had written to her dutifully enough. He had even sent her gifts, as well as the mementos she was to keep for him, like the three-foot-long plait of hair given him by his Spanish landlady in Seville. For himself he had brought in his luggage marble relics, a silver funeral urn, four Athenian skulls, a collection of live tortoises, a phial of Attic hemlock, and the manuscript of his poem, *Childe Harold's Pilgrimage.* For her there was a shawl and a great deal of attar of roses, which he had promised her. Yet never for a moment had he forgotten the nightmare of their life together.

The end had been characteristic of her. Hanson had told him in London that his mother had fallen down in a fit brought on by rage on opening the upholsterers' bills he had run up before leaving England. The upholsterers had taken two years to send them, waiting for his return. The bills were for fifteen hundred pounds, and that was a lot, of course, for fitting up rooms he didn't mean to use much. Then, halfway on the journey to Newstead from London, a messenger had met him with the news that she was dead. So like her, to put him in the wrong to the last. She was only forty-six, too young to die. He had been born when she was exactly as old as he was now, twenty-three.

He remembered her as he had last seen her, two years and four months ago, with her great face disappearing into two double chins, and her gross arms, rolling towards him with her clumsy gait, overdressed as always, to say good-bye to him. He had flinched from her embrace.

Now the carriage was entering the Abbey grounds. His heart melted, as it always did, at sight of the Abbey. Rundown or not, it was his and he loved it, stretching there before him with all its Gothic splendours. There was the great ruined chapel, where the monks had once prayed, and the ornate fountain, which had been moved from the cloisters to the front of the Abbey. At once Fletcher, his valet, jumped down from the box to open the carriage door for him, and young Robert Rushton, his page, came running out of the Abbey.

Byron got down from the carriage. He was not tall, only five foot eight inches, but his body was compact and muscular from boxing, fencing and swimming. He had a bad limp, but he moved swiftly, gliding along the ground with his lame foot so that it looked almost as if he were running. When he stopped he planted his sound foot firmly and slid the bad one up to it. There was something a little shocking in the contrast between his handsome face and the clumsiness of his gait. He was a satyr, he used to say bitterly.

Rushton was standing beside him, saying, "My lord, the housekeeper asks if you will go and see your mother at once."

"No, I'll not see her now," Byron replied violently. He spoke with a slight Scottish burr and a lisp. Then he touched Rushton on his shoulder, as if in apology, and tousled his fair hair. He had been his catamite for three years. His father was one of the farmers on the Newstead estate, and had let the boy come to work for him in the Abbey. Now he slept next to his bedroom. Byron had had him painted full length, standing beside him on the seashore two years ago—the very year in which he discovered that Fletcher had taken the boy to a strumpet. He had dismissed them both in his fury, then relented and taken them abroad with him. He had sent his page home from Gibraltar, saying that Turkey was too dangerous for boys to enter. The real reason was that Robert Rushton would have been jealous of all the boys he meant to have in Turkey, though the Turks certainly did kidnap pretty boys and make eunuchs of them. He paid twenty-five pounds a year for him by reducing his father's rent, and promised to make him independent. A pretty boy, yes—but not as pretty as Nicolo Giraud of Athens.

Now Byron went into the vaulted entrance hall and from there into the old Prior's dining room, looking approvingly at its panelled walls and at the gilded and painted chimney piece, surmounted by the arms of his spendthrift ancestor, known as Little Sir John with the Great Beard. He stood before the portrait of his great-uncle, the fifth Lord Byron, the so-called Wicked Lord, from whom he had inherited the title and the Abbey. Wicked, indeed. He had killed his neighbour and cousin, Chaworth of Annesley Hall, in a duel fought with swords by the light of a single candle in a locked inn room, and been sent to the Tower and tried for murder by his peers in the Lords—and acquitted and freed. His real wickedness lay elsewhere. He had devastated the Abbey and its lands to spite his son—and only because he had eloped with his cousin on his wedding day instead of marrying the heiress his father had marked down for him. He had sold five thousand pounds' worth of ancient oaks, killed and sold for pence two thousand seven hundred head of deer, and disposed illegally of the Rochdale coal mines. He had driven away his wife and settled down with one manservant, a village woman for mistress, called "Lady Betty," and the household crickets for pets. He had trained the crickets to run races over his body, they said. His son had died, and his grandson killed at the battle of Calvi, and then he, Byron, was suddenly the sixth Lord Byron and owner of Newstead Abbey, or what was left of it.

Byron pulled back the rich red hangings he had put up before his departure, and, glancing round suspiciously, went to an elaborate Boulle cabinet. He caressed its smooth surface of walnut, ebony and tortoiseshell inlaid with pewter, then slid down a central panel. Yes, it was there. Smiling, he drew it out, a large skull mounted in silver to form a drinking cup. They had found the skull in the grounds. Doubtless it had belonged to one of the old monks. It held more than a bottle of claret, and no one had ever drained it without falling down dead drunk. He read aloud the verse he had inscribed on the silver.

Start not, nor deem my spirit fled,
In me behold the only skull,
From which, unlike a living head,
Whatever flows is never dull.

Suddenly he put it back in its hiding place, and went determinedly out of the room, heading for the cloisters. He made straight for a memorial standing beyond them. It had been a good joke, that, to erect a tombstone to a dog on the site of the high altar. Poor, beautiful Boatswain, his Newfoundland dog, had gone mad three years ago. He had been gentle to the very end. Why, he had wiped the foam from the dog's lips during his worst paroxysms, and Boatswain had never tried to bite him. He read over to himself the last couplet of the verses he had composed and had had carved on the tomb.

To mark a friend's remains these stones arise;
I never knew but one—and here he lies.

That was the truth. His own mother had been an enemy.
At last Byron returned through the hall and went into the great drawing room, up to the gallery, and then laboured up the twisting stone staircase which led to his private apartments. Quickly he crossed the anteroom, went into his small bedroom, and limped the few steps to the window to gaze at the entrance court and the distant lake. He was standing beside the pretty round table, with drawers circling it and with curved cabriole legs, on which, he recalled, he had written *English Bards and Scotch Reviewers*—his invective had made him dangerous enemies. There, too, was the heavily carved and gilded looking glass over the mantelpiece, and the fine bed he had bought in Cambridge, a little four-poster, barely six feet long but with high bedposts and four heavy gilded

coronets on the corners of its domed silken canopy. There was a cornice to it, too, double tiered, of gilded bamboo from which fell curtains of olive green, looped up with black and red silk cords. Beneath them were the bed-curtains themselves, of greenish Oriental chintz with a pattern of pagodas and palm trees. He was home again. He sank on the bed with a sigh.

Soon there was a timid knock on the door, and the fair-haired page, Rushton, came in. Mrs. Byron, he said, had charged him with messages for her son. Byron listened while Rushton, often incoherently, stumbled through his task. He told his master how his mother, in dreadful pain and mortally ill from she knew not what, had been certain she would not live to see her son again. With her ebbing strength she had fought to hold at bay the disasters he had brought on them both by his mad extravagance. She had struggled against the lethargy of Hanson, the solicitor, and the obstinacy of tenants, to raise the rents, to make the farms pay, to preserve the game, and to reduce the staff. She had charged Rushton, who obviously hardly understood what she had told him, to say that she had refused Hanson's advice to convert her three thousand pounds of capital into an annuity—just as well for him, Byron thought, since she had only two years to live. She had quarrelled with neighbours and tenants in protecting the estate. But in the end the bailiffs had arrived, demanding that she settle Byron's debts. To her shame they had nailed a copy of the debt summons on the door of the Great Hall. The very day the bailiffs came she had written to him, but had said nothing—to spare him. Yet she had been in anguish that the bailiffs might seize her own property—her plate, linen and furniture—and she expected Byron's other creditors to follow Brothers' example. They were after him for his debts of ten thousand pounds, to say nothing of the annuities he had arranged in exchange for cash—approaching three thousand pounds a year—with no funds to meet them. "All this she told me to tell you, my lord, saying she would not see you again."

Byron listened in silence. At the end he dismissed Rushton with a gesture of the hand.

It was late at night before Byron brought himself to visit his mother in her coffin. There was a candle burning in the room, and an old woman sitting beside the corpse, keeping vigil. He gestured her silently away, and she crept out.

Now he stood looking down at the open coffin. There she lay, stiff and cold and expressionless, her great arms bent at the elbows to allow the small fat hands to meet on her massive bust. Those breasts had given him suck. That boxlike frame had carried him in its womb. There was more dignity to her in death than there had ever been in life. At last she was silent, and still. She wore no jewelry in death, not even her wedding ring, that poor thin piece of gold, hardly thicker than wire, which was all that his father had given her. She had lost that, somewhere here at Newstead Abbey, years ago.

What a fool she had been! And the greatest of her follies had been marrying "Mad Jack" Byron. Captain Byron had been the son of Admiral Byron, "Foulweather Jack" to the Navy. *He'd* been no angel, but even he had disinherited his son. Handsome, greedy, unscrupulous, Mad Jack had been a disaster to any woman who crossed his path, and worst of all to his two wives.

He had been a guardsman of only twenty-two when, in the summer of 1778, he had met the brilliant and beautiful Marchioness of Carmarthen, only child and heiress of the last Earl of Holdernesse. She had married her marquis for love, and had had three children by him. When Mad Jack met her she had just come into four thousand pounds a year, and had gone off with him at once. Her marriage had ended in divorce, by Act of Parliament, and she married Byron's father at once and bore him a child a month later. There had been two more children, but only the last, Byron's half sister Augusta, had lived. She had been born in 1784, so she was four years older than he. Her mother had died in childbirth and taken her four thousand a year with her.

Mad Jack was soon on the lookout for another rich wife, and by the spring of 1785 he was haunting the ballrooms of Bath in search of an heiress. There he had met Miss Catherine Gordon, thirteenth laird of Gight, seeking a husband. He was twenty-nine and she was twenty, and had a fortune of twenty-three thousand pounds. On May 13, 1785, she and Mad Jack were married in Bath, and the silly girl had not even insisted on a marriage settlement. (Unlucky thirteen again, for the thirteenth laird of Gight. No wonder she was superstitious, and her son, too.) All her money was his by law.

Mad Jack's new wife was a plain, coarse, awkward Scottish girl with an ugly, rolling gait, a dumpy body, the temper of a termagant and a bad heredity—both her father and her grandfather had been suicides. Soon Mad Jack found her unbearable. Still, he liked her money, and before a year was out most of it had gone, and all the lands she owned in Scotland and everything movable had been sold at knockdown prices. He sold Gight Castle for seventeen thousand eight hundred and fifty pounds—but what was that to Jack's creditors? A mere seven or eight thousand pounds was all that was left.

Catherine, big with child, had followed her Jack to Paris, and watched him spending what was left, while she stayed at home nursing her four-year-old stepdaughter Augusta through a frightening illness. Then, drearily, she had gone back to England with Augusta, put her in the care of the child's grandmother, and, with a pathetic fifty guineas for the lying-in expenses, awaited the birth of Mad Jack's child in a furnished back sitting room on the first floor of number 16 Holles Street, in London, alone. Mad Jack had followed Catherine, and, hiding in the country during the week, visited her on Sundays, when creditors were debarred from arresting debtors, to wheedle what he could from her. (He had already had a taste of the King's Bench Prison, for debt.) Oh, his mother had told Byron of it all often enough, cursing him for following in his spendthrift father's footsteps.

Then Byron had been born, with a caul—and a clubfoot. That had been on Tuesday, January 22, 1788. He had been christened at St. Marylebone Church, with the Duke of Gordon and Colonel Duff of Fetteresso as godfathers. His mother had named him George Gordon after her father. Had *his* father been there? He had never asked her. Now it was too late.

When Byron was nearly three Mad Jack had abandoned his wife and child. He had lived with his sister in France at Valenciennes, and, after a few months of whoring and gaming, died destitute. In his will he had left four thousand pounds he did not possess to his sister, and appointed his infant son, "Mr. George Gordon," his executor, with the duty of paying his debts, legacies and funeral expenses—his last, bad joke. His mother's cries when she received the news could be heard in the street. She had never ceased to love him, and Byron himself loved his memory and yearned for him all his life. But his parents' quarrels had left him with a horror of matrimony which would last his lifetime.

How he had hated his mother—for calling him a lame brat; for scolding him when the moneylenders caught him at eighteen; for falling in love with that French dancing master, Monsieur Louis, and trying to run off to France, taking him, too. Most of all, he had hated her probings—especially about his childhood infatuation for his cousin, Mary Chaworth, when as a shy, fat fifteen-year-old and sick with love, he refused to go back to school at Harrow. He had been heartbroken when he overheard Mary say to her maid, "Do you think I could care anything for that lame boy?" He had rushed out of the Chaworths' house, and home to Newstead. Now Mary was married to her fox-hunting squire, John Musters, and happy, no doubt.

Well, he had kept two secrets from his prying dam. The first had been about May Gray, the maid they had brought from Scotland. Hanson had found out that she beat him until his bones ached, brought her lovers into his room, stayed out late at night so that he had to put himself to bed, took the chaise boys into the chaise with her and drank with them at every alehouse. Hanson had found out, too, that she used to get into bed with him and debauch him—"play tricks with my person," he called it when relating it to Hanson—at under ten years old. Hanson had not informed his mother about *that*. He had been cunning, and told her that May had traduced Mrs. Byron herself. She had been sent packing at once.

The other secret had been about Lord Grey de Ruthyn, the twenty-three-year-old tenant of Newstead, who had leased the estate for five years when he was fifteen. De Ruthyn had asked him to stay, and then attacked him—forced him. He had left the house at once and had never forgiven him, though his mother had badgered him ceaselessly. *She* had fallen in love with de Ruthyn, and made herself ridiculous, lying about her age and throwing herself at him. He had never told her. He had never even told Augusta. It was strange, in a way, that he had minded so. Hadn't he perverted enough boys himself, at Harrow and since? There had been Lord Clare, and his pretty fags John Wingfield, Lord Powercourt's son, and the young Duke of Dorset, and Earl Delawarr.

Then at Cambridge there had been John Edleston, the choirboy at Trinity Chapel, two years younger than he was —though that passion was pure in those days. Edleston had presented him with a cornelian, stammering shyly, his head low. They had met every day they could, summer and winter. Poor Edleston was no gentleman—he had left Cambridge to go into some mercantile business. He would pay for him to become a partner one day, or take him to live with him. He loved Edleston better than any human being—any male human being. They had not met for years now. What he felt for boys was always more passionate than what he felt for girls, even very young girls with all the sweetness of boys. He had had enough of both in the past two years. He had abandoned Constance Spencer Smith of Malta for Teresa Macri, his maid of Athens, that lovely twelve-year-old child. As for boys, what an orgy it had been in Turkey, and best of all had been Nicolo Giraud. He had been clapped again and again, but what was a dose of gonorrhea? His friend and boon companion, John Cam Hobhouse, who had travelled with him on his tour, had been shocked—so much that they parted company. Not, however, before news came that Edleston had been accused of a homosexual offense. Poor Hobhouse. The height of *his* sexual exploits had been seducing a housemaid at Newstead.

Suddenly, as he looked down at his mother, the hatred left Byron's heart, and a feeling of guilt and remorse flooded through him. Poor stupid creature, she had done her best for him. She had tried, God knew, at monstrous expense, to get his foot put right by the best London surgeons. If she had railed at him about his debts it was only because she feared to see him end like his father. She had taken nothing for herself, and sent him to Cambridge with one of the best incomes in the college—able to keep three horses, not one, and two menservants, to say nothing of a bear—and provided for them all in the vacations as well. He had been mad, spending like a lunatic, buying a carriage, and rushing to the moneylenders —over five thousand pounds in debt by the time he was twenty, and over twelve thousand at twenty-two.

She *had* loved him, of course. What if she had been unable to control her temper? Wasn't it the same with him? He shouldn't have been ashamed of her. For that was it, of course. He sighed heavily.

A moment later the door opened, and a plump, red-cheeked woman came in. He recognized his mother's maid, Mrs. Bye. She looked down at him, sitting there in the dark.

"I heard you sighing," she said. "Don't give way, my lord. She's only gone to a better world."

Suddenly he flung his arms about her waist and burst into tears.

"Oh, Mrs. Bye. I had but one friend in the world, and she is gone."

"Hush, my lord," she said before she could stop herself. "That's what you said of Boatswain."

Then she clapped her hands over her mouth. But he had not heard her.

His mother had not yet been buried when the news came that Charles Skinner Matthews, the most brilliant of his Cambridge friends and very dear to him, had died horribly the day after his mother. He had been bathing alone in a pool of the river Cam, and been caught in a bed of weeds at the bottom. They had seen him leap breast high from the water in a desperate attempt to free his arms and thighs from the thick ropes of water weeds, but he'd been dragged down and had drowned. Byron wrote to Scrope Davies at once, "Some curse hangs over me and mine. My mother lies a corpse in this house. One of my best friends is drowned. Come to me, Scrope. I am almost desolate—left alone in the world."

Next morning, as he dressed for the funeral, he swallowed two glasses of brandy. In his mind's eye he saw the church at Hucknall Torkard, hung with those yards of black bombazet and bombazine, the pulpit swathed in black crepe, and the coffin draped with black velvet. At last he threw back his shoulders and went to stand at the Abbey door. The procession was gathering below; at least forty men and women were waiting for the carriages. The undertaker's men wore black scarves round their hats, black cloaks, black handkerchiefs, black ribbons and black stockings. The mutes carried tall staffs draped with crepe. Suddenly he could think of nothing but the cost. He was bled dry, and there would be a mighty bill at the end of the day—why, he had had to order thirty-five hatbands for nearly thirty pounds, thirty-five ties at seventeen shillings and sixpence each, thirty-five pairs of black gloves at over three pounds each, and twenty-nine mourning cloaks. There would be refreshments for them all afterwards, too. The bill would be nearly two hundred pounds for the clothing alone.

Suddenly Byron felt Rushton touch him, and turned round. The pallbearers were behind him, bearing his mother's coffin on their shoulders. He shrank back as they moved slowly to the door and down the steps. He watched, strangely removed, as they put it in the hearse and arranged the wreaths over it. The horses stood, their heads adorned with tall black plumes. Now carriage after carriage moved up behind the hearse, and the waiting men and women got into them. His carriage was the first in line, waiting for him. They would put her in the vault, and he would have to watch. Rushton was standing beside him, in black, too, with a mourning band hanging from his hat, his fair hair bright against his dark clothes. It was time to go.

"Fetch me the gloves!" he cried sharply. Rushton hesitated, and he shouted, "Fetch them!"

Soon Rushton returned with the boxing gloves they used for sparring. At Byron's gesture he removed his hat and coat, and flung them on the floor. Byron did the same. There, where they stood in the hall, Byron laced up Rushton's gloves, and Rushton did the same for him. Then suddenly Byron leaped at Rushton and struck him a violent blow on the chin. Rushton flung up his arms, then recovered and returned the blow. Byron was seized with an intense desire to make him weep, and struck him again. Blood came from Rushton's mouth. It gave Byron pleasure, and he lunged for his eyes but missed. He could see that Rushton was terrified. Byron laughed loudly, then flung away the gloves and went up to his room.

After a while the procession moved off to the church, without him.

*　*　*

Next day news came of a third death—John Wingfield, one
of his pretty Harrow fags. The tears ran down Byron's face,
and he was filled with despair. At times of great emotion he
always thought of his own death. He would make his will.
Newstead Abbey, he wrote, was to go to George Byron, his
cousin and heir to the title. He would leave seven thousand
pounds to Nicolo Giraud of Athens, when he reached twenty-
one. Scrope Davies was to be paid, and Fletcher and Rushton
were to have fifty pounds a year each for life. His body was
to be buried beside Boatswain, and if any of his heirs objected
to that then the whole estate was to go to his half sister
Augusta and her heirs on similar conditions.

Next day Byron awoke to the worst blow of all, the fourth
death. A letter arrived from Ann Edleston saying that her
brother John had died of consumption, at twenty-one. Byron
staggered as he read, and groped for a chair. After a while
he got up. For him there was only one outlet for such pain.
He wrote:

> *Thou too art gone, thou loved and lovely one!*
> *Whom youth and youth's affections bound to me;*
> *Who did for me what none beside have done,*
> *Nor shrank from one albeit unworthy thee.*
> *What is my being! thou hast ceased to be!*
> *Nor staid to welcome here thy wanderer home . . .*
>
> *Oh! ever loving, lovely and beloved!*
> *How selfish sorrow ponders on the past,*
> *And clings to thoughts now better far removed!*
> *But time shall tear thy shadow from me last.*
> *All thou couldst have of mine, stern Death, thou hast;*
> *The parent, friend, and now the more than friend.*

Childe Harold's Pilgrimage needed an ending. He would
close it with this poem. But no one must ever know that it

was written to Edleston, a man. He had given Edleston's cornelian to—who was it?—Elizabeth Pigot, a friendly girl. He must get it back from her. It was all that was left to him of Edleston's love.

He was sitting, still grieving, when he realized that Mrs. Bye was standing before him, holding out a box.

"My lady asked me to give this to you, my lord. She hid it from the bailiffs, she said."

He opened the box. Treasure lay before his eyes: diamond brooches, bracelets, earrings and necklaces, a diamond tiara, a diamond cross, a diamond feather of great beauty. There was a hoop of rubies, and tassels of pearls, pearl bracelets, and pearl necklaces of many strands. There were topazes, and a parure and a necklace and a stomacher of amethysts. Scattered among the jewels were a gold thimble, a gold fruit knife, a gold vinaigrette, a gold and enamel bonbon box, some jewelled fans, and some ornaments of beryl. His mother had never owned these jewels and precious trinkets of gold and silver when she was married to his father. Mad Jack would soon have got them from her and sold them. They must have belonged to old Margaret Duff, his great-grandmother, the rich banker's daughter. She had died ten years before. His mother must have hidden them all that time, these glorious family jewels.

Mrs. Bye watched him as he plunged his hands into the sparkling hoard, and held up one beautiful object after another to the light.

"My lady said you was to give them to the heiress you should marry, seeing that she would not be here to do so."

He laughed. He would sell them all, at once. They would pay some of his debts and hold off the bailiffs for a few months more.

* * *

CHAPTER
❧ 2 ❧

It was August 12, 1812, a year after Byron had buried his mother. Lady Caroline Lamb was standing before the long mirror in her bedroom on the top floor of Melbourne House —the apartment fitted up, for her and her husband William and their little five-year-old son, by William's parents, Lord and Lady Melbourne.

It was a boyish face Caroline was examining so disapprovingly, with large, dark hazel eyes, very white teeth, and short, fair, curly hair falling engagingly about it—a pretty face, if not a beautiful one. She knew that Lord Byron did not care for her figure. It was too thin and angular. He preferred the voluptuous women of the East, with their little feet peeping from their flowing draperies. When they were young, he said, skinny women reminded him of dried butterflies, and when they were old, of spiders. She knew she looked best in boy's clothes, and when she wore her pageboy's scarlet and sepia livery and carried a feathered hat she came, she thought, nearest to pleasing him. He liked her, too, in her scarlet hussar's jacket and pantaloons. He had confided to her that in his Cambridge days he had taken a girl with him to Brighton dressed in boy's clothes and had lived with her there.

Six months ago she had been happy—or at least not unhappy. She was fond of William Lamb. Then, her in-laws, Lord and Lady Melbourne, had plenty of money. Her mother, Lady Bessborough, was blue-blooded, as they called it. So, one way or another, she had all that high lineage and money could give her. She had been happy and content with her life.

In March everything had changed. Samuel Rogers, the poet and a munificent host, with a face like a death's head, had lent her a copy of *Childe Harold*. The first edition had sold out in three days. As soon as she had read it she said to Rogers, "I *must* meet him."

"He has a club foot," Rogers had replied, "and bites his nails."

She had answered, "If he's as ugly as Aesop I must know him."

But when she had been led up to him at Lady Westmorland's house to be presented she was infuriated by the sight of all the other women waiting to meet him, ogling him and trying to catch his eye. Suddenly she had turned on her heel and walked away. She had seen the spark of interest light in his eye. Then when, a few days later at Lady Holland's, he had been announced and presented to her, he begged permission to call on her. After that first meeting she had gone home to write in her diary, "Mad—bad—and dangerous to know." Later she had added, "That beautiful pale face is my fate."

So that had been the beginning. It was he who had made her give him the first kiss in a carriage; he who had tormented her with accusations that she loved William more than him, the poor lame thing, the satyr; he who had forbidden her to waltz since he could not dance and could not bear to see her in the arms of other men. He was a rake—*and* a prude. Yes, she had swept him off his feet, and he had hardly been near the House of Lords since. True, she had met folly with folly. They had become the scandal of London drawing rooms. She had offered him all her jewels if he needed money, had followed him like a shadow during those first six weeks of his fame, had sat by him at supper parties and in ballrooms, and, when she had not been invited, actually waited long hours for him in the street outside, and got into his carriage with him afterwards. She had been mad with love for him—and jealous. Once she had bitten through the glass she was holding at the sight of him bending over a pretty woman, and hadn't even noticed until she saw the eyes of Lord John Russell, Bedford's younger son, on her. They had quarrelled desperately a score of times, and made it up again. No man had ever roused her before, certainly not William. The love token she had sent to Byron, the most private a woman could give a man, a curl of pubic hair, revealed her passion. "Give me the same," she had written, "and be careful, you might cut yourself."

What a lover he had been. He had called her heart "a little volcano," but swore he did not wish it colder. "You know," he had written, "I have always thought you the cleverest, most agreeable, absurd, amiable, perplexing, dangerous, fascinating little being that lives now, or ought to have lived two thousand years ago. I won't talk to you of beauty; I am no judge. But our beauties cease to be so when near you, and therefore you have either some, or something better."

Yes, he *had* loved her. He had told her everything, even his most dangerous secrets. Hadn't he told her about that night in May when he and two friends went at three o'clock in the morning to watch the hanging of Bellingham, the man who had shot and killed the Prime Minister, Spencer Perceval, in the lobby of the House of Commons? They had hired a window opposite Newgate Prison. She could see his face now, as he had described it all. As they walked towards the house he noticed a woman lying on the steps, and he bent and offered her a few shillings. To his astonishment she pushed his hand away, and jumped up screeching, and began to mimic his lameness. He was struck dumb with misery. But as he stood in the window watching Bellingham brought out he forgot even that humiliation. The sight of the man, led out by two warders, held him taut with interest. He bent forward to see him mount the scaffold, then have his eyes blindfolded, and the noose put round his neck. Byron wanted to look away then;

but he wasn't able to. Then came the hanging body, the twitching legs, and, at last, the still body with the head to one side, the neck broken. He wasn't able to take his eyes from it, and only came to himself when his friends, growing impatient, urged him to go with them. They had not been as moved as he was. Then when she had asked him why it had had such an effect on him, he answered bleakly, "Sodomy's a hanging offense." Then out it had all come—about Lord Grey de Ruthyn and his Harrow fags, and Edleston, and Rushton, and Nicolo Giraud. He said it was all over now she had come into his life; and that he was purging it all by telling her. That was how close they had been—no secrets between them whatever.

But now Byron had cooled. He spent too much time with her mother-in-law, Lady Melbourne. He was dancing attendance, too, on Annabella Milbanke, that dowdy country cousin of the Melbournes. It was a pity Annabella had so much to be smug about. She was adored by her parents, since she was an only child born to her mother in her forties. She was a brilliant mathematician. Then she was destined to inherit the estates of her rich uncle, Lord Wentworth, and, exceptionally for a woman, his peerage. There were plenty of men after her money already. The more jealous Caroline grew of Byron's attentions to Annabella and Lady Melbourne, the colder he became towards her. Now she went more often to his rooms in her page's dress, but he did not respond. Yet as recently as July he had been willing to elope with her.

As Lady Caroline was standing before the mirror brooding on her jealousy and love for Byron, there was a knock on the door and, to her astonishment, her mother, Lady Bessborough, entered. Lady Bessborough's face was determined.

"I've come to take you away, Caroline," she said. "I'm taking you to Ireland, *now*. William will follow shortly."

Then followed the scandalous farce that was to become a favourite saga of society gossip. Caroline rushed out of Melbourne House into Whitehall, pawned a ring and hired a carriage. Her mother and her mother-in-law rushed after her, into another carriage, and drove straight to Byron's lodgings. As soon as they arrived a cab was seen to draw up at the door, and Fletcher brought Byron the news that the coachman had a message for him from Lady Caroline. Caroline, it transpired, was at a surgeon's house in Kensington. Leaving the two women in his lodgings, Byron set off at once in his own coach. An hour later he returned, bringing with him a hysterical Caroline, whom he coldly and sternly handed over to her mother and mother-in-law.

The rapprochements that followed at Melbourne House were for Caroline no more than a yielding to exhaustion and despair on her part. She trailed into her bedroom, and sat at the end of her bed. The tears ran down her cheeks, and she made no effort to wipe them away. Then, for the second time that afternoon, there was an unexpected knock on her door. A page entered with a letter. It was from Byron, sealed with his "Crede Byron" seal. "Trust Byron." Could she?

"My dearest Caroline," the letter read. "If all I have said and done, and am still but too ready to say and do, have not sufficiently proved what my real feelings are, and must ever be towards you, my love, I have no other proof to offer. I was and am yours freely and most entirely, to obey, honour, love —and fly with you when, where and how you yourself *might* and may determine."

Caroline could hardly believe her eyes. She dried her tears and went to bed, with his letter under her pillow. Byron loved her, after all, to distraction.

Within a few days Lady Caroline set out with William Lamb and Lady Bessborough for Ireland, still content. Byron was hers; he must be, forever.

Byron was torn between happiness and misery. Newstead had been sold to a solicitor, Thomas Claughton. Claughton had offered a hundred and forty thousand pounds for the whole estate, all three thousand two hundred acres of it—abbey, park, farms, timber and furniture. Byron was relieved, too, to have escaped from his liaison with Lady Caroline. He had made up his mind to break it, but he hadn't told her that. He had his eye on another lady, who would do him more good if his plans worked. He remembered his first meeting with Annabella Milbanke at Lady Caroline's. Lady Caroline had just come in from riding, splashed with mud, and had run out of the room to beautify herself, when he noticed the very small girl sitting alone on a sofa in a corner of the large room. She had seemed out of place, and he thought she was a paid companion.

"Who is that?" he had asked Tom Moore, the Irish poet.

"She's a great heiress," Moore had answered. "You'd better marry her. But I warn you, she's pursued by two ardent suitors, Augustus Foster and William Bankes."

What chance had he, Byron, the impecunious, against the son of the second Duchess of Devonshire, or even against his old Cambridge friend, Bankes, with his eight thousand a year? Still the young woman had attracted him, with her quiet, modest air. She wasn't more than twenty to Caroline Lamb's twenty-seven. She wasn't beautiful, but she was pretty.

"She's Miss Annabella Milbanke," Moore was saying conspiratorially, "the only daughter of Lady Melbourne's brother, Sir Ralph Milbanke. She's brilliant, too, a mathematician, a classical scholar, and a philosopher."

She looked manageable; and he needed an heiress. All his affairs, until Caroline, had been with servant girls or whores, except for his pure boy's love for Mary Chaworth. He'd gotten Lucy, the servant girl at Newstead, pregnant, but the child died at eighteen months. He had been in love—really in love—with Susan Vaughan, the scullery maid, till he learned how she had betrayed him with Rushton, and sent her packing. He had taken it badly, feeling that not even a scullery maid could love the wretched cripple he was. Well, he would try to catch the heiress, and kill the Caroline Lamb affair. Of course he didn't love her, but what of it? Let her love him. If she was no beauty he needn't worry about being cuckolded. He would go on writing to Caroline, keep her quiet till it was done. He knew she was sending Lady Melbourne extracts from his letters; but he had told Lady Melbourne that he was trying not to hurt her feelings. He would write to Lady Melbourne and ask her to help him propose to her niece.

It had been done. Lady Melbourne had written to ask the young woman what qualifications she wanted in a husband. A long and sanctimonious list had arrived from Annabella. Byron had laughed and thrown it aside. Then Lady Melbourne had forwarded Byron's proposal to Annabella. She had taken a long time to reply to Lady Melbourne. Her letter began with a broad hint that she was in love with George Eden, Lord Auckland's heir, the man she had turned down a year ago. She was, she said, "not inclined to return" Byron's attachment.

As he read her elaborate evasions and circumlocutions, his anger nearly choked Byron. He could feel Annabella's fingers on his cheek. No one, he vowed, should know how he felt. He wrote to Lady Melbourne that he hadn't been much interested, and had half-regretted his proposal. He only really regretted losing his chance of being her nephew. What should he do now? Advertise? He ended, "I thank you again for your efforts with my Princess of Parallelograms, who has puzzled you more than the hypothenuse. Her proceedings are quite rectangular, or rather we are two parallel lines prolonged to infinity side by side, but never to meet." She could tell Annabella that he was more proud of her rejection than he could ever be of another's acceptance.

He had met Lady Oxford, he consoled himself, and she was ripe for an affair. She was forty, but she was there; and she had a pretty little daughter, Lady Charlotte Harley, eleven years old with golden hair. He liked her best of all the "Harleian Miscellany," as people called her family, since they said there was a different father for each child. He would set off for Eywood at once.

Byron was still at Eywood in November, making love to the mother and caressing the child, when Lady Oxford received Lady Caroline's tirade. Wild with jealousy of her rival, Lady Caroline was demanding to know where she stood with Byron. He read her letter and replied at once, furiously.

"Lady Caroline, our affections are not in our power. Mine are engaged. I love another. Were I inclined to reproach you I might for twenty thousand things, but I will not." He sealed his letter with Lady Oxford's seal.

Lady Caroline received his letter in Dublin, where she had arrived on her way to England. She fell in a faint, and was put to bed, bled and leeched. They kept her for a week at the Dolphin Inn at Rock, then said she might travel. She arrived at Melbourne House looking ill and frail. From there she wrote to Byron, begging for a meeting. His letter of cold refusal came by return. By the same post he wrote to Lady Melbourne, "How thankful I am to have escaped from marriage with your niece—that would have been but a *cold collation*, and I prefer hot suppers."

Then Lady Caroline grew hysterical, trying to get her letters back from him, but refusing to let him have his, and demanding the return of the presents she had given him. He wrote to her through Lady Melbourne to say that he had given away all her presents in his anxiety to be rid of them—and long before he had met Lady Oxford.

At last, in misery, Lady Caroline departed for Brocket, the Melbournes' country house in Hertfordshire. She was alone except for her little son, Augustus. There was nothing for her to do but ride that cold winter.

In London in December, suddenly there was news of her

dramatic, bizarre revenge on Byron. She had gathered some village children, dressed the little girls in white, and, lighting a great bonfire in the park, made them dance round an ugly waxen effigy of Byron. Then Lady Caroline herself, dressed in the livery of one of her pages, threw into the flames, first, Byron's ring, then his chain, and, finally, copies of his letters. She watched his effigy melt, then slowly collapse in the flames. The village maidens danced, and she declaimed:

> *See here are locks and braids of coloured hair*
> *Worn oft by me, to make the people stare,*
> *Rouge, feathers, flowers, and all those tawdry things,*
> *Besides these pictures, letters, charms and rings.*

Against the wintry background the flames made a bright picture. Above their crackling Lady Caroline's high voice rose eerily.

> *Burn, fire, burn, while wondering boys exclaim,*
> *And gold and trinkets glitter in the flame.*

Then she turned to address her rustic audience.

> *Oh! look not thus on me, so grave and sad,*
> *Shake not your head, nor say the lady's mad.*

Pivoting on her heels, she pleaded,

> *Upon my youthful faults few censures cast,*
> *Look to the future—and forgive the past.*

She ended on a dramatic note:

> *Young though I seem, I quit the world forever!*

The Melbournes had been angry, Lady Bessborough distraught, and Byron, at Eywood, furious. What none of them heard was that as Lady Caroline's thin voice faded into silence a manservant came running out from the house and panted, "My lady, the nurse begs you to come at once to Master Augustus."

She ran up to the house, up the stairs and into the nursery. There was no need for words. The nurse held her son in her arms; he was racked with convulsions, his jaws clenched, his eyes rolled back in their sockets. It was no new sight. The fine big baby whose birth had brought so much joy to her and William, after their first child had been lost in a miscarriage, had had convulsions since his teething days. He could hardly speak even now, and the fits seemed to grow worse. Yet the doctors said that the condition would probably right itself in the natural course of events. But there was no sign of any such improvement so far.

"What is the use of sending for me?" she cried angrily to the nurse. "What can *I* do?"

She turned and fled from the room and the sight of her child.

*　*　*

CHAPTER
⚜ 3 ⚜

Lady Caroline was impossible. She had even forged a letter in Byron's writing so as to extract from his publisher the one picture of him Lady Oxford wanted. Lady Melbourne had got it back for him, but she had to promise a copy of it in return. He had told Caroline that she could have her meeting, but only in Lady Oxford's presence—and that silenced her. He had written to Lady Melbourne, "To the latest hour of my life I shall hate that woman."

Everything was going wrong. Lord and Lady Oxford had sailed for Sicily without him; he felt abandoned. The solicitor, Claughton, who had offered a hundred and forty thousand pounds for the Newstead estate, failed to produce the money, and his creditors were persecuting him. He had only spoken once in the House of Lords, and that merely to present a petition for the reform of Parliament—his swan song. He must either get married to money or go abroad, the only two ways of dealing with creditors. He had ordered Hanson to sell everything at Newstead not committed to Claughton—plate, linen, pictures, a silver vase and a silver cup. Give him a few thousand pounds, and he would stay abroad for ten years— perhaps forever.

Byron was in the depths of despair when Augusta appeared in London, seeking refuge from her own creditors. He had always been fond of this half sister of his, four years older than he and the daughter of his own father, Mad Jack. He had seen her only occasionally when he was a schoolboy, and hardly at all since her marriage to her cousin, Colonel George

Leigh, six years before. They had almost quarrelled when he had attacked their guardian, Lord Carlisle, in his *English Bards and Scotch Reviewers*. He had called him "paralytic and puling." Since his return from the East, however, they had written to each other again. He had invited her to Newstead during that terrible autumn of deaths in 1811, but she hadn't come. Now she had three children—two daughters and a son. They lived somewhere near Newmarket, where Leigh busied himself about the Prince Regent's racing stables. The house itself was a gift from the Prince, and without it they would have had nowhere to live—couldn't even have married. Augusta had never been good at handling money, poor goose, but Leigh was worse. He followed the races from track to track, betting heavily and living as well as his rich companions. Now they were deep in debt, and Augusta had asked him to help her. So he would have, willingly; but Claughton's delays were awkward.

How glad he was to see her. What a pretty woman she was, with her large eyes and her straight nose and her sweet, laughing mouth, and her rich dark-brown hair cascading down in long curls to brush her cheeks and temples. She looked a Byron—looked like him, with those well-marked brows and that long upper lip. She frowned and pouted like him, and she too could not pronounce her r's. She too was shy in company. They laughed at the same jokes. Was she wicked as well? Her figure was soft and rounded—voluptuous.

That July of 1813 he took her everywhere, to theaters and balls and assemblies. He even begged a ticket for her for the masquerade ball at Almack's—Almack's, which had turned away the Duke of Wellington himself for not being properly dressed. She loved it all; and two weeks after the Oxfords had sailed he was quite consoled.

Then Lady Caroline devastated them all. He had been polite to her in private—even had Murray send her a copy of his new poem, *The Giaour*, on publication. But he had been wary of her in public, and she hadn't liked that. That Monday evening he was due to go to a small party at Lady Heathcote's. Augusta hadn't been asked, and he decided to make his excuses. Then, at the last moment, he went after all.

As soon as he entered the room he saw Lady Caroline, and the devil took possession of him. He went up to her and said, "Tell me, is there anything I can say, do, or not do, to give you the least gratification?" She turned away without answering. He was left, obviously snubbed, with at least twenty people staring. He shrugged. Soon the dancers took the floor. He tried to put it out of his mind.

The hours dragged by, slowly for one who could not dance; but at last it was suppertime. He was taking in Lady Rancliffe, when he ran into Lady Caroline again. The music had stopped, and he was standing in a doorway. As he moved to pass her he felt her seize his hand and press something sharp against it. "I mean to use this," she whispered. "Against me, I presume?" he asked coldly and brushed past her. He was shaking with anger, afraid that Lady Rancliffe might have overheard her, but sure it was only one of her usual threats.

After supper he met her again in the same doorway and paused. "Caroline, you should waltz," he said bitterly. "You dance well, and if you do not I will be blamed for it." At that moment Lady Heathcote bustled up, crying, "Come, Lady Caroline, you must begin."

"Oh, yes, I am in a merry humour," Lady Caroline answered; but she turned to Byron as she went and whispered, "I conclude I may waltz *now!*"

"With everybody in turn. You always did it better than anyone. I shall take pleasure in watching you." His tone was caustic. Lady Caroline swept on to the dance floor with her partner.

As the waltz ended Lady Caroline left the floor. She moved across to the small inner room where supper had been laid out. Byron and Lady Rancliffe followed.

"I have been admiring your dexterity," Byron sneered.

Lady Caroline seized a knife. He laughed. "Do, my dear," he said. "But if you mean that, mind which way you strike with your knife. Point it at your own heart, not mine. You have struck there already."

"Byron!" Lady Caroline cried, and ran away with the knife. Lady Rancliffe screamed and called out, "She'll kill herself!" A dozen people ran after her and struggled with her, trying to get the knife from her. Suddenly there was blood on her gown. It was all over very quickly; but there had been a public scandal and it would never be forgotten.

Next morning the papers were full of it. When Lady Caroline saw William Lamb open *The Satirist* and then, jumping up, throw it down angrily, she knew that something dreadful had happened, and that there would be no going back. William was never disturbed about anything. He could ignore things other men fought duels over. Trembling, she picked up the paper. There, under the headline *Scandalum Magnatum*, she saw it. First there were two lines of doggerel verse:

> *With horn-handled knife,*
> *To kill a tender lamb as dead as mutton . . .*

The report went on to tell "how Lady C. L. in a fit of jealousy over Lord B——n took up a dessert-knife and stabbed herself."

William was staring at her as she read. He was white with anger. He must take her out of London, he thought. In the seclusion of the Melbournes' Hertfordshire estate she would be out of reach of the mischief-makers.

"We go to Brocket today," he said. "Get ready, Caroline."

On the very day of the Heathcote dance Hanson, the solicitor, had written to say that Claughton looked as if he would at last produce the purchase money for the Newstead estate.

Byron was elated. Now he could go abroad. He had already run up large bills for equipment and presents to take with him. He had bought swords, guns, mahogany dressing cases and writing desks, a great number of uniforms and other clothing, nankeen trousers by the dozen, and blue-and-scarlet staff officer's coats with very rich gold epaulets. He already had a tailor's bill for nearly nine hundred pounds, and he owed Love and Kelly, the jewellers and goldsmiths, over seven hundred pounds. Now he ordered seven fine gold boxes as presents for foreign potentates and others. The finest was a gold and enamel music box, with figures set with pearls, for a hundred and five pounds. For the seven boxes alone he owed three hundred and fifteen pounds. Now he was tired of spending money and waiting. He wanted to get away. How he missed Augusta. He would go and see her at Six Mile Bottom, her house near Newmarket.

It was growing dark when he arrived; and he leaned out of the carriage to get a look at the house. What a barracks it was, hardly better than the stabling which justified its existence. No form, no style, no grace of any kind—a haphazard, rambling place, unpainted, uncared for, its chimney pots as ill-placed as if they had fallen onto its jumble of roofs from the skies, its front door crushed into a corner, its windows ill-matching. No wonder Augusta liked to get away when she could—she who was used to the glories of the Duke of Devonshire's Chatsworth, and of the lovely country houses of all her aristocratic relations. It had no gardens either. He jumped out impatiently, and hammered at the door knocker himself. A surprised-looking, slovenly servant girl appeared.

"Mrs. Leigh," he said peremptorily. "Tell her her brother is here."

In a moment Augusta came running down the stairs, and threw her arms round him as he stood stripping off his gloves in the hall.

"Baby Byron!" she rejoiced. "Dear George is away—but you knew that. Are you tired? Are you hungry? Let us eat. The children are fed. There's nothing much—only a chicken, but never mind, there's plenty of wine." She was gabbling, warm and welcoming, like a good fire. He felt loved, and he hugged her.

"Yes, I'm hungry," he laughed. "Yes."

So there they were, eating and drinking and laughing and joking as they did with no one else. They sat a long time at table, and then moved lazily to the sofa next door. They sat close together, and Byron held a glass in one hand, his other arm about her shoulders as if he could not bear her to move from him. Then, suddenly, Augusta was weeping and telling him how, when he had been abroad, George Leigh had been threatened with a court-martial because of his dishonest handling of regimental funds. He had been trying to recoup his gambling debts. Byron's mother had written to him that George Leigh had lost the Prince Regent's favour when he cheated him in selling a horse for him, keeping part of the purchase money for himself; but this was new, a low, sordid story. Leigh had connived at the exorbitant profits made by the paymaster from his regiment out of the supply of military equipment and soldiers' clothing; he hadn't credited the regiment with the full government allowances for postage and stationery and coal and candles, and the veterinary and riding-school accounts; and had made improper charges for the non-commissioned officers' expenses, and for remount horses and coach hire and farriers' bills—petty theft. The Prince Regent had wanted him out of his regiment, out of Newmarket and out of the turf.

"And what we are to do I know not," Augusta wept. "I'm forbidden to tell you this, but—"

"I'll look after you, come what may. You and the children."

Augusta flung her arms around him. Her face was radiant. "Oh, brother Byron. I knew you would. God bless you."

They sat in silence for a long time. Then, somehow, they were talking of their father, Mad Jack.

"I love to talk of him to you," he said. "You were older than I, and can remember more of him—of my mother, then, too, I suppose."

"Her, too. She was very good to me in Valenciennes. I should have died if she had not nursed me through that terrible illness. He was always out enjoying himself, but she stayed to look after me—day and night, and all night, too, though she was with child."

"It was not man's work."

"Perhaps. Baby Byron, I know your love for him, and I share it. But he was not all that you believe him."

"What are you saying, Guss?"

Augusta examined her hands. "I have seen letters about him—and from him to his sister Fanny, whom he lived with there, when she'd left her husband, the General. Her sister, Aunt Sophia, showed them to me."

"Well?"

"He was very immoral—and so was she. He slept with all the whores in Valenciennes, he gambled, he drank, and lived on her—"

"I daresay all that's true." He was untroubled.

"But there's worse, Baby Byron."

"Worse?"

She was silent.

"Go on."

She raised her head and looked at him at last.

"It's quite clear from the letters. In Valenciennes Mad Jack and his sister Fanny Leigh committed incest."

He sat looking into his wineglass. Then he said at last, "You're sure?"

"I am sure. Aunt Sophia means to leave me the letters when she dies. I'm to do what I think best about them."

Finally he looked up; and she saw that he was smiling. He

put down his glass. "It wasn't such a bad idea if she was like you!" Suddenly he pulled her to him and pressed his lips to hers. She pushed him away, protesting, "Byron, you are out of your mind!" But it was a gentle push, and there was no anger in her voice. She was actually laughing. She rose, yawning lazily, and tidied her dress.

"I can see we shall have to marry you off, and soon, my dear brother. I'm going to bed now. Your room is the first one at the top of the stairs."

"And which is your room?"

Augusta laughed again. Then she bent over him and kissed him. "Good night. I shall see you in the morning."

He waited by the fire. After a little while he followed her upstairs. He opened the first door at the top of the stairs—the room was empty and ready for him. He opened the next door —there was a sleeping child inside. Then the next—another child. But the fourth room was hers. She was sitting before her dressing table in her petticoat, brushing her long shining hair. He went to her and stood with his hands on her soft, plump, naked shoulders. Then he pulled her to her feet, and with his arm tight about her waist began to draw her towards the large bed. "No!" she protested, but he silenced her with a kiss.

She hardly struggled at all.

He left her in the small hours, fast asleep. No word had been spoken. They met again at breakfast, with the children. Augusta said nothing. My sweet sister, he thought, you are like me—with the morals of a rabbit.

"You'll come abroad with me," he said, pointing a knife at her. "Get away from debts and brats and that useless husband of yours."

He waited for reproof; but she laughed, a little wildly, and tossed her head. "Very well, I *will*."

He was surprised by his own delight. She shooed the children away, and he kissed her while the servants were out of the room. Then he shouted for Fletcher and ordered his carriage.

"I'll prepare everything," he promised her at the door. "Be ready, that's all."

But back in London, he found that he was frightened at what he had done. He was seized by an overriding compulsion to tell Lady Melbourne, but he did not know how to do so. Would she be shocked? He wrote to her, dropping hints about something he had done. Then, abruptly, he told her that Augusta was going abroad with him. At once he had a letter, full of alarm, and commanding him to visit her. So he went.

She received him, smiling, tolerant, unemotional as ever, but she spoke directly. She was surprisingly attractive for her age, he thought.

"What is all this, Byron, you've been hinting at? This something terrible that you've done?"

So out it came in a rush, with all the details. He even told her how easy it had been. And crudely. His sense of relief at the confession was enormous; but at the end he looked up to see that even she was shocked and frightened. She was frightened for him, and that frightened him in turn.

"Your sister is a depraved woman. She is four years older than you. It is all her fault."

"No. No. It was not her fault, but my own folly and her weakness. We did not mean this, either of us. It was I who did it, not her. *I* was the cause of it all. *She* was not to blame for one thousandth part in comparison! She did not know she was in danger until it was too late."

Still Lady Melbourne did not seem convinced. She sat for a long time in silence. When at last she looked up, she said, "There's only one way out of this. You must get married. Or at least find another woman to fall in love with."

"That's exactly what Guss says."

Lady Melbourne said, "It should not be too difficult."

"Not Caroline. Never again."

"No, not Caroline."

"I can't marry Annabella Milbanke. She won't have me. As for falling in love, Lady Oxford's abroad."

"There are others closer at hand." Lady Melbourne, he saw, was smiling into his eyes. "Lord Melbourne," she went on, "is out, and will not return till dinnertime."

She rose, took his hand and drew him towards the door. Lord Byron followed, shaken to the core.

Back at his rooms in Bennet Street Byron found a letter from Annabella Milbanke. It said nothing about George Eden; and in it she asked him to keep it a secret from Lady Melbourne that she had written to him. She seemed to want his friendship. Well, he would play that fish on the line as long as it rose to the bait. He answered at once. "On the score of friendship I must be candid with you. It is a feeling towards you with which I cannot trust myself. I doubt whether I could help loving you." A good letter—he was satisfied with it.

Poetry was the best outlet for frustration. He would write about himself and Augusta.

> *I grant my love imperfect, all*
> *That mortals by the name miscall;*
> *Then deem it evil, what thou wilt;*
> *But say, oh say, hers was not guilt.*

Lady Melbourne would see the reference to Augusta when she read that verse in print.

Then, he thought, I will play at my other hobby. In half an hour he had drafted a will, superseding the one of 1811, in which he had left seven thousand pounds to Nicolo Giraud. Now there would be nothing for Nicolo. Instead he would leave half his estate to Captain George Anson Byron, his cousin and the heir to the title, and half to Augusta. In the morning he would give it to Hanson. He would begin a new poem, too, one about a brother and a sister who loved each other as he and Augusta did. They would be called Selim and Zuleika. There was nothing left for him to do but write poetry, though he would never descend to taking money for it—writing poetry and hunting down heiresses would be his life. Tally ho! for Miss Mercer Elphinstone and Miss Annabella Milbanke.

As Byron finished the draft Fletcher knocked at the door, and brought in a letter on a silver salver. There was Augusta's neat, firm writing on the envelope. He tore it open. Inside was a curl of her hair tied with white silk. It was enclosed in a sheet of paper with her pretty signature on it—*Augusta.* There was a message too: *"Partager tous vos sentimens, ne voir que par vos yeux, n'agir que par vos conseils, ne vivre que pour vous, voila mes vouex, mes projets, et le seul destin qui peut me rendre heureuse."* He translated it as he read, smiling over the misspellings of *sentiments* and *voeux*. So, to share all his feelings, to see only through his eyes, to act only by his advice, to live only for him, were her desires, her intentions, and the only fate which could make her happy. Elation surged in him. On the outside of the packet he scrawled the words, "La Chevelure of the *one* whom I most *loved*," and added a + after "loved"—that would be their secret sign. Augusta, Augusta, his one, his perfect love. No one should come between them.

* * *

CHAPTER
❦ 4 ❦

Augusta's letter arrived, telling him she was pregnant. Of course the child was his. They were both sure of that. She was frightened, and he decided at once to take her to Newstead Abbey. There they would have their honeymoon.

So Augusta had hurried to London, and now on Monday, January 17, 1814, they were driving together in his huge coach into the Abbey grounds. He watched her face and saw it soften at the sight of the great park white with snow and the bare black branches of the oaks stark against the sky.

"*Must* it be sold? It is so beautiful," she pleaded.

"It must."

Inside the snowbound Abbey he and Augusta were snug, with the large fireplaces blazing with coal fires, and plenty of wine from his cellar. Never had there been a colder winter. The roads were impassable, and they could not drive even as far as Nottingham. The mails came on horseback when they arrived at all. It was a good excuse not to visit Mary Chaworth Musters, that childhood love of his who had so wounded him with her sneering reference to him as "that lame boy." She had written to him on Christmas Eve—a desperate letter, saying her husband was unfaithful and that she was sick, thin, pale and gloomy. Could he, she implored, come to her? Obviously she wanted help, he thought, and that always meant money. He had not replied. Annabella Milbanke had written to him again, too, on Boxing Day, urging him to visit her at Seaham, her parents' home in Durham. But Augusta and Byron thought only of themselves and their coming child. If it was a girl, they agreed, they would call her Medora, after the girl in *The Corsair*, the poem he'd finished on New Year's Day. There was no need to worry about George Leigh, Augusta assured him. She had slept with him at about the right time, and he would never suspect.

They had three weeks together—alone except for a visit of two days from Claughton at the end. They did not leave until the sixth of February. Augusta was well and happy; and as for him, he had never been so happy for so long.

Back in London, however, with Augusta at Six Mile Bottom, he worried and fretted. Everything *seemed* to be going well. *The Corsair* sold ten thousand copies at once, which his publisher Murray called unprecedented, and he reprinted edition after edition—in a month they had sold twenty-five thousand copies. The only snag had been Byron's insistence on including his *Lines to a Lady Weeping* in the book. The Tory press was full of indignation at his giving publicity to Princess Charlotte's having burst into tears at a banquet because her father, the Prince Regent, had abandoned his Whig friends and kept the Tories in power. Murray, the Tory, had withdrawn it from the second edition, but Byron had made him put it back in the third. Suicidal, Murray had called it, but *The Corsair* had gone on selling. Byron had been accused of pocketing large sums of money, too, from it; but that had been refuted in print. He hadn't taken a penny. No gentleman could.

He was worried and unhappy, however, torn between guilt and ecstasy. His dentist pointed out that he was grinding his teeth in his sleep. He would write his thoughts in his journal, then get up in the morning, racked with fear, and tear out the pages. It was too dangerous—the Catholics were wise, with their secret confessionals. Hobhouse called him "a solitary hobgoblin," since he never went out. His only amusement had been the wedding of Hanson's daughter, Mary Anne, to the simple-minded Earl of Portsmouth. He had given the bride away at her father's request. It was clearly a put-up job, to make the girl a countess—she was twenty-four to the idiot's forty. Portsmouth had stood at the altar, his mouth open and his eyes glazed, looking around him as if he didn't know what it was all about. Byron had been fond of the girl once himself, when he was at Harrow. She had wanted to marry him, but that was not for him. Well, there was no harm in helping her become a countess if that was what she wanted, though Portsmouth was a nasty, sadistic creature. He had an obsession about what he called "black jobs"—funerals. His attendants—for the earl had to be watched—had to pretend to be mourners, and load a log on their shoulders and pretend it was a corpse, to please him, every so often.

Well, by the end of March Byron had paid off his debt of four thousand eight hundred to Scrope. After five years Scrope had been nearly out of his mind with worry over it. They had dined at The Cocoa Tree on the strength of it, with Scrope as host. He had moved into chambers in Albany, too, a fine apartment thirty feet by forty feet, subleased for seven years from Lord Althorp. He might as well live in comfort and style if he could not go abroad. He had written to Annabella again, insisting that he wanted to see her—and she had waited a month before replying. Evasively, too.

Suddenly he could bear it no longer. On Saturday, April 2, 1814, he ordered his coach and set off for Six Mile Bottom. He found Augusta alone there, awaiting the birth of her—their—baby. She was hugely swollen, and they laughed about that. He could see how joyous she was to have him with her; they talked and talked while she sewed clothes for the baby, and they told each other everything that was in their hearts. It was there that he heard that Paris had capitulated to the allies, and that, unbelievably, Napoleon had not committed suicide. It was the end of the Napoleonic Wars in Europe. He had written his *Ode to Napoleon Bonaparte*, all ten stanzas and ninety lines of it, in one day. Augusta and he could not be as happy as they had been at Newstead, but they were happy enough just to be together. It was hard to tear himself away and return to London.

But then, no sooner was he back than he heard that Claughton had defaulted on his promise to pay another five thousand pounds on account towards the purchase money for the Newstead estate. Now he couldn't go abroad. Anyway, he thought, this was no time to leave Augusta.

The news came at last. On April 15, 1814, Augusta had given birth to a daughter—his!—and she would call her Elizabeth Medora. He was full of strange feelings. It had not been like that when Lucy the servant girl had produced her bastard boy. He wrote immediately to tell Lady Melbourne. Her chilly answer came at once: "Do you think, my dear Byron, that the danger you are running in this affair is really worth while?" Exultantly he answered her, "Oh! but it is worth while; I can't tell you why, and it is *not* an ape, and if it is, that must be my fault. However, I will positively reform. You must however allow that it is utterly impossible I can ever be half so well liked elsewhere, and I have been trying all my life to make someone love me, and never got the sort of love that I preferred before. But positively she and I will grow good and all that, and so we are *now* and shall be these three weeks and more too." Lady Melbourne was a cultivated woman. She would understand his allusion to the medieval belief that the child of incest would be an ape.

It was while he was tormented by conflicting emotions that Annabella's next letter came. "Am I mistaken in imagining that you are disposed to visit us?" she asked outright. Should he go to Seaham or not? Lady Melbourne should decide. She wrote her approval. So on April 20 he wrote that he would be glad to avail himself of a possible invitation from her father, Sir Ralph Milbanke.

Meanwhile he consoled himself, as he always did, by spend-

50

ing money on anything that took his fancy—jewelry, furniture, a macaw and a parrot. He boxed and fenced every day. He was bored with society, but went wherever he was asked. But one invitation he had refused firmly. The Prince Regent went to meet Louis XVIII, and escorted him from Stanmore, with white horses, trumpeters in gold lace, a hundred gentlemen on their own steeds, and outriders, to Grillon's Hotel in Albemarle Street. Murray had invited Byron to watch the procession from his first-floor balcony. "I'm a republican," he had said, "and I won't watch the triumph of Louis the Gouty."

All too soon Sir Ralph's letter came, inviting him to Seaham—and with it a letter from Annabella suggesting they discuss their religious beliefs. Augusta was religious, he thought, and gave away Bibles to her friends, but *she* was never tedious about it. This girl annoyed him. He told Lady Melbourne, "I am not in love with her; but I can't be at all sure that I won't be so, and, seriously, I do admire her as a very superior woman, a little encumbered with virtue." But in his journal he wrote, "What an odd situation and friendship is ours, without one spark of love on either side."

Lady Melbourne knew what the trouble was. He was receiving almost daily letters from Augusta, and he was sending them on to her, and Annabella's, too. Soon they were reduced to referring to "my A" and "your A" in their letters, to distinguish Augusta from Annabella. Lady Melbourne was urging him to go and visit Annabella. "If you don't like her," she wrote, "you can talk only of the prayer-book, and if you do that subject will easily make way for another." She still blamed Augusta, and he still defended her; but he admitted that his feelings for her were a mixture of the good and the diabolical. As for Annabella, he wrote, "The fact is that my wife, if she had commonsense, would have more power over me than any other whatsoever, for my heart always alights on the nearest perch. If it is withdrawn, it goes God knows where

51

—but one must like something." Then, when Moore asked him to write some words for a song, he sent him some impassioned verses.

I speak not, I trace not, I breathe not thy name,
There is grief in the sound, there is guilt in the fame;
But the tear which now burns on my cheek may impart
The deep thoughts that dwell in that silence of heart.

Too brief for our passion, too long for our peace,
Were those hours—can their joy or their bitterness cease?
We repent, we abjure, we will break from our chain,
We will part, we will fly to—unite it again!

With him love always expressed itself in giving generous presents. He knew what Augusta wanted; and that May he sent her three thousand pounds to clear her husband's debts.

It was "the summer of the sovereigns," as everyone called it. London was full of the powerful—foreign royalty among them. Alexander, the Czar of Russia; the King of Prussia; Metternich; Blücher—all were there. He was going to a never-ending round of parties, and spending wildly. He sent Kean, the actor, fifty guineas for his benefit night, and followed that with a handsome snuffbox and an expensive Turkish sword. He tried to ignore Lady Caroline, who was still demanding her letters—everybody had read them by then, in any case. She was spreading a story that he was to be married, too. He saw silly girls who wrote to him, and slept with some of them. He was writing poetry, and well. The mere sight of the beautiful Mrs. Wilmot at a party, in mourning with spangles on her black dress, had inspired him.

She walks in beauty, like the night
Of cloudless climes and starry skies;
And all that's best of dark and bright
Meet in her aspect and her eyes.

Mary Chaworth Musters had written him more than fifty letters in six months, but he didn't want to see her. Then, he tried, for a little while, to be kinder to Lady Caroline. She'd written him a terrible letter of farewell, referring to herself as "ugly and thin and mad and despised as I am." She *had* grown thin—so thin he felt he was haunted by a skeleton. She invaded his chambers at all hours unannounced. He even threatened to run away with Augusta to Lady Melbourne, hoping the threat would get to her and put her off. Bolts, bars, silence—nothing kept her away. One day she had found him out when she made one of her visits. She had picked up a copy of Beckford's *Vathek*, which was lying on a table, and written on its first page, "Remember me!" He returned to find the book open and the words staring at him. He stood looking at them for a long time. Then he wrote under them:

Remember thee, remember thee!
Till Lethe quench life's burning stream,
Remorse and shame shall cling to thee,
And haunt thee like a feverish dream!

Remember thee! Ay, doubt it not;
Thy husband too shall think of thee;
By neither shalt thou be forgot,
Thou false *to him, thou* fiend *to me!*

In July Byron made one of his sudden visits to Newmarket. He spent three days with Augusta and the baby Medora. When he left he had persuaded her to go with him to Hastings for a holiday with her four children. He had already taken Hastings House for a month, at ten guineas a week. Augusta followed him back to London and stayed at the London Hotel in Albemarle Street. On July 20 he took her to Hastings. Mary Chaworth Musters had arrived in London, but he left without seeing her.

For three weeks Byron was happy with Augusta and her children by the sea. He swam, he ate turbot, he walked on the cliffs and up and down the hills; he laughed with Augusta, their arms around each other, the wind blowing their hair and whipping her skirts. On the first of August another letter arrived from Annabella, referring to his proposed visit. Impatiently he challenged her. Was she in love with George Eden or not? He waited. Two days later her answer came, "Nothing could now induce me to marry him." He and Augusta were sitting together.

"What shall I do, Guss?"

"You must marry, Byron. It's the only chance of redemption for us both. But not that girl. She's not for you. Marry Lady Charlotte Leveson-Gower."

He'd met Lady Charlotte and liked her—one of the great tribe of the Carlisles, and Augusta's friend. She was very young, very pretty and very shy—so shy he called her "the Antelope." "Well, you write to her and arrange it," he said. "I'm too busy. That Musters woman is threatening to come here, by the way. She and her husband have separated. And here's a letter to say that Claughton's offer has fallen through. He'll give up twenty-five of the twenty-eight thousand pounds he's paid and give the property back to me. I must go to London and sign the papers."

Still he didn't go; and soon he wrote to Annabella again, "I did—do—and always shall love you. But I will not ask you to account for your feelings." Annabella must make the next move.

His new poem, *Lara*, published anonymously, was selling well, and now for the first time he accepted money for the copyright—seven hundred pounds. He no longer cared whether that was gentlemanly or not—he needed money. On August 20 he signed the papers discharging Claughton's contract for the purchase of the Newstead estate, sent to him by Hanson at last. He was torn between delight that Newstead was his again and despair that he had lost the rest of the money.

That very day Byron set off with Augusta and her children for Newstead Abbey. He did not know, and would not hear until late October, that Mary Chaworth Musters had gone to Hastings and moved into the house where he and Augusta had been so happy, and there had gone mad.

At Newstead Byron was again as near to perfect happiness as he could be. No sooner did he reach the Abbey than he wrote to Annabella that he would be unable to visit Seaham that year. He caught perch and carp in his lakes, he swam, he rowed, he shot everything that flew overhead. He devoted time, too, to target practice with his pistols, shooting at empty soda-water bottles. Augusta wrote long letters to her little friend, the Antelope, and was full of hope.

Then, suddenly, in September came a flustered letter from the Antelope to Augusta, refusing Byron's offer.

"I did hear a rumour," Augusta mourned, "that her parents hoped for the Duke of Norfolk's son—young Howard, Earl of Surrey, you know."

"Well, that's that. You see that after all Miss Milbanke is to be the one—I'll write to her."

"She is wrong—*very* wrong for you."

He wrote to her all the same. When he handed his letter to Augusta, she read it, frowning. As she read, however, her brow cleared. Then she said, "Well, really, this is a very pretty letter. It's a pity it shouldn't go."

"Then it *shall* go." He sealed it, called Fletcher, and sent it off at once. In his letter he had asked, "Are the 'objections' to which you alluded insuperable? Or is there any line or change of conduct which could possibly remove them?"

The letter was posted on September 9. Nine days later Byron and Augusta were sitting at dinner when the servant waiting at table was summoned to the door. He returned to

55

Byron and asked, "Will you have a word with the gardener, my lord? He says he has something to show you." Byron nodded, and the old gardener came in, his cap in one gnarled hand, and the other held out before him. In the palm was a golden wedding ring. Byron took it in his hand. It was very thin, hardly more than a thick wire.

" 'Tis your mother's wedding ring, my lord. She lost it here. I was digging up the mould under her window—and there 'twas."

At that moment Fletcher came in, holding a silver salver with a letter on it. Byron recognised Annabella's writing.

"Miss Milbanke has answered," he said. "If it contains a consent I'll be married with this ring." He opened the letter.

"I have your second letter," he read, "and I am almost too agitated to write, but you will understand. It would be absurd to suppress anything—I am and have long been pledged to myself to make your happiness my first object in life. I will *trust* to you for all I should look up to—all I can love. This is a moment of joy which I have too much despaired of ever experiencing. There has in reality been scarcely a change in my sentiments."

There was another sheet. She said that she had sent a second letter to Albany in case he was in London, with a few lines from her father, as she did not want to cause him a moment's anxiety. Apparently the other letter was even more effusive, for she added, "I hope you will find in my other letter *all you wish.*"

Byron passed the letter across the table to Augusta. He looked so pale she thought he was going to faint. "It never rains but it pours," he said.

Augusta read Annabella's letter. "Well," she said after a while, "it is the best and prettiest letter I ever read."

Byron caught the desperate effort in her voice. "The stars, I presume, did it," he said drily.

After dinner he forced himself to answer Annabella as

lovingly as he could. Then he wrote to Lady Melbourne—but he did not show that letter to Augusta. "May I hope for your consent too? I mean to reform," it said.

"Byron," Augusta implored him when she had read his letter to Annabella, "you must set off for Seaham at once."

"No," he said stubbornly. "Not before I must. Come and walk with me."

"Oh, not tonight," Augusta said. He could not move her.

In the morning, he insisted. First he took her through the Abbey rooms on a slow, loving tour, and before long he saw that she was as moved as he was. Then he drew her outside, and they walked in the great park and by the lakes.

"I cannot bear to give it up," she sighed. "And for what?"

"For the marriage settlement," he said. "What else?" Then he said, "Come into the Devil's Wood with me, there, behind the Abbey."

"Why is it called the Devil's Wood?"

"Because the Wicked Lord put statues of satyrs and nymphs in it; and the country people were convinced he held orgies there. Perhaps he did."

He paused before an old silver birch. It was of an unusual shape—springing from the base into two boles. He took out his penknife and carved his name slowly, carefully and deeply into it—BYRON. Then he carved hers—AUGUSTA. Underneath he carved the date, 20 September 1814.

Next morning they set out, Augusta for Six Mile Bottom and Byron for London. She had been away from home for almost three months.

* * *

CHAPTER
❦ 5 ❦

Well, here he was at Seaham, come to marry Annabella—
and, thank God, Hobhouse was with him. He was in disgrace,
he could see that. He had been so late turning up that he and
Hob were shown to their rooms by the servants—a clear snub.
Lady Milbanke was in her room, and didn't appear to greet
them—a worse one.

He still winced at the memory of his earlier, first visit in
November. Everything had been wrong—his coming at a
snail's pace from Six Mile Bottom; Annabella's taking offense
when he didn't step forward from the mantelpiece to greet
her, never thinking of his bad foot; his bringing her no ring,
no poetry and no presents; the boredom of old Sir Twaddle
—as he called Sir Ralph—with his endless, half-drunken
anecdotes at dinner; the peremptory, managing ways of Lady
Milbanke; and Annabella's sitting, staring at him with those
great critical eyes, in deadly silence. On the very first morning, while he was sleeping until noon, as usual, she waited for
him on a cold cliff top, ready for a walk. To crown it all, she
seemed to be taken ill every three days with God knew what.
She prated about her feelings from morning till night, and in
the end she made a scene, declaring he didn't love her, and
they had better break off the engagement. He turned green
and actually fainted, and she said, "Now I'm *sure* you must
love me." After that he gave up argument and took to action;
physical passion had worked wonders with her—the Princess
of Parallelograms was hot-blooded, it seemed. Then after two

weeks of that she urged him to go, frightened of what might happen.

At least the lawyers had agreed without squabbling. She would have twenty thousand pounds settled on her by her father—little enough, in view of her expectations from old Wentworth. But he would have to settle sixty thousand on her.

Byron's tongue had run away with him, and he talked too much of Augusta, and said that no one would ever have as much of his love as she did. He said, "You remind me of her when you are playful," and watched her trying to be playful. She made him want to be cruel. He even said, "If you'd married me two years ago you would have saved me from what I can never get over." She listened, saying nothing, staring at him with those cold eyes, taking it in, storing it up. He was glad enough to go, but resentful at being ordered away. How good the five days at Six Mile Bottom on his way back to London seemed. Then his old life in London had been tainted by her letters, growing warmer and warmer, demanding him, troubling him—"I wish for you, want you, Byron mine, more every hour."

He had found one excuse after another for deferring the wedding—even grasping at Hanson's being distracted by the prospect that the marriage of his daughter to the imbecile Earl of Portsmouth would be annulled. Portsmouth's brother had taken out what they called a Commission in Lunacy, which would have that effect. He had been furious at it—they had married off the Earl to a woman past child-bearing age for his first wife, so the brother would inherit; but when she died Hanson had jumped in quickly with his daughter. Then the eternal delays in concluding the sale of the Newstead estate to Claughton had provided another excuse—it wasn't cut and dried. Annabella would hear of no delay, however. He was sure she wanted a big church wedding, too, as her parents did, with all the county invited to eat slices of rich wedding cake and drink their healths. He wouldn't have that. "I will have it by special license," he had written firmly, "because I think it will be quieter to be married in a room, and mama will lend us a cushion each to kneel upon." Of course, he didn't want a great church wedding, because he would have to wear knee breeches and silk stockings and court shoes for that, and then his thin leg and his club foot would be on display to all. In his wide trousers he was left with his dignity. He *would not* be stared at.

It was not until December 18, 1814, that he named the date of his departure—Christmas Eve. Even then, he warned them, he might have to be a witness at the Portsmouth lunacy trial, and return as soon as he was married. On December 22 he collected the special license from Doctors' Commons. He knew very well that Annabella and her parents had counted on having him there for Christmas, but he had meant to have Christmas with Augusta. He had insulted them; but be damned to them.

Byron and Hobhouse had set out from London on December 24, and parted at Chesterfield, Hobhouse for Cambridge and he for Six Mile Bottom. It hadn't been a merry Christmas, for George Leigh was at home, and sick, and Augusta was busy spooning his medicines into him. It was freezing, too, and they couldn't leave the house. Still he had eaten Augusta's mince pies and played with the children, particularly Medora —their Mignonne, as he and Augusta called her. Augusta whispered that Mignonne looked more like him every day. On Christmas Day he had forced himself to write to Annabella, "I am thus far on my way, and as warm as love can make me with the thermometer below God knows what," warning her that the snow might delay him.

On Boxing Day he had set out, picking up Hobhouse in Cambridge, and had gone on. But he had stopped at Wansford; and so it had gone on, at even more of a snail's pace than his last journey to Seaham, in the bitter cold, the ground covered with snow and the frost so biting the servants could hardly stay on the outside of the carriage. Hobhouse sat beside him, his face, with its long nose and quizzical eyebrows, unsmiling. He was jealous of Annabella, of course. Hobhouse had always wanted to own him, dear fellow.

"I don't love her, I'm *not* in love with her," Byron burst out suddenly. "And I didn't want to marry till my money affairs were all arranged. I don't like marrying without a good income. I've offered to wait a year or two, engaged to be married, but she wouldn't have it!" He told Hobhouse he had written to Annabella from Six Mile Bottom, trying to break the engagement, but Augusta had stopped him sending the letter. He had seen Hobhouse scribbling in his journal, and had stolen a look. "The bridegroom less and *less* impatient," his friend had written. "He feels towards her indifference, almost aversion."

Not until eight o'clock on Friday, December 30, a week after he had left London, and four days after leaving Augusta, did they finally arrive, to their chilly reception. The die was cast. There was no going back.

Hobhouse came out of his room first, and was taken to the library. Then the red-faced Sir Ralph tottered in, looking like a caricature of Lady Melbourne, his sister. Hobhouse stammered his excuses for the delay, embarrassed by their inadequacy, and trailed into silence. In a few moments Annabella came in and took Hobhouse's hand. Hobhouse examined her critically. She was rather dowdy looking, he thought. He didn't like that long dress of hers, though she had good feet and ankles. The lower part of her face was bad, the upper part expressive but not beautiful. Yet he admitted grudgingly that she grew on him even as he looked at her. Then Lady Milbanke came in, still chilly, and greeted Hobhouse. She wore a very obvious wig, he thought, and she was clearly a formidable woman. She had been dashing in her day, they said, and she was obviously intelligent, but seemed pettish and tiresome.

Suddenly Annabella heard Byron coming out of his room. She ran to meet him, and in the doorway she threw her arms about his neck and burst into tears. Byron made no excuses for his slowness. Hobhouse watched Annabella, struggling against his surging jealousy, admitting that she was silent and modest, and very sensible, and decent and frank and unaffected; but he was resentful at the way she gazed and gazed at Byron.

Byron and Hobhouse refused supper, saying that they had eaten early. Soon everyone went to bed.

Next morning the real business began. Before noon both the clergymen and Sir Ralph's attorney, Mr. Hoar, arrived. The Reverend Thomas Noel, Rector of Kirkby Mallory, the parish in which Lord Wentworth's estate was situated, was to conduct the service. Noel was, Byron knew, Wentworth's illegitimate son. The other clergyman was called Wallace, and he was to make the responses.

The signing of the deeds for the settlements did not take long, and everyone stayed for the midday meal. Time seemed to hang heavy after that. Then the Reverend Thomas Noel bustled up to Byron.

"We must rehearse the ceremony tonight," he said, "but it would be more amusing, don't you think, to change the parts about?"

So, after dinner they had the mock marriage. Hobhouse took the bride's part, and Hoar gave him away, and Noel conducted, and everybody laughed a good deal, except Annabella. They shook hands at midnight, and wished each other a happy new year, 1815.

It was January 2, 1815, the wedding day. Byron was up before Hobhouse. He walked into his dressing room. There, spread out on the bed, were his wedding clothes—the blue coat with the gold buttons which had cost so much money, and the finely embroidered white waistcoat, and the ruffled white shirt, and the white kid gloves. He was proud of that waistcoat—it had belonged to King George II. But now he took no pleasure in it, or in the coat, or in those small gloves of the finest kid. He couldn't bear to put them on. When at last he was dressed he went outside and walked about the grounds alone. At a little before half-past ten a manservant came to summon him.

Byron laboured upstairs to the drawing room. Hobhouse was there, in full dress and white kid gloves, too. Wentworth's bastard was there, and the other clergyman—both in full canonicals. Then Sir Ralph and Lady Milbanke came in, in all their finery. Lady Milbanke went over to a tray in the corner, and began to make tea; but her hand shook so much she had to gesture to the maid to take her place. She was, Byron thought, on the verge of hysterics.

At half-past ten, after their refreshment, they separated. Hobhouse and Byron went to Byron's room on the ground floor. The others went upstairs. Byron and Hobhouse waited for ten minutes, then walked upstairs to the drawing room. Now hassocks had been laid down for the bride and groom and the others.

Almost at once Annabella entered, with a plain, stiff woman who held her head high. "That's Mrs. Clermont," Hobhouse whispered to Byron. "She was her nursemaid, and then her governess." Annabella was dressed in a white muslin dress trimmed with lace at the hem, and a white muslin jacket. She wore nothing on her head. Her wedding dress seemed very plain, Byron thought, but it was delicately embroidered—the hem of the petticoat and the detachable cuffs of the dress had an edging of embroidery of rose and pale green, and the petticoat showed between the fronts of a kind of overdress. The gown was long. It was fresh and sweet, and she wore a fragile pair of white lace gloves. Yet his heart was cold towards her.

Now Noel was gesturing to Annabella and Byron to kneel, and Lady Milbanke was beckoning to Sir Ralph to stand beside his daughter. Hobhouse at once moved next to Sir Ralph. Then Lady Milbanke joined Mrs. Clermont in a corner, where they could see everything. Noel took his place, and the ceremony began.

Annabella was as firm as a rock, her voice bell-like. She looked steadily at Byron, and her voice rang out firm and clear. But Byron stammered over the "I, George Gordon." Then, when he came to the words "With all my worldly goods I thee endow," he could not help looking up at Hobhouse with a half-smile. He was very uncomfortable, and the hassocks were hard.

At eleven o'clock Byron and Annabella were man and wife. Annabella went at once to show her wedding ring to her parents. It was the one which the gardener had found at Newstead Abbey—his mother's wedding ring. The thin gold band, which had been chosen for Mrs. Byron's fat finger, was too large for Annabella's slender one. Moving up behind Lady Milbanke to join his wife, Byron heard her say to Sir Ralph, "Imagine not bringing her even a diamond hoop ring—I don't like it, any of it!" A deep crimson spread over Sir Ralph's face as he realized that she had been overheard, but he said nothing. Then Lady Milbanke saw his eyes fixed on someone across her shoulder, and turned round. She kissed the bridegroom, unaware that he had overheard her. She and Mrs. Clermont were both weeping.

Annabella was signing the register, and Hobhouse and Wallace were poised to witness her signature. Annabella turned, looked at her father and mother, and tears gushed to her eyes. She left the room swiftly.

Annabella returned within twenty minutes. Now she was wearing a dove-coloured pelisse of the finest satin, beautifully stitched and trimmed with white fur. She sat down in the drawing room without speaking. Byron was calm, and Hobhouse moved to his side. "I feel," he whispered to him, "as if I had buried a friend."

There was no reception. Everyone was given a slice of the huge wedding cake, brought in after the ceremony and now dominating the room. It had four tiers, covered with icing and decorated with white ribbons. Everyone drank the health of the bride and groom in champagne, and Sir Ralph read a wedding poem which he had composed weeks before the occasion. Everything seemed grim, forced and desperately unhappy. More slices of cake were passed round, but hardly anyone took a second slice. Everyone was conscious that the carriage was waiting, and that the couple had to travel forty miles in wintry weather before nightfall.

Suddenly Hobhouse slipped away, picked up a large package he had left outside the drawing room, and took it down to the carriage—it was a complete collection of Byron's poems bound in yellow morocco, his wedding gift to the new Lady Byron. Then he slipped back into the drawing room, went to Annabella and offered her his arm. He led the way downstairs, and the others followed.

Outside, Hobhouse helped Annabella into the carriage. "May you have many years of happiness," he said.

"If I am not happy, it will be my own fault," Annabella answered firmly. Byron swung up into the carriage beside her. Then Hobhouse clasped Byron's hand warmly. Byron clutched it and did not let it go. He was still gripping it, leaning out of the window, when the carriage moved off.

Lady Milbanke stood beside Hobhouse in the little crowd by the front door as the carriage drove off. "Didn't I behave well?" she asked him. At that moment the little bells of Seaham Church struck up and drowned Hobhouse's reply. Then half a dozen of the Milbankes' servants ran out to the front of the house and fired off muskets. By noon, Hobhouse decided, he would leave Seaham. He was engaged that evening to dine with Billy Hoar, and Sir Ralph and Lady Milbanke would be among the guests—it was a sort of wedding dinner but, he felt, a heartless one.

In the carriage there was silence for several miles. Then Byron broke out into one of the wild Albanian songs he had learned abroad. Annabella shrank into her corner, tears in her eyes. Soon, as they clattered into Durham, the bells rang out for their wedding day. Sir Ralph had formerly been the Member of Parliament for twenty-two years, and the bridal carriage had been eagerly watched for. "Ringing for our happiness, I suppose," Byron sneered. Then he rounded on her ferociously. "It *must* come to a separation. You should have married me when I first proposed."

They drove on in silence until they came to Rusheyford, and stopped at the inn to rest the horses. "I wonder how long I'll be able to keep up the part I've been playing," Byron jeered. She did not reply, and he shouted, "I detest your mother, and I think the settlements are niggardly!"

"You speak of me as if I were a beggar."

"Oh—*you*. Lady Melbourne and I plotted to avenge your refusing me. It was something to outwit a woman like you, who'd refused so many men. But, even so, it was only to spite another girl that I proposed again." She believed him, he saw, and smiled. Then he added, "I've longed to break off the engagement, but they said that as a man of honour I must fulfil it. But now you are in my power, and I shall make you feel it."

After that there was complete silence. At last they reached Halnaby Hall, in Yorkshire, which the Milbankes had lent them for the honeymoon. Byron looked out approvingly at the splendid red-brick seventeenth-century mansion set in fine grounds, but then at once jumped out of the carriage and walked away. Annabella was left alone until the old butler, the husband of her maid, Mrs. Minns, came tottering down the steps to help her down. The butler looked at her, staring at her agonized face and her listless body. He looked at this bride plunged in despair, and longed to offer her his arm but did not. He was only a butler.

As soon as Annabella was inside the door she was greeted by Mrs. Minns, her maid for the past ten years, who had been sent ahead to look after her. Mrs. Minns led her and Byron upstairs to their inter-connecting rooms. They were not large and they faced north, but they looked snug and comfortable, with blazing coal fires. One of the four-poster beds was curtained in a red woollen material called moreen.

Soon they followed Mrs. Minns down to the dining room for their wedding dinner. Annabella remembered that at that very time they were being toasted by Sir Ralph and Lady Milbanke. They ate in silence and climbed the stairs again. Mrs. Minns, Annabella saw, had unpacked for her, and had laid out her nightdress. They stood, totally alone for the first time, staring at each other, despair in both their hearts. Tears streamed down Annabella's face.

"Do you mean to sleep in the same bed?" he demanded. "I hate sleeping with a woman, but you may if you want to." He glared at her, then added, "Provided a woman is young, one is as good as another."

Suddenly he seized her and dragged her to the sofa. "Best get it over with," he said harshly.

After a while Annabella protested, "My lord—"

"Be quiet!" Byron shouted.

After that there was no protest. When he released her she went, still weeping, to sit for a long time on the bed. He went to his dressing room. Fifteen minutes later he returned to her in his nightshirt, and flung himself into bed. She washed, put on her nightdress and followed him.

Late that night, between the firelit crimson curtains, she woke to hear him cry out, "Good God, I am surely in hell!"

* * *

Next morning Annabella woke early to find him gone. She went downstairs to the sitting room, but Byron did not appear until noon. "It's too late now," he said. "It's done and can't be undone." "I don't repent," she replied, wearily.

The park was covered with snow and the pond with ice. They could not even walk outside. But when his valet, Fletcher, brought a letter to Byron he was all happiness. "It's from Augusta," he exulted. "Listen! It begins, 'Dearest, first and best of human beings'—there, what do you think of that? And she says that at the hour of my wedding she was upset, dreadfully upset, 'as the sea trembles when the earth quakes.' She wouldn't come because she couldn't bear to see me married to you." Yet an hour later he was kind, calling her Pippin because of her round, rosy face. Enchanted, she called him Dear Duck. "You should have a softer pillow than my heart," he said bitterly.

"I wonder which will break first, yours or mine."

"If you'd married me two years ago you'd have spared me something for which I'll never forgive myself. I could tell you, but it's another's secret."

"Does Augusta know it?"

He looked terrified. "Oh, for God's sake don't ask her."

She picked up a book and sat down to read it. It was Dryden's *Don Sebastian*. After a while she said, "This is a dreadful story, about a brother and sister who sleep together, not knowing—"

"What did you say?" he shouted, and she looked up to see him holding over her the dagger he usually wore. "Oh, it's only this book," she answered. "What is it?"

He put the dagger down. "If anything could make me believe in heaven it's the expression of your face at this moment," he said. Yet within the hour he was tormenting her again, telling her he had tried to seduce Lady Oxford's twelve-year-old daughter, and urging her to say that she would condone his affairs with other women. "I want to terrify you into running back to your father like the spoiled child you are. Now go out of the room. I don't want you."

That afternoon came the worst outburst. Annabella had wound a black ribbon round her wedding ring to keep it from falling off. She came into the sitting room and moved to the fire.

"A black ribbon!" Byron cried. "Take it off at once. It's an evil omen."

She took it off. A moment later the ring fell into the fire. Byron threw himself at the hearth scraping frantically at the coals. At last he found the ring and pulled it out. He was upset for hours afterwards.

So it went on, each day bringing some new anguish to Annabella. At last she went to Mrs. Minns. "I can't bear it," she sobbed. "I must tell somebody." She told her everything she had endured since leaving her father's home. "I'm sure there's been something dreadful between him and his sister," she ended despairingly.

"You *must* write to your father and take his advice," Mrs. Minns cried. "You cannot bear this alone."

"Perhaps. If I can't bear it, I will. But you must promise me never to reveal what I've told you."

"Very well, though I don't like it."

Now Annabella knew that she had been married without love, and that all Byron's letters—those letters which had rained on her—had been calculated works of art. Every day now she listened to his threats of suicide, his exultations at her defenselessness, his hints that he was a murderer and his cruel speeches charged with references to incest. Once he said, "I'll live with you *if I can*, until I've got an heir—then I'll leave you"; and once, "I only want a woman to laugh, and don't care what she is besides. I can make Augusta laugh at anything—no one but Augusta makes me happy."

One night he brought out her letters to him, written before

and during their engagement. Taking them one by one from a red portfolio, he read out passages, sneering at them, his rage so extreme that she was afraid he would strike her. She threw herself on her knees and flung her arms round his neck. "You forget we *are* married," she cried, and that calmed him, but not for long.

At last their time had dragged to an end. "The treacle-moon is over," Byron announced. "Now we'll go to Six Mile Bottom."

Annabella was looking forward to her visit with trepidation. Augusta herself had been making excuses, but Byron had refused to be fobbed off.

On March 12 they arrived. There was no one to greet them, and Byron said, "You stay in the carriage. I'll go and prepare Guss." He pushed the front door, which was open, and went in. Then he came out again, looking upset, to hand her out. "There's no sign of her," he said. Inside Annabella looked around. She had seen Augusta at a party in 1813, but they had not been introduced. What was she like? Suddenly there was the sound of footsteps, and Byron called out joyfully, "Guss!" Augusta was running downstairs. She ran to Byron and kissed him. Then she went to Annabella and greeted her warmly, but she did not kiss her. Byron watched them, a cruel smile on his lips. Annabella could not take her eyes from Augusta's silky brown hair about her pretty face, her brown eyes, her long neck, her large, pretty mouth, her fine teeth, and her long, narrow, fashionable dress and ornate bracelet. She found she was saying to herself, "She's freckled, I didn't remember that."

Byron had picked up a letter and opened it. "You're out of humour," Augusta chided him.

"It's this letter about Newstead. Claughton again," he fretted.

Annabella followed Augusta upstairs. In her bedroom she

kissed Augusta and said, "I hope we'll be friends—sisters." Augusta seemed taken aback, but she embraced her warmly. When they returned to Byron, Annabella told him she had kissed Augusta. "*You* should have kissed her first, Guss," Byron reproached his sister.

After supper Annabella got up to go to bed, and waited for Byron to follow. "We don't want *you*, my charmer," he snarled. She climbed the stairs alone.

It was late before Byron came to Annabella's room. He stood over her and said deliberately, "Now I have *her* you will find I can do without *you*—in all ways."

At breakfast next morning Byron greeted his sister, "Here is my inflammable one!" Annabella noticed that Augusta looked as if she were about to faint.

Later that morning a package arrived from Byron's London jeweler. He opened it and took out two gold brooches inset with hair and with crosses engraved on them. He gave one to Augusta, saying, "There, that's my hair." Then he pinned the other to his coat with "And here is *your* hair, Guss. If she knew what these mean! Do you remember our signs at Newstead?" He paused, then said, "Well, Guss, I'm a reformed man, ain't I?" Augusta seemed put out. "I *have* observed some improvements lately," she said crossly, but she pinned the brooch to her dress.

When late that night Byron at last left Augusta, Annabella trembled at the sound of his footsteps on the stairs, and quailed as he swore at Fletcher.

From then on he came to her in the same mood every night, and if she turned over in bed he cried, "Don't touch me!" in hatred. At last one night she got up. "Where are you going?" he growled. "To my own room." There, in her bed, she cried herself to sleep. She forced herself to seem calm and gentle; but Byron saw through the pretense and did all he could to torment her. Her life, she felt, was a kind of death. Once she spoke of Byron's bad temper to Augusta. "It's his indigestion," she replied. "Don't mind it." Augusta never said, she noticed, that Byron loved her. She decided, at length, to try to gain Augusta's friendship, but she was upset by the glances passing constantly between her and her brother. Once she saw Byron looking at Augusta's youngest child, and said to her, "I should like to have him painted when he is looking at Medora—he looks so tender." She was astonished at the expressions on their faces and at Byron's emotion. He was drinking more and more, and complaining about his money troubles. Only Napoleon's escape from Elba cheered him a little.

The next night Byron pointed to Medora and said, "You know, that is my child. Let me see, Colonel Leigh was certainly away from home. She couldn't possibly be his, now, could she, Guss?" Augusta gave a little cry of terror. "He's joking," she said faintly. "But it's wicked, Byron, to talk so."

Annabella and Augusta went for walks together, but they did not confide in each other. Once or twice Annabella thought that Augusta wanted to speak out to her, but it came to nothing. They were neither friends, she felt, nor enemies, brought together by Byron's behaviour, his malice, and his insults. It was the most terrible two weeks of Annabella's life, worse even than those at Halnaby Hall. She wrote in her diary, "My heart is withered away, so that I forget to eat my bread."

The day came when it was clear that Augusta was anxious for them to go. On March 28, 1815, sixteen days after they had arrived, they set out for London. As they drove away Byron looked back and waved to Augusta as long as he could see her. Then he sank back, giving Annabella a black look. "What do you think of her?" he asked.

Annabella did not reply. She was preoccupied with a discovery. She was pregnant.

* * *

CHAPTER

❦ 6 ❧

At last they were installed at number 13 Piccadilly Terrace. Hobhouse had taken for them the fine mansion facing south over London's Green Park owned by the widowed Duchess of Devonshire, who had gone to live in France. It cost seven hundred pounds a year, furnished, to rent, and would eat up all Annabella's pin money. Only stark necessity had made Byron agree to live in a house with so unlucky a number. There was nowhere else for them to go.

They arrived on March 31, and for ten days Byron was kind to Annabella. Augusta came on April 7. Byron tried to prevent it, but Annabella insisted. "Very well," he replied grimly. "But you're a fool for letting her come here, and you'll find it will make a great difference to *you* in every way." Even Augusta was horrified at the cost of the house. "But what will you live on?" she asked. "Then, there are so many servants, a carriage, and a coachman—and Mrs. Mule." For Byron had brought the hideous old woman who had been his firelighter at the Albany, and had rigged her out in new clothes. "Typical sentimentality," Augusta smiled.

Soon all the agonies of the Six Mile Bottom visit began again. It was almost a relief to Annabella when news came that her rich uncle, Lord Wentworth, was seriously ill, and she had to leave at once for Kirkby Mallory to be with him until her mother could come from Seaham to nurse him. Three nights passed before Lady Milbanke arrived. Next day Annabella had a note from Byron. "Dearest, I won't have you worried any longer. Pray come home." The sickbed had been better than what she had left behind, Annabella thought, but she set off at once.

No sooner was Annabella back at number 13 Piccadilly than news came that Lord Wentworth had died. "Now," Byron said, "there will be some money. It has worked out very well." But word followed swiftly that it was her mother who was to inherit the Wentworth fortune. Not until her death would there be anything for Annabella. Byron went into a rage that terrified her. Now, he declared, the whole dismal charade of his courtship and marriage had been in vain. "There'll be no money, and I'll be burdened with you and the child for nothing."

Money was certainly very short. They could have retrenched. Annabella was in mourning, and so there was no need for her to entertain. But Byron was going out more and more, especially to the theater and to supper parties. All his creditors had descended on him like vultures at the news of Wentworth's death. His *Hebrew Melodies* was out, with the lovely poem about Mrs. Wilmot in it, and had sold ten thousand copies; but he refused to take any of the five thousand pounds' profit it had made for Murray. This time his name was on the book, and he dared not be thought a literary hack.

Annabella watched Byron and his sister together, consumed by jealousy. She admitted to herself that there were moments when she could have plunged a dagger in Augusta's heart; but she managed to hide her feelings from them both. Week after week went by, with no relief.

In June came news of the victory of Waterloo. Annabella's uncle, Sir James Bland Burges, brought it to them, all smiles. "Well, I'm damned sorry for it," Byron cried surlily, and Annabella saw the shock in her uncle's face. Next day Annabella said outright to Augusta that she wanted her to go home. She went, and Annabella rejoiced more than at the nation's triumph. Byron at once grew kinder. They even dined together now and then, though Byron was scornful of her hearty appetite. "Women should never be seen eating or drinking, except lobster salad and champagne," he said, glaring at her as she ate a large meal of mutton chops. In her condition, too, she took violent fancies for certain dishes. When her favourite goose pies arrived from her mother Byron ate them greedily and rebuked her for wanting any. For the most part, however, she ate alone.

Annabella said nothing to her parents of her miseries, writing home gaily about how she had been caught between two posts in Hyde Park, and had been hard put to it to extricate herself, so large had she become; and threatening to have a crescent cut out of her writing table so as to accommodate her great protuberance. To Augusta, however, she wrote frequently, in a different tone. Now she found herself torn between the attraction which Byron's sister held for her and her jealousy. All her life she had been strongly drawn to women —much more so than to men—but never had she been so drawn to any particular woman. She loved the very childishness, the effusiveness, the incoherence, and the levity of Byron's Guss, so different from her own solemn nature, and so like what she called Byron's "child side." She wrote to her now, fully and frankly. Once, even, she wrote piteously, "Augusta, will you be my *only* friend?"

Annabella was consumed with jealousy, now, of Mary Chaworth Musters. She had recovered from her madness, and was reconciled to her husband. When Annabella met her at Lady Caroline Lamb's she wrote to Augusta, "Such a wicked-looking cat I never saw. Somebody else looked quite virtuous beside her." But soon Annabella did not need to worry about that "somebody else." "Caroline Lamb has gone to Brussels to nurse her brother, Frederick," Byron informed her casually. "He was seriously wounded at Waterloo. And Hobhouse's brother was killed." Hardly had Lady Caroline gone than

London was full of scandalous tales of her misbehaviour, first in Brussels and then in Paris, and of her affair with the Duke of Wellington.

Byron was thinking of nothing but money. Again the sale of his Newstead estate to the solicitor Claughton had been postponed. Lady Milbanke had become Lady Noel, as a condition of inheriting the Wentworth fortune; but the expected income of seven thousand pounds a year from the estate seemed to vanish like smoke. Then the Durham Bank had failed, taking a good deal of Sir Ralph's money with it; and he had even lost fifteen hundred pounds when he had been let down by a man for whom he had stood surety. The Noels seemed nearly as badly off as the Byrons, who had gained nothing at all from the Wentworth inheritance—but at least *they* had no creditors ready to pounce.

Suddenly Byron decided to make a new will to supersede the one of 1813. On July 29, 1815, he signed it. This time, he stipulated, after all his property had been sold and the sixty thousand pounds of Annabella's marriage settlement been paid, the entire residue was to go to Augusta and her children.

"Do you accept that?" he asked Annabella.

"I do. You are doing the right thing." The words choked her. But she felt she must seem to take it in good part.

Seaham was theirs, Lady Noel wrote, for the lying-in. She and Sir Ralph would go to Kirkby Mallory, so as to leave Seaham to the Byrons entirely. They did not leave London, however. Byron was now interesting himself in the actual management of the Drury Lane Theater. Annabella loathed it, and detested the actors and actresses who absorbed so much of his time. But he was deaf to her protests. She had met Douglas Kinnaird, Byron's close friend, too, and abominated him. She hated his small, mean, bewhiskered face, his small, mean body, and the way he stared at her as if she were an unwelcome visitor. He was even more jealous of her than Hobhouse, she thought. But they could not leave London for fear their creditors would send in bailiffs and warrants of execution. Besides, Newstead and the Rochdale property were both up for sale at the end of July at Garraway's, the auctioneers.

On the day of the auction they all went along. Even Annabella went. Hobhouse proved a good friend, and a useful cheat. He forced the price up by bidding, with no intention of buying. It did no good, however. Both Newstead and Rochdale had to be withdrawn. Lady Noel could hardly contain her impatience for the properties to be sold; but the best offer for Newstead had been seventy-nine thousand pounds—and the settlement on Annabella was sixty thousand. The difference would not have paid even Byron's most pressing debts.

"Hobhouse," Byron complained in Annabella's hearing as they left, "she and I are quarrelling about money, and I'm driven mad by threats of execution. I'm going to see Augusta."

To Annabella the debacle of the auction seemed like a deathblow to their marriage. From then on Byron was consistently unpleasant, and often ferocious, to her. Then, at the end of August, he went to Six Mile Bottom. Colonel Leigh was away as usual, and he stayed for five days. Yet, with a sudden change, he wrote to Annabella cheerfully and affectionately—asking for his laudanum, which Fletcher had forgotten, and complaining that he had nearly lost a toe from one of Augusta's mousetraps. "Goose is taking a quill from her wing to scribble to you," he ended, and added, after his signature, "A-da." Ada was the name they had decided to call their child if it was a girl. But Annabella was not cheered. She was lonely and dispirited, with her parents away at Kirkby, and most of her friends out of town for the summer. Mrs. Clermont had come to London to care for her, but even she was living out of the house. The servants treated her as if she were not there.

When Byron returned to London he seemed angry with Augusta. She refused to sleep with him, Annabella decided. Besides, he told her, Augusta had offended him by taking the part of her parents when he abused them. Annabella now desperately longed for the comfort of her old home and her mother and father. She begged him to go to Seaham.

"No. We *can't* go to Seaham," he insisted. "The moment we leave they'll take out executions. Go by yourself."

"I will not."

"Why don't your parents help? They've got plenty of money. In any case, the theater opens on September the ninth for the autumn season."

"Lady Hardwicke told me what you're doing is only fit for a six-and-eightpenny man—you're only an acting manager. It's demeaning."

Annabella even wrote to her father, complaining of this low occupation of Byron's. But she did not tell him of how Byron boasted to her of his many mistresses at the theater, saying, "They're to vex Augusta as much as you."

She knew that Byron was sleeping badly, and was full of nervous fears. At three or four o'clock in the morning, night after night, he would wake up, trembling, his eyes wild, swearing that someone was lurking in the house, waiting to kill him. "Go, go and find him," he besought her. "It's safe for you. I'm the one he means to harm." So though she was within a few months of the birth of her baby Annabella would get out of bed, light a candle and search the house for the murderer he feared. She could not believe that this poor, terrified creature was the same man she had fallen in love with. Where was the enchanting lover whom women pursued? Where the delightful friend who commanded such love and loyalty from men? All the sweetness and openness of his nature had gone. Now she never heard his engaging, musical laugh. There was only malignancy and calculated, gratuitous cruelty for her.

78

Things had been bad before, but never so bad as they then were.

One morning Annabella was in the library copying out the last words of his poem, *The Siege of Corinth*. Suddenly she heard voices raised below. She crept out and hung over the banisters.

"Yes, sir, a bailiff, sir. I have a warrant of execution, and *must* enter."

Byron's angry voice came up to her, swearing loudly. The bailiff's calm tones reached her again: "It'll be a question for the police, sir, if you lay hands on me." Annabella crept down a few steps.

"Well, get below then," Byron shouted. "Into the kitchen with you."

My God, Annabella thought, he has sold all the furniture at Newstead already. Now his books will have to go. Yet he had property worth a hundred thousand pounds—more, probably. And my child is about to be born. She saw him approach the staircase, and fled back to the library. He came in and walked up to her, clearly suspicious. She was writing steadily, as if she had not stirred.

"I thought I heard voices," she said carelessly, eyes on her work.

"It's nothing. Fletcher is attending to it." Then he said, "I must go abroad as soon as the child is born. A woman always loves her child better than her husband."

"You'll make me hate my child if you say that," she answered, throwing down her quill.

"I'm going to sell my library."

"Oh, no."

"I must. Murray's offered me three and a half thousand for it, but I won't take it—not from him."

He stood lowering. He was thinking of the presents he had been giving to Susan Boyce, the little actress, and the rent he was paying for her room in New Ormonde Street, where he visited her—her sister had objected to his visiting her at her house. She was pregnant, too. That meant more money, he fretted.

Annabella could bear it alone no longer. As soon as he left her she wrote to Augusta, begging her to come: "Don't be afraid for my health—it will do very well. But let me see you the middle of next week—at latest. Hobhouse has come—I have good reason to think to arrange a plan for going abroad with Byron. My heart aches—you will do good, I think, if any can be done. My dearest A, I feel all your kindness."

On November 15, 1815, Augusta arrived. Byron met her coldly; but before the day was over he resumed his old insults to them both. To Annabella, Augusta seemed wretched, even more so than she was herself.

The next morning Byron came into the room where they both were. He was drunk and abusive.

"I'll bring a mistress into the house," he swore. "See if I don't." He stumbled out of the room.

Augusta sat, her embroidery forgotten on her lap. "Ah, you don't know *what* a fool I've been about him," she cried, throwing her hair back from her forehead with a trembling hand. Annabella rose, kissed her, and left the room.

The heavy drinking continued, the rages grew worse. Then Byron locked a door against Annabella, shouting that he was going to renew his incestuous intercourse with Augusta. That night he discharged a pistol in her bedroom.

"Was that an accident?"

"Yes."

"You meant to make me lose my child."

Now Augusta felt that she could no longer control Byron. She wrote to Mrs. Clermont, Annabella's old governess, and to George Byron, her cousin and Byron's heir, asking them to come and stay. "If Byron goes on in this way," she wrote, "God knows what he may do!"

They arrived, and Mrs. Clermont at once asked Fletcher to sleep in the room next to Annabella's bedroom. Byron, to her surprise, raised no objection. Fletcher himself was frightened by his master's behaviour; and everyone was careful to do nothing to upset him. But they tried to make sure that Annabella was never left alone with him. Augusta and Mrs. Clermont guarded her particularly, and Augusta sat up with her every night. Then the night nurse came and acted as an extra guardian. Captain Byron was very disturbed by all that he saw and heard.

Annabella longed for her mother. Lady Noel had arrived to stay at Mivart's Hotel in Lower Brook Street, but she had fallen ill. There was no question of her coming to the house.

It was all the worse for Annabella because she was suffering from a particular fear. She had never cared for dolls, and now she was certain that she would not love her child. She told nobody. But she thought of the baby only as "it." At her mother's wish, Dr. Le Mann had been chosen as her *accoucheur* in preference to one of the fashionable London doctors. Her mother told her to choose the best clothes for her lying-in and for her baby's layette, and to send her the bill from Bontner's. Annabella looked at the baby clothes without interest. But every day she wrote merry letters to one or the other of her parents. She joked about Byron's throwing the parrot and his cage out of the window, and her relief when the parrot came down safely, calling out, "Johnny!" She told them how delighted Byron was at the thought of making Lady Noel a grandmother. But in private she was composing verses about her misery.

At last she had made a decision. Byron must be mad. There was no other explanation for such behaviour. She must take advice So, large as she was, and averse to all effort, Annabella went to consult Samuel Heywood, the sergeant-at-law. She told him that Augusta had agreed to the consultation, and that they both suspected that Byron was insane. Should she leave the house? she asked him. He hummed and hawed, and said he would write to her.

Next day Byron came to see her. "I hope you'll die in labour," he said, "and that the child won't live. If it does, I'll curse it." Oh, God, Annabella thought, I'll wait till the child is born, and then decide whether to leave this house. After all, I might die and be spared having to do anything about it.

Three hours later, on that Sunday, December 10, 1815, Annabella felt her labour pains begin. Fletcher was sent off for the doctor and the midwife, and she went to lie down. Lady Noel had been summoned, too, but had sent a message to say that she was too ill to come. She was, in fact, dangerously ill.

The doctor arrived after what seemed a long time—a big, red-faced, cheery man. "If only my mother wasn't ill," Annabella fretted.

"She'll have a fine grandchild to make her better," he comforted her. Then startled by the sound of blows on the ceiling of the room below, and of furniture being flung about in it, he asked, "What is that noise?" Annabella turned her head away without replying. What was Byron doing? Was he throwing his soda-water bottles at the ceiling to prevent her sleeping?

At one o'clock she gave birth to a girl. The news was sent down to Byron at once. Augusta tiptoed in, admired the baby and said, "Byron will come soon." Then she slipped away.

Ten minutes later Fletcher knocked on the door and spoke to the midwife. "His lordship says that Lady Byron is to be told that her mother is dead," he said.

"I can't tell her that," the midwife protested. "This is no time—"

"I'm sorry," Fletcher said. "It's his lordship's orders."

Reluctantly the midwife went to Annabella and whispered to her. "No!" Annabella screamed. "No! No! No!" Terrible sobs racked her. Then, "Mrs. Leigh," she begged. "Please call Mrs. Leigh."

Augusta came quickly. She held the sobbing Annabella to her, stroking her hair.

"Oh, Guss," Annabella wept, "that my mother should die at this moment."

"Your mother? Dead?" Augusta was incredulous. "I've heard nothing about that. Who told you?"

"Byron—a message."

"I'll send at once to Mivart's Hotel." Augusta ran out of the room, scribbled a hasty note, pressed it into Mrs. Clermont's hand, and sent her off in the carriage.

"Now," the doctor said, "the father may see his child." Tactfully he left the room.

Byron was summoned, and came into the bedroom. "The child *was* born dead, wasn't it?" he asked sneeringly. Yet Annabella saw that his eyes were on the baby, and his face was tender. She turned her face away without answering or mentioning the message he had sent her. It is strange, he loves it more than I do, she thought miserably, I still feel nothing for it. Byron swung on his heel and left the room.

At last Mrs. Clermont returned and came up, with Augusta.

"It's not true, my lady," she reported indignantly. "Lady Noel is very ill, but she is alive and very angry at the lying story. I saw her myself. She rejoices at the birth of her granddaughter."

Now Annabella wept even more than before, but it was from relief, and she was smiling.

On December 20 the baby was registered as Augusta Ada, daughter of Lord and Lady Byron. Annabella was still confined to her room. Augusta had been asked to be a godmother, and the baby was to be named after her.

Byron was behaving worse than ever. His paroxysms of frenzy and his horrible threats were exhausting everyone.

83

Once he threw down a favourite old watch of his and ground it to pieces in the hearth with a poker. He was still throwing money away—suddenly he gave fifty guineas to Charles Maturin, the dramatist, who was supposed to be starving. Murray had sent him a thousand guineas from the sale of *The Siege of Corinth* and *Parisina*, but he had refused them. At any rate, he had at last received six thousand two hundred pounds from Hanson, raised on the security of Newstead, and his creditors were staved off, at least temporarily.

Annabella was quite certain that Byron was insane, but she wanted medical proof. On January 2, 1816, he ignored their first wedding anniversary. Next day he came to her room and began to talk in obscene detail about his affairs with actresses. She endured it in total silence, and at last he went away. After that he did not come near her or the child again.

Two days later Annabella drove in the park for her first outing since the birth. Determined to be silent and brave, she still said nothing of her misery to her mother, to her visitors, or to anyone else. She even managed to be playful when she wrote to her mother: "I'm giving suck while I write, and oh, dear, she pinches me!" However, she warned her parents in the same letter that she and her family might descend on them at Kirkby Mallory, where they had now returned.

Two more days went by. On the third morning Annabella awoke as drearily as usual, expecting nothing out of the ordinary. Then Fletcher brought her a note from Byron. "When you are disposed to leave London," it read, "it would be convenient that a day should be fixed—and, if possible, not a very remote one for that purpose. As Lady Noel has asked you to Kirkby, there you can be for the present, unless you prefer Seaham. The child *will* of course accompany you. There is a more comfortable and safer carriage than the chariot (unless you prefer it) which I mentioned before. On that you can do as you please."

Annabella went to him. "What do you mean by this?" she demanded angrily, waving the letter. "I won't go."

"You will—or I shall leave this house."

She drew a deep breath. It was better, she remembered, not to provoke him, however monstrous his conduct. "Very well," she said. "I will go."

Next day she wrote a note to him and sent it to his room —"I shall obey your wishes, and fix the earliest day that circumstances will admit for leaving London."

That day Annabella waited for Byron to leave the house, and slipped into his room. She looked through his drawers and trunks and letter cases. She found his laudanum and the novel *Justine* by the Marquis de Sade, which had been banned, but nothing else. Then she looked at *The Medical Journal*. She decided that he was hydrocephalic, and marked the passage with pencil in the margin.

Next day Annabella went to see Hanson at his house. She told him of her fears, and handed him a list of sixteen symptoms she said Byron was suffering from. "I'm going away to stay with my parents," she said.

"You don't mean to restrain him personally, I hope?" Hanson asked nervously.

"No, I don't. But he may take his own life if he is *not* restrained."

"Are you afraid of him?"

"Oh, no, not in the least. My eye can always put his down."

"Hmmm. Don't take him too literally. He's always been irritable."

"Irritable! If I'm wanted in London, let me know. I'll come at a moment's notice."

She could delay no longer. Yet she did not feel that she and her child were strong enough yet to travel. She had hoped for a definite decision about Byron's mental health before leaving.

She felt it would be a positive relief if his monstrous rages and cruelties were due to a deranged mind. It would be better than if he were himself a monster of evil. She would have delayed longer, but Captain Byron came to her. "I won't allow you to stay another day in this house," he said. "If you do I'll inform your family of what has been going on myself."

"Well, I don't want that, so I must go. Let it be January the fifteenth."

On January 14 Annabella went into the room where Byron was sitting. She was holding her baby.

"Byron, I have come to say good-bye."

Byron put his hands behind his back. He rose and backed away to the mantelpiece.

"When shall we three meet again?" he asked.

"In heaven, I trust," Annabella replied firmly. For a moment Byron looked shocked. Then he laughed. Annabella left the room, went up to her bedroom and fell into a deep sleep.

Next morning Annabella woke, still exhausted. She could not eat. She rose, dressed and went downstairs, holding her baby. The carriage was already at the door. She passed Byron's room. There was a large mat outside it on which his Newfoundland dog used to lie. For a moment she was seized with an overwhelming desire to throw herself on it and wait for him to come out. It lasted only a moment. She passed through the door, her baby clutched close to her, and entered the carriage. The coachman flicked his whip and drove away.

* * *

CHAPTER
✻ 7 ✻

Annabella and her unweaned baby were travelling alone, on the long, cold drive to Kirkby Mallory. The coach stopped at Woburn for the night. Cradling her baby in one arm, Annabella wrote to her husband.

"Dearest B— The child is quite well and the best of travellers. I hope you are *good*, and remember my medical prayers and injunctions. Don't give yourself up to the abominable trade of versifying—nor to brandy—nor to anything or anybody that is not lawful and *right*.

"Ada's love to you with mine. Pip."

Next day she reached Kirkby Mallory. She said nothing to her parents, but went to bed at once. The following morning she wrote again to Byron.

"Dearest Duck, If I were not always looking about for B I should be a great deal better already for country air. *Miss* finds her provisions increased and fattens thereon." She paused, then added, "Love to the good goose and everybody's love to you both from here. Ever thy most loving Pippin . . . Pip. . . . Ip."

Annabella did not hide her misery from Augusta, however. The same day she wrote two long letters to her. Her mother and father, she said, wanted Byron to come and stay. Would Augusta make him come? He had said that he would get a male heir and go abroad. So Augusta could tell him to go to Kirkby Mallory and get his heir by her. Would Augusta, too, fill his laudanum bottle three-quarters full of water? She had, she said, told her parents only her fears about his threats to go abroad, his use of laudanum, his paroxysms, and her dread that he might be deranged. She wanted to get him away from London. Annabella wrote to Byron's cousin and heir, Captain Byron, too, asking him to persuade Byron to go to Kirkby Mallory. Then she induced her mother, Lady Noel, to write to Byron, pressing him to come for a visit.

The letters had gone to be posted. Annabella was sitting in the drawing room with her parents. Suddenly she burst into loud sobs and cries. Lady Noel flew to her, and Annabella flung her arms about her mother. She sobbed out all that had happened at number 13 Piccadilly—but she said nothing of her suspicions of Augusta. Sir Ralph sat in stupefied silence.

"It's too much," Lady Noel cried. "You must never return to that beast. If he is sane you must promise never to go back."

Annabella nodded miserably.

Next day Lady Noel sat over Annabella while she drew up a statement of Byron's misdeeds.

"Now I shall take that to London and see a lawyer," Lady Noel said.

"I expect he will get better. Then I can go back."

She was terribly torn. Sometimes she even contemplated suicide. In that mood she wrote to Augusta, "I mean to break my neck upon my old horse, which is here." At other times she was cold and numb, uncaring. Then, at others, she would have abandoned everything and everyone to fly back to Byron. Every day, it seemed, a letter came from Augusta, telling her about Byron's activities, his words and his silences. She lived in spirit in the house she had left, and wrote, "O, that I were in London, even if in the coal-hole!" Yet that very day Lady Noel left for London with her statement.

As soon as Lady Noel arrived in London she went straight to the great lawyer, Sir Samuel Romilly. He listened gravely, and in silence, then said, "Don't let Lord Byron stay at Kirkby Mallory. That would be condonation." Then he advised her to put the whole matter in the hands of Dr. Stephen Lushington. "He is a most distinguished barrister of the Inner Temple. We will have a conference, dear lady."

Next day they had their conference. Then Lady Noel saw Annabella's doctor, Dr. Le Mann, Augusta, and her housekeeper, Mrs. Clermont, separately.

"I haven't seen any proofs that the patient is insane," Le Mann said uneasily. "I believe he is, but I can't say there's any settled lunacy there."

To Augusta Lady Noel said, "He's bad, not mad." She stared at Augusta's figure—she was pregnant again.

"But he may take his own life," Augusta protested, in tears.

"So much the better," Lady Noel answered bitterly. "It is not right that such men should live." But even she sat in shocked silence while Mrs. Clermont described all that she had seen and heard of Byron's behaviour.

Lady Noel had only just left the house when Captain Byron went to see Byron.

"You see, Lady Noel is here," he said. "It's because you were cruel to your wife, I'll be bound. Her parents will take up the matter."

"Let them," Byron answered. "I'll glory in it. As for her— I want a separation. I prefer the pretty actresses at the theater. They're better in bed and in every other way. I'll marry Miss Mercer Elphinstone if I can get rid of that vixen."

On January 28, 1816, Lady Noel and Mrs. Clermont arrived at Kirkby Mallory. Augusta had sent Fletcher's wife with them to help Annabella with her baby. Lady Noel brought a letter drafted by Sir Samuel Romilly for Sir Ralph to send to Byron. It proposed a quiet separation. Annabella read it, weeping bitterly. But she nodded, and it was written out and posted.

Two days later at breakfast the letter reappeared. Augusta had intercepted it and returned it. "Please think again," she implored Annabella. Annabella passed her letter to Lady Noel in silence.

"Sir Ralph, you shall go to London," Lady Noel said firmly. "This will never do. You must deliver the letter yourself."

So the next day Sir Ralph and Mrs. Clermont travelled up to London and put up at Mivart's Hotel. That day, February 2, the letter was delivered to Byron in person. He had just ordered a coach and horses to take him to Kirkby Mallory the following Sunday. He read:

"Very recently, circumstances have come to my knowledge, which convince me that with your opinions it cannot tend to your happiness to continue to live with Lady Byron, and I am yet more forcibly convinced that after her dismissal from your house, and the treatment she experienced whilst in it, those on whose protection she has the strongest natural claims could not feel themselves justified in permitting her to return thither. I am willing to bring the whole matter before the public, if necessary, but I hope that you will agree to appoint a professional friend to consider with one of my appointment the terms of a separation."

Byron was thunderstruck.

"Guss," he said, waving the letter at his sister, "write to Annabella and ask if she's responsible for this."

Augusta wrote, and they waited. Annabella's reply came. She had agreed, she said, to her father's proposal for a separation. Augusta, distressed, withheld that letter too from Byron.

Then at last Byron wrote to Annabella. It was a carefully phrased letter. He did not understand, he said, what part of Sir Ralph's letter meant. He would abide by her decision, but requested her most earnestly to weigh well the probable consequences. He signed himself ever her most affectionate Byron.

Annabella did not reply. Instead she urged Augusta to give Byron her previous letter, which he had clearly not received.

By Monday February 5 Byron had still had no word from Annabella, and Hobhouse called to find him very depressed and blaming Lady Noel and Mrs. Clermont.

"I swear to you, Hobhouse, that Annabella and I parted friends. I can't guess the reason for all this. Look at this letter." He thrust the letter beginning "Dearest Duck" into Hobhouse's hands.

"Shall I write to her for you?"

"Yes, do, my dear fellow. Tell her on no account to take such a step. I'll write to her, too."

"I loved you," he wrote, "and I won't part from you without your express and expressed refusal to return to, or receive, me."

Augusta was in anguish. She had been appointed a lady-in-waiting to Queen Charlotte the previous March, and had rooms at St. James's Palace. There must be no gossip concerning those in personal contact with the Queen, and if Byron's troubles reached the law courts there was danger that she would lose her position. It was high time, in any case, that she went to the Palace to stay.

Now, indeed, the gossip which Augusta feared began. Lady Melbourne wrote to Byron that she had heard rumours of a separation—false, of course, she was sure, but widely believed. "Can't you get Annabella to come to town, or go to her yourself?" she asked him.

Annabella received Byron's letter the day after he had written it. She read it, fell to the floor and began to roll about, apparently in agony. Mrs. Fletcher ran to her, terrified at what she saw. When at last Annabella was persuaded to go to bed Mrs. Fletcher wrote to her husband: "My mistress is in the height of distress and agony. She was rolling on the floor at having promised to separate from Lord Byron. She shows by every word and deed that 'tis her family which has compelled her to quit her husband."

Hobhouse's long letter had been sent on the day of Annabella's attack. By then, too, Byron had received both Annabella's letters. Augusta had not dared withhold them any longer. Terribly shaken, Byron wrote to his wife:

"Were you then *never* happy with me? Did you never at any time or times express yourself so? Have no marks of affection passed between us? Or did in fact hardly a day go down without some such on one side and generally on both? Had I not—had we not—the days before and on the day when we parted, every reason to believe that we loved each other, and that we were to meet again? You are much changed within these twenty days, or you would never have thus poisoned your own better feelings—and trampled upon mine."

As he ended Hobhouse arrived. Augusta took him in to her brother and waited.

"Here are her two letters," Byron blustered. "Do they show misery and ill treatment? I never did anything to hurt or harm her. Augusta, was I not a loving husband?"

Augusta was silent.

"Well? Well?"

"Yes," Augusta said, her face tortured. "Yes, a very loving husband—and she is a loving wife, too." She left the room.

"Douglas Kinnaird told me this morning," Hobhouse said abruptly, "that Lady Caroline is accusing you of—well, you know what of."

Byron paled, remembering the hanging man. He could never forget that the penalty for sodomy was death. He did not reply, and after a while Hobhouse left the room. He found Augusta waiting for him outside. "I'd like to speak to you alone," she said. "I want to tell you the truth."

She spoke to him for half an hour. Then he cross-examined her. At length he said, "Let me go to him."

When Hobhouse came out he went to see Augusta again.

"He has confessed it all," he said miserably.

"What, exactly?"

"To very great tyranny, to menaces, to rages, to neglect, even real injuries. He admitted that he had told her he was living with another woman, and also that he turned her out of the house. He told me he locked her in and out of rooms, threatened her with pistols—and frowned at her in bed! After he had denied it all to me, too. Now he says, 'Yet she loved me once,' and now, 'I'm glad to be rid of her.' He said if I go abroad with him at once he'll separate from her. And he threatened to blow out his brains again and again."

"I'll go and see how he is," Augusta said. She was gone a long time, Hobhouse thought, but it was only a quarter of an hour.

"He is crying bitterly in his room," she said, weeping herself.

"Poor, poor fellow!" Hobhouse said. "I'll make it my business to try to prevent rumour becoming scandal. *You* try to get a reconciliation."

He took his leave, mounted his horse and rode away, his head hanging dejectedly.

No one could change Annabella's mind. She wrote to Byron for the first time, saying that she had believed him to be mad, and so had written him affectionate letters. Now, she said, she knew him to be sane, and her resolution could not be changed. To Augusta she wrote, "*Happiness* no longer enters into my views. I deem it my duty to God to act as I am acting." She scoffed at Byron's threats of suicide. "I know him too well to dread the fatal event which he so often threatens."

Then at last Byron wrote his final appeal to Annabella.

"And now, Bell, dearest Bell, I can only say in the truth of affliction, and without hope, motive, or end in again saying what I have lately but vainly repeated, that I love you, bad or good, mad or rational, miserable or content, I love you, and shall do, to the dregs of my memory and existence."

Annabella tried to harden her heart as she read. It was a work of art, she told herself, only a work of art, like all those he had written when he was courting her. The next sentence made her blood run cold.

"I have hitherto avoided naming my child, but this was a feeling you never doubted in me. I must ask of its welfare." Would he try to take the child from her by law? Her new barrister, Dr. Stephen Lushington, said that no one could be sure of preventing that.

On February 10 Hobhouse called at number 13 Piccadilly Terrace again, and found Captain Byron there. Captain Byron told him what Douglas Kinnaird, the banker and a great friend of Byron's, had reported was said openly by a woman at a party. Augusta had not actually been named, but the word incest had been used.

"I'll deny it, I'll disprove it," Hobhouse protested. "I'm his closest friend, and will be believed."

"Perhaps."

That night Hobhouse sat with Byron until half-past one in the morning. He told him the worst he had heard against him, and he used the word incest. To his astonishment Byron received it all without apparent surprise or discomposure. Yet Hobhouse could see that he was very worried, and very frightened.

Annabella had had an interview with Dr. Lushington. She had written asking for it, saying, "There are things which I, and I alone, could explain to you, that may be of great importance to the thorough understanding of the case." She added, "As to terms, I want simply not to be molested, and to have the child—I cannot think of anything else."

When Annabella had said all she meant to, Dr. Lushington said, "This has changed my opinion of the case completely,

Lady Byron. No reconciliation is now possible. You said nothing of these, humph, relations with his sister in your statement."

"I hoped it wouldn't be necessary to bring it out."

"My advice is to seek a separation."

"In court?"

"In court, if necessary. You should rest your case on Lord Byron's brutally indecent conduct, and you should use as part of your evidence his crude references to intercourse with Mrs. Leigh as a means of torturing his wife. But no effort should be made to establish the *fact* of incest."

"But as his wife I cannot give evidence against him."

"Quite. So if your evidence is legally excluded you cannot prove incest."

"I will not appear at a public hearing."

"Then we are left with only one weapon. You and your counsel must use all possible means to get Lord Byron's friends to persuade him to agree to a private settlement and a quiet separation."

"Very well."

"Meanwhile you must not see Mrs. Leigh."

"I will never agree to that. She has done me no harm."

"Then you must sign a statement, to safeguard your position—a limited personal correspondence only, and a single interview."

"Well—if I must."

There was, it seemed, to be nothing quiet about the separation, however. As the rumours grew and grew, with Byron's name linked with Augusta's, Byron asked Annabella for an interview; and she refused it. Then the lawyers on the two sides began to wrangle about a settlement.

First Byron received a proposal for giving up five hundred pounds a year and half the Noel reversion to Lady Byron. There was no mention of the sixty thousand pounds he had settled on her; nor of the fact that on Lady Noel's death he would get between three and four thousand pounds a year.

"I'll sign nothing which binds me to a definite division of the Kirkby property," Byron swore.

"At least," Hanson pleaded, "bring a suit to force Lady Byron to return to you before the other side enters suit."

"No. I'm told I have a good defendant's case."

Augusta and Annabella had their meeting, and Annabella said again and again that she had not been coerced into asking for a separation. "It's my own wish. See that he understands that."

"Byron may kill himself," Augusta pleaded.

"I cannot help it. I must do my duty."

The day after that Hobhouse found a letter from Annabella to Byron on Byron's writing table. He picked it up and read it. In it she claimed that, of his own act and will, Byron had promised to consent to a private arrangement.

"Did you promise that, Byron?"

"Yes—yes, I did. Through Augusta."

"You'll have to keep to it, then," Hobhouse said grimly. "She can enforce it." Byron admitted, too, that he had already made overtures for a mediator to try to arrange a private separation.

Byron was feeling reckless, careless of what might happen. He ignored a letter from Lady Caroline, offering to swear that she had spread injurious reports for the purpose of deceiving his wife: "There is nothing, however base it may appear, that I would not do to save you and yours from this. Do not, oh, do not, believe those who would lead you for one moment to think she knows anything for certain. Be firm, be guarded."

Byron could not ignore the next disaster. He packed up his library and sent it away till it could be sold. It should, he was sure, fetch nearly five hundred pounds. But hardly had the books gone than he heard that the sheriff had traced them, and they had been attached against his debts. He had to return the five hundred pounds Murray had advanced on them. "This is about the tenth execution in as many months," he wrote to Murray, "so I am pretty well hardened to them."

At last the agreement was drawn up. Annabella had refused Byron's offer to resign the whole of her present allowance of a thousand pounds a year. She asked for only five hundred pounds a year, leaving Byron the other five hundred. When her parents died, she said, she wanted the Kirkby property to be divided on fair terms of arbitration. She agreed to sign a statement that neither she nor her family had spread any reports injurious to Byron, and that neither incest nor sodomy made any part of her charge.

"She does not say that they are not true," Hobhouse objected. "Only that she will not bring them forward in court."

"That's as far as she will go," Byron said.

"Very well. I suppose it's better than nothing. You'd better accept," Hobhouse said. He added, "Your sister seems near a breakdown, Byron. She says she's not seen three of her children since November; and all the world can see she's far gone in pregnancy now—it's embarrassing for her. She's very upset by all these rumours. She's given the lie to them by staying, ignoring them. And Colonel Leigh has supported her handsomely. But I think she should go back to the Palace now."

"Very well. Very well. Let everyone abandon me."

Next day Augusta left number 13 and went to her rooms in the Palace. To her relief the Queen said nothing to her about the rumours. Yet Augusta was sure she could not fail to be aware of them. She was overcome with gratitude. She would not have been surprised to have been sent away.

The day after, Annabella signed another statement, more formal than the first one. She had added to her barrister Dr. Lushington's draft that Augusta had always been kind, that she had sometimes shown deep remorse, and that she, Annabella, believed it possible that there had been no incestuous intercourse between her and Byron since her own marriage to him.

On March 17, 1816, the basis for the separation was finally agreed on. On March 22 Hobhouse found Byron, to his astonishment, in great spirits at the prospect of going abroad soon. He seemed to be thinking only of packing. Hobhouse watched him sorting out a few prints, a silver cup, and a large screen covered with pictures of actors and pugilists and scenes from boxing matches. They would be auctioned, he said, with such books as were left to him after the sheriff's seizure. To Hobhouse it seemed somehow to mark the finality of what had happened—to cut the cord that tied Byron to England with one blow. Yet his friend gave no sign of distress. He wondered whether he would ever really understand this strange man of whom he was so fond.

* * *

CHAPTER
𝕏 8 𝕏

Byron was being pursued. He had received a letter written from 21 Noley Place, Mary le Bonne, signed by the name E. Trefusis, which meant nothing to him and which was written in very frank terms. "If a woman," it ran, "whose reputation has yet remained unstained, if, without either guardian or husband to control her, she should throw herself upon your mercy, if with a beating heart she should confess the love she has borne you many years, would you betray her, or would you be silent as the grave?"

He had not replied. Next time a letter came signed G.C.B., which again meant nothing to him. It read, "Lord Byron is requested to state whether seven o'clock this evening will be convenient to him to receive a lady to communicate with him on business of peculiar importance. She desires to be admitted alone and with the utmost privacy."

This time he returned a curt answer. "Ld. B is not aware of any 'importance' which can be attached by any person to an interview with him, and more particularly by one with whom it does not appear that he has the honour of being acquainted. He will however be at home at the hour mentioned."

At seven o'clock his visitor arrived. She was about eighteen, with black curly hair, and she was quite plain. She seemed intelligent and very solemn, this dumpy girl in the red dress with a frilly white collar framing her round face.

"I'm Mary Jane Clairmont—but please call me Claire."

She explained that she was the daughter of the second wife of the famous William Godwin by her previous husband. (She did not tell him that she was, in fact, illegitimate.) William Godwin's first wife, Mary Wollstonecraft Godwin, author of *The Vindication of the Rights of Women*, had died at the birth of her daughter Mary. So when Mrs. Clairmont had married Godwin there were two Marys in the house. "It was *I*, of course, who had to lose my name. They called me Jane. But *I* call myself Claire—it is prettier." She prattled on, telling him of her own dedication to the right of women to lead their lives as they pleased, whether they were married or not.

"My stepfather is all for free love, in theory, but he didn't like it at all when Percy Shelley deserted *his* wife and eloped with Mary two years ago. He called him 'that atheist.'" She told him, too, how she had gone with Shelley and Mary on their honeymoon elopement through France and Switzerland, and how now, back in England, she still spent part of her time with Mary and Percy at Bishopsgate, and the rest with the Godwins at Skinner Street. Shelley had supported her, and she loved him. But Mary had grown jealous, and had wanted to break up the trio. "She calls it a *ménage à trois*. She doesn't want me."

And now, Byron thought cynically, she wants to show Mary that she can get a poet of her own, and one more famous than Shelley. She knew that he kept women. Had she heard too that his wife had left him? He kissed her hand and ordered Fletcher to show her out.

Claire Clairmont came again and again. Now she begged him to help her become an actress, now to read her efforts at writing, and now she tried to use Shelley or Mary to interest him. Byron was upset by Annabella's unforgivingness, harassed by the arrangements for his departure, and in need of love—from anyone. Then he discovered that Claire had a beautiful voice—always an irresistible charm for him. She sang to him, and after that he no longer sent her away when she came.

* * *

One evening Byron was sitting in his rooms in a miserable mood. He had just written a poem for Annabella.

Fare thee well! and if for ever,
Still for ever, fare thee well:
Even though unforgiving, never
'Gainst thee shall my heart rebel.
Would that breast were bared before thee
Where thy head so oft hath lain,
While that placid sleep came o'er thee
Which thou ne'er canst know again.

The tears poured down his face as he read it—how easily he wept, he thought. But she *had* been cruel.

Though my many faults defaced me,
Could no other arm be found,
Than the one which once embraced me,
To inflict a cureless wound? . . .
When our child's first accents flow
Wilt thou teach her to say "Father."
Though his care she must forego? . . .
All my faults perchance thou knowest—
All my madness—none can know;
All my hopes—where'er thou goest—
Wither—yet with thee *they go . . .*
Fare thee well! thus disunited—
Torn from every nearer tie—
Seared in heart—and lone—and blighted—
More than this I scarce can die.

He addressed the poem to her, with a note, "I send you the first verses that ever I attempted to write upon you, and perhaps the last that I may ever write at all." Would Annabella reply? Probably not. In that case he would give them to Murray. She had never replied to anything. Lord Holland and Samuel Rogers and Douglas Kinnaird had all written letters testifying that he, Byron, had never said anything but good about her. She had sent them back, with no answer. He knew who to blame—he would teach her. A different sort of poem this time, for Mrs. Clermont.

> *Born in the garret, in the kitchen bred,*
> *Promoted thence to deck her mistress's head;*
> *Next—for some gracious service unexpressed,*
> *And from its wages only to be guessed—*
> *Raised from the toilet to the table, where*
> *Her wondering betters wait behind her chair.*
> *With eye unmoved, and forehead unabashed,*
> *She dines from off the plate she lately washed.*

Now he would describe her:

> *A lip of lies; a face formed to conceal,*
> *And, without feeling, mock at all who feel,*
> *With a vile mask the Gorgon would disown,*
> *A cheek of parchment, and an eye of stone . . .*

And now he would curse her:

> *May the strong curse of crushed affections light*
> *Back on thy bosom with reflected blight! . . .*
> *Down to the dust! and, as thou rott'st away,*
> *Even worms shall perish on thy poisonous clay.*
> *But for the love I bore, and still must bear,*
> *To her thy malice from all ties would tear—*
> *Thy name—thy human name—to every eye*
> *The climax of all scorn should hang on high,*
> *Exalted o'er thy less abhorred compeers,*
> *And festering in the infamy of years.*

He did not know that two days previously Annabella had accepted Lady Caroline Lamb's invitation to meet her, sacrificing her pride to her curiosity; and that she had found it rewarding. Bitterly, after the interview, she had written to Dr.

Lushington that it had changed her "strong impression into *absolute* conviction." Now she could no longer doubt that Byron's taunts of having committed incest with his sister were true, and not merely made to torment her.

On April 3 Hobhouse came to stay at number 13. That night he and Byron dined with Leigh Hunt and Scrope Davies, his old friend who had lent him money to go abroad in 1809. They talked of the time when Tom Moore, the Irish poet, and Byron had dined with Leigh Hunt while Hunt was in prison in the Surrey Gaol for libelling the Prince Regent; and Byron chatted gaily. Hunt was horrified at the way Byron expressed his most shocking thoughts to everyone. "He looks jaundiced," he muttered to Hobhouse, his eyes shifty under his shock of hair.

"He's well—seems well," Hobhouse said. "But he won't be still—and he drowns his sorrows." He was depressed because he could not go abroad with Byron. He had been refused a passport for some time to come because he had written a book about the Hundred Days of renewed imperial sway, which had put the nations of Europe once more in terror. Hobhouse's book, favouring Napoleon's case, had been considered near-treason.

On April 8 Byron's remaining books were sold at auction. Hobhouse bought thirty-four pounds' worth, and Murray bought some for Augusta; some for Samuel Rogers, the poet, banker, connoisseur and literary patron; and some for himself, as well as the screen. The sale brought seven hundred and twenty pounds less expenses. Had Byron's signature, Murray told him, been in each volume, they would have sold for twice as much.

That night Lady Jersey, the beauty and reigning queen of the most select London society, was giving a party.

"Come with me, Augusta," Byron said. "It will put a stop to the gossip if we are seen together. No one would believe we would dare to face the world together if we were guilty."

Augusta felt a little ill and more than a little shy about her pregnant figure, but she dressed and went with him. They arrived in good spirits. Then as she entered the drawing room, Augusta saw to her horror eyes shifting from her and faces turning away. She moved towards an acquaintance, and found a back presented to her. It happened again and again. She was being cut. "Take me home, Byron," she begged, and he saw that she was chalk-white. "No," he said. "See it through. You must." So she stayed by his side.

He saw that he, too, was being cut by women who had once crowded about him. He turned to the men. Some of them also turned their backs on him. He stood his ground, looking as cool as he could. Only Lady Jersey, his hostess, came to speak to him. He stood, leaning on a small table, his heart cold. He was absolutely alone but for Augusta. Woman after woman swept by him without speaking, and left the room.

Suddenly one of them stopped, and he recognized her. It was Miss Mercer Elphinstone, who had flirted with him in his great summer of 1812. She was rich enough not to care, he thought—only she. Her red hair was heaped high, and she looked very lovely to him. Now she gave him a little nod and stopped by him. "You should have married *me*," she said, "and then this would not have happened to you."

I will never forget this, he said to himself, never. He took Augusta away, and she went back to the Palace. That night he sent Miss Mercer Elphinstone a book which he had saved from his library for himself.

It was after that dreadful night that his friends deliberately set out to make up to him for the slights. They saw him every day, and dined with him whenever they could. Sometimes, after dining out, they stayed with him until six o'clock in the morning. All his friends were kind, he thought—only Annabella was cruel. And when Augusta sent her a precious family heirloom, a lock of the hair of Charles I, to be given to Ada one day, and received only a formal note from her solicitor, Hobhouse had a difficult time trying to calm her and her brother.

Time was going by, however slowly. On April 14 Hobhouse decided to go home to his father's house at Whitton, so that Byron might have a whole day alone with Augusta in which to make his farewells to her.

Augusta came from St. James's Palace. Now she was heavy with child and very near her time. She was almost hysterical at the slights she had suffered at Lady Jersey's party. She declared that the rumours about her were growing more and more vicious. She was very upset, too, that Annabella had deserted her.

"I am going home tomorrow to Six Mile Bottom," she said.

Byron handed her a poem he had written for her.

"There, Guss," he said. "This will show you how I feel."

Augusta read, and as she read Byron rehearsed the lines in his mind.

> *When fortune changed, and love fled far,*
> *And hatred's shafts flew thick and fast,*
> *Thou wert the solitary star*
> *Which rose and set not to the last . . .*
> *Still may thy spirit dwell on mine,*
> *And teach it what to brave or brook—*
> *There's more in one soft word of thine*
> *Than in the world's defied rebuke.*
> *Thou stood'st, as stands a lovely tree,*
> *That still unbroke, though gently bent,*
> *Still waves with fond fidelity*
> *Its boughs above a monument . . .*
> *Then let the ties of baffled love*
> *Be broken—thine will never break;*
> *Thy heart can feel—but will not move;*

Thy soul, though soft, will never shake.
And these, when all was lost beside,
Were found and still are fixed in thee;
And bearing still a breast so tried,
Earth is no desert—ev'n to me.

The tears were falling slowly down Augusta's cheeks. At the end she embraced him silently, and they clung together for a long time. Then Augusta gave him her own parting present—a Bible. "I feel," Byron sighed, "that we will not meet again."

Not until the end of the day, however, when Augusta was about to leave, and for the first and only time, did Byron express remorse for his guilt. That Easter Sunday they parted, never to meet again.

Byron had sent his poem about Augusta to Murray; and Murray had circulated it. Worse, he had shown it to Lady Caroline Lamb. At once she wrote a frantic letter to Byron. "I do implore you for God's sake not to publish the verses. You will draw ruin on your own head and hers if at this moment you show these. If you could hear all that is said at this moment, you would believe one who would perhaps die to save you." Byron wrote angrily to Murray, blaming him for showing the poem to Lady Caroline against his frequently repeated instructions. "You do not know what mischief you do by this," he wrote.

Then Byron wrote his last letter to Annabella.

"I have just parted from Augusta—almost the last being you had left me to part with, and the only unshattered tie of my existence. Wherever I may go—and I am going far—you and I can never meet again in this world, nor in the next. Let this content or atone. If any accident occurs to me be kind to *her*; if she is then nothing, to her children. And recollect that, though it may be an advantage to you to have lost your husband it is sorrow to her to have the waters now, or the earth hereafter, between her and her brother."

Annabella did not reply.

Byron had incurred the disapproval of Samuel Rogers and Leigh Hunt, Hobhouse found, for having published *Fare Thee Well.* It was, they thought, most ungentlemanly. The papers were full of violent abuse of him. Hobhouse tried to prevent him seeing them; but he bought them all and pored over them.

"It's time you went, Byron," Hobhouse said.

"Yes, it's time. I'll go."

He had found someone he thought would be very useful to him on his travels on the Continent. He was a doctor and a scholar and a language teacher—Dr. John Polidori, the son of an Italian exile. He was young, vain and cocksure, but a doctor was always useful, and he spoke French and Italian as well as English. Byron's coach was ready, too—an exact copy of Napoleon's green carriage which had been captured at Genappe. It had a bed, a library, a plate chest, and everything necessary for dining in it. The price was five hundred pounds, but payment, he decided, could wait. He was doing everything he could to raise money for the trip.

As the time drew near for Byron's departure the efforts of the girl who had written to him so importunately to get him to bed grew more and more feverish. He was cold to this Claire Clairmont, and made no attempt to hide his boredom, but that did not deter her. It was already past mid-April, and he was expecting to leave as soon as the separation deeds were signed. He discovered, too, to his horror that Claire was planning to meet him in Geneva. She wanted Shelley and Mary to go there with her. Shelley, she told him, had already made up his mind to leave England, and Mary was eager to go to Italy by way of Geneva. Shelley was engaged in a complicated wrangle about his grandfather's will in the Court of Chancery, to be settled in a day or so.

Now Claire offered herself to Byron outright. "I don't expect you to love me," she wrote. "I am not worthy of your love. I feel you are superior, yet much to my surprise, more to my happiness, you betrayed passions I had believed no longer alive in your bosom. Have you any objection to the following plan? On Thursday evening we may go out of town together by some stage-coach or mail-coach about the distance of ten or twelve miles. There we shall be free and unknown; we can return early the following morning. Will you admit me for two moments to settle with you *where*? Indeed I will not stay an instant after you tell me to go."

So they went, and returned. She had had her way.

On Sunday, April 21, 1816, at half-past three in the afternoon Hanson brought the separation deed. Hobhouse, Byron thought, had witnessed the deed for the marriage settlement, on December 31, 1814, and now he was to witness the separation deed. He and Annabella had parted not long after their first wedding anniversary. They would be legally separated in less than sixteen months. Byron signed the deed and handed it to Hanson theatrically, with the words, "I deliver this as Mrs. Clermont's act and deed."

Monday, April 22, was Byron's last day in London. His last-minute packing was interrupted by a constant stream of visitors come to say good-bye to him. He found time, however, to write a brief note to Augusta.

"My own sweet Sis, The deeds are signed, so that is over. All I have now to beg or desire on the subject is that you will never mention nor allude to Lady Byron's name again in any shape, or on any occasion, except indispensable business."

Hanson came to bid him farewell. He had just left Lady Byron, he said, and she had signed the separation deed. "She looked well," he said, "but she was dreadfully torn."

Samuel Rogers, the poet and connoisseur, came to say good-bye, too, as did Douglas Kinnaird and his old friend Scrope Davies. "Do you really mean never to return?" Scrope asked.

"Good God! I never had it in contemplation to remain in exile. Why do you ask that question?" Scrope made no reply.

Claire sent him note after note begging for a last-minute meeting, and imploring him for his address in Geneva. At length he gave it—*poste restante, à Genève.*

The day for Byron's departure came—April 23, 1816. Despite his hatred of early rising, it was, he knew, vitally important to start before the bailiffs arrived. It was only a matter of hours, everyone knew, before they came.

It was a largish party which was setting off with him— Polidori and three servants. There were Fletcher and Robert Rushton, both leaving their wives behind, and a Swiss named Berger. Hobhouse was going to see him off at Dover, and Scrope Davies had decided to do so, too.

Hobhouse was up at six, and had finished breakfast soon after, but the party did not get off until half-past nine. Polidori and Hobhouse travelled in Scrope Davies's chaise, and Byron and Scrope went in Byron's bright new Napoleonic carriage. There was a crowd about the door as they set off.

At Canterbury they stopped to admire the cathedral, but soon pressed on. They arrived at Dover at half-past eight in the evening. They had had nothing to eat all day except snacks in the carriages, and now they dined well at The Ship Inn, and drank light French wines. It was very late when they went to bed.

Next morning they heard by letter sent by special messenger from Kinnaird that the bailiffs had entered number 13 Piccadilly just after they had left, and had seized anything and everything Byron had left behind. "Nothing, in short, but the birds and the squirrel," Byron laughed.

"Byron, you must get the carriage aboard," Hobhouse pressed him. "They may be following now, and will seize it. The seizure's for the half-year's rent owing to the Duchess of Devonshire."

So they got the carriage aboard ship. But they could not

sail. There was a strong wind, and the captain refused to put out. They had dinner at five o'clock, then walked out to see the grave of Charles Churchill, the satirist and friend of John Wilkes, the revolutionary parliamentarian of the days of George III. Churchill's *Rosciad* had been one of the models which had inspired Byron's *English Bards and Scotch Reviewers*. Byron lay down on the grave, and gave the gravedigger a crown to returf it.

The news was spreading fast that Byron was in Dover. Word passed from mouth to mouth, and soon ladies were borrowing the chambermaids' uniforms so that they could have a close look at him without loss of dignity.

Next morning the wind had moderated and shifted. Now the captain was anxious to set sail. But Byron and his party were not on board. Hobhouse had risen at eight and had done his best to rouse Byron. The captain swore he would not wait, but Byron refused to get up. Even the carefree Scrope Davies was worried.

At last Byron came down, strolling casually out of the inn. He took Hobhouse's arm and walked down to the quay. They walked all the way through a lane of spectators in an atmosphere of bustle and hubbub. Byron was clearly enjoying himself. He climbed aboard and went to the ship's rail.

As the packet glided off, Hobhouse saw that suddenly Byron looked stricken. Hobhouse ran to the end of the wooden pier. The vessel tossed by, and Hobhouse caught sight of him again. Byron pulled off his cap and waved it at him. Hobhouse gazed until he could see him no more.

"God bless him for a gallant spirit, and a kind one," he said aloud.

* * *

CHAPTER
❦ 9 ❧

Here he was, surprisingly, settled in a fine villa on Lake Geneva—the Villa Diodati—with Percy Shelley and Mary Godwin, and Claire Clairmont, as neighbours. He had meant to be in Venice by now.

A good deal lay behind him. He would not easily forget those sixteen hours of seasickness to Ostend, and the squalid inn at the end. All the same, he had not been too ill to fall on the chambermaid there—like a thunderbolt, Polidori said. Then he had gone through Ghent and Antwerp, bored to death by the Rubens paintings. The field of Waterloo had been a different thing—he had charged on horseback, singing, across it, pretending he was leading a charge against the enemy. Then he had written the first draft of his poem commemorating Lady Richmond's ball, at which the gay young officers had danced before going to their deaths.

> *There was a sound of revelry by night,*
> *And Belgium's capital had gathered then*
> *Her beauty and her chivalry—and bright*
> *The lamps shone o'er fair women and brave men;*
> *A thousand hearts beat happily; and when*
> *Music arose with its voluptuous swell,*
> *Soft eyes looked love to eyes which spake again,*
> *And all went merry as a marriage bell;*
> *But hush! hark! a deep sound strikes like a rising knell!*
>
> *Did ye not hear it?—No—'twas but the wind,*
> *Or the car rattling o'er the stony street;*

On with the dance! let joy be unconfined . . .
But hark!—that heavy sound breaks in once more,
As if the clouds its echo would repeat;
And nearer—clearer—deadlier than before!
Arm! Arm! it is—it is—the cannon's opening roar!

So it had gone, faultlessly, to the splendid last lines.

The earth is covered thick with other clay
Which her own clay shall cover, heaped and pent,
Rider and horse—friend—foe—in one red burial blent!

When they had reached Geneva he'd put his age in the inn's register as a hundred—felt it, too. A letter from Claire Clairmont was awaiting him there, and she followed it as soon as he arrived. She was pregnant. That didn't stop her pestering him to sleep with her at the inn. As usual he had given way, now and then, out of sheer weakness.

At last he'd met the boy wonder Shelley, and found him pleasant. Shelley was only twenty-three to Byron's twenty-eight, and was living with the two women, Claire and Mary Godwin, at the Maison Chappuis on the lake. He was not at all the ethereal and unworldly figure he had expected. He was very tall but terribly bent, and so thin his bones and joints stood out quite horribly. He didn't walk, but loped in the most awkward way. Shelley wore a schoolboy's jacket, and no gloves, and unpolished shoes. His voice was high-pitched and strident. Yet no one could possibly take him for anything but a gentleman, and there was nothing pathetic about him. This was a tough man, determined to have his own way if it smashed everything and everyone about him.

So there he was, in his Villa Diodati, away from the prying English, who had actually used spyglasses to stare at him when he was at the inn, and from the gossiping of the narrow-minded Swiss. Shelley and Byron often went sailing together on the lake, and Byron dieted off a good deal of the fat he had put on in those last, horrible days in London. He ate nothing but a slice of bread and a cup of tea for breakfast, only vegetables and seltzer water at noon, and only a little tea without milk or sugar at night; he was so hungry he had to chew tobacco and smoke cigars to quell the hunger pangs. But without Claire it might all have been extremely pleasant. She was the only flaw—always pleading with him to *like* her, and to say that he would be very pleased to have a little baby, and would take care of it. He refused to be involved—it was all her fault, not his.

To his surprise he quite liked Mary Godwin, though he distrusted clever women. A strange girl, only eighteen but very clever—as the daughter of Godwin and Mary Wollstonecraft should be—solemn, and more than a little in love with him, he thought. She was not a beauty, but she had a fine brow and a very fair skin, speaking grey eyes, delicate features, and very silky, thick, light-brown hair falling in ringlets on her shoulders. She had beautiful white arms and hands, too. Mary was a little too rounded, perhaps. But it was her coldness that chilled him—she was too intellectual, and he had had enough of that with Annabella. He never forgot the night when they had played a game, all of them making up ghost stories. He had started one about a vampire, but she had begun a ghoulish tale about a monster created by a Count Frankenstein; and then kept on with it when they had all abandoned theirs. A determined miss.

Shelley was a brave fellow. Suddenly one day on the lake there had been a squall, and they had been in danger. It looked as if the boat would sink before they reached the shore. Then Shelley had admitted that he couldn't swim, and Byron offered to save him if it came to it. Shelley had refused outright. He had no notion of being saved, he said, and added that he, Byron, would have enough to do to save himself, and he wouldn't trouble him. Well, luckily, it hadn't come to that. Yet—did Shelley want to die? It had looked like it.

It was at the Villa Diodati that the news came of the dreadful book which Caroline Lamb had published—her *Glenarvon*—with a quotation taken from *The Corsair* on the flyleaf.

> *He left a name to all succeeding times*
> *Link'd with one virtue and a thousand crimes.*

It was a dreadful novel, a libel, which everyone took for the truth, with a vile picture of him, and a worse one of her, as characters in it. She published it anonymously, but it was an open secret, and it was said the whole of English society was agog with it. Well, he could do nothing about that.

Then the matter of Claire's pregnancy became urgent. Shelley and Mary Godwin agreed to take her back to England to give birth. She had been violently angry when he suggested giving the baby to Augusta. "A child needs its parents till it's at least seven years old," she cried. So he had given way and agreed to take the child, and promised never to part with it to strangers until it was seven years old. Claire was to be known as the child's aunt, so that she could see it and watch over it without arousing scandal. Even in the midst of all that hullaballoo he had written *The Prisoner of Chillon* after a visit to the Castle of Chillon. He had composed a tender poem to Augusta, too, expressing his aching longing to live with her.

> *Go where I will, to me thou art the same—*
> *A loved regret which I would not resign.*
> *There yet are two things in my destiny—*
> *A world to roam through, and a home with thee . . .*
> *For thee, my own sweet sister, in thy heart*
> *I know myself secure, as thou in mine;*
> *We were and are—I am, even as thou art—*
> *Beings who ne'er each other can resign;*
> *It is the same, together or apart—*
> *From life's commencement to its slow decline*

We are entwined—let death come slow or fast,
The tie which bound the first endures the last!

Yet Augusta's letters to him were strange and incoherent, anxious, and full of vague alarms—what he called her damned crinkum crankum. He had done his best to comfort her, and had written, "We are the last persons in the world who ought or could cease to love one another. Ever dearest thine + B." But no answer had come from her.

At last Hobhouse and Scrope Davies had arrived at the end of August. They had come through Calais, where they had seen Scrope's old gambling companion, George Brummell. Beau Brummell had fled the country owing fifty thousand pounds—a change from his gay days, when he had set the tone with his clothes and cravats, and even the Prince Regent followed his lead. Byron had always been a little jealous of Brummell. The night before Hobhouse and Scrope arrived he saw Claire for the last time, at the Villa Diodati, and dismissed her without a farewell kiss. It was all arranged. She would never hear from him again directly. Everything would be managed through Shelley. Three days later she and Shelley and Mary left—with the third canto of *Childe Harold* and *The Prisoner of Chillon* for Murray. Murray was to look at his *Epistle to Augusta*, too, the first of his two poems to her, but *she* was to decide whether it was to be published or not.

So then he and Polly Dolly—as he called Polidori—and Scrope and old Hob went travelling to see Mont Blanc and the other sights, until Scrope too departed, taking Robert Rushton and more of Byron's manuscripts back with him. Only to Augusta did Byron write his true feelings—that the separation had broken his heart: "I feel as if an elephant had trodden on it. I breathe lead." Still, nothing came from her to ease his pain. Then, when at long last she wrote, she babbled only of

Annabella's kindness. "Do not altogether forget," he replied, "that she has destroyed your brother."

In October the news reached him that his wife was ill. At once he wrote his verses to her—as vengeful and excoriating as he could make them.

> *And thou wert sad—yet I was not with thee;*
> *And thou wert sick, and yet I was not near,*
> *Methought that joy and health alone could be*
> *Where I was* not—*and pain and sorrow here!* . . .
> *I am too well avenged!—but 'twas my right;*
> *Whate'er my sins might be,* thou wert not sent
> *To be the Nemesis who should requite* . . .
> *Even upon such a basis hast thou built*
> *A monument, whose cement hath been guilt,*
> *The moral Clytemnestra of thy lord!* . . .
> *The means were worthy, and the end is won—*
> *I would not do by thee as thou hast done!*

It was another ungentlemanly poem. Of course it was, but what of that? He hated her.

Other things changed. He tired of Polidori and dismissed him, but with a generous payment, in September. He had borne with him until he went too far. Polidori had dared to ask him, "And, pray, what is there excepting writing poetry that I cannot do better than you?" He had replied, "Three things. First, I can hit the keyhole of that door with a pistol shot. Secondly, I can swim across that river to yonder point. And thirdly I can give you a damned good thrashing." That had finished Polidori for him.

He had broken new ground in another way. Murray had offered him fifteen hundred pounds for his new *Childe Harold* cantos and for *The Prisoner of Chillon,* and Kinnaird raised that to two thousand pounds. This time he meant to take the money, though his name was to be published.

So now, while Claire and Mary Godwin awaited the birth

of Claire's child in Bath, he met Claire's letters with silence, and worked on a new poem, *Manfred*, which throbbed with his love for Augusta, its theme clearly incestuous.

> *She was like me in lineaments—her eyes—*
> *Her hair—her features—all, to the very tone*
> *Even of her voice, they said were like to mine;*
> *But softened all, and tempered into beauty;*
> *She had the same lone thoughts and wanderings . . .*
> *Her faults were mine—her virtues were her own—*
> *I loved her, and destroyed her!*

He made Manfred conjure up Nemesis to call the phantom of Astarte, his love, his Augusta. But no pleas of his can make her speak to him.

> *Astarte! my beloved! speak to me . . .*
> *. . . . . .Thou lovedst me*
> *Too much, as I loved thee: we were not made*
> *To torture thus each other—though it were*
> *The deadliest sin to love as we have loved.*

She will not speak—as Augusta would not speak. She utters his name, says "Farewell!" and disappears. Farewell, Augusta?

So at last on September 18 he left for Venice at six o'clock in the morning, without a good-bye to anyone. That had been Switzerland.

*   *   *

CHAPTER
❧ 10 ❧

He arrived in Venice with Hobhouse. It was not as he had expected. They left the carriage and horses at Mestre and embarked, in pouring rain, in a gondola. Now he felt as if he were in a black box, or a hearse. For an hour and a half they saw nothing but the stakes in the water.

Milan, where he had stopped on his way, had been disastrous, thanks to Polidori. He had turned up after crossing the Alps on foot, and they went to the theater. There Polidori fell afoul of an Austrian officer who refused to remove his grenadier's hat, which was blocking his view. Polidori was taken off to the guardhouse, and released only on condition that he leave Milan next morning for good. That was Byron's first experience of Austrian bullying, begun after Napoleon's fall, when the Congress of Vienna divided Italian territory into several states small enough to present no problems, and gave Lombardy and Venice outright to Austria, leaving Piedmont and its island of Sardinia as the Kingdom of Sardinia. Thanks to Polidori, he knew, the Austrians would be watching him from then on with their secret police.

In Milan, too, he had been devastated by a letter from Augusta, saying that if he came back to England she would not see him alone. He wrote back that no human power would prevent him from seeing her whenever and wherever and however he pleased, and that anything which divided them would drive him insane. He told her, too, of his fits of giddiness and deafness, his greying, thinning hair, his loosening teeth, and

118

his enduring bitterness against Annabella. She didn't answer him.

Now lights were reflected in the black, smooth, rain-dappled water, as they glided past tall houses and stone piers, and under a bridge—*the* bridge, Shylock's bridge, the Rialto. Then, suddenly, they were landing at the Hotel Gran Bretagna on the Grand Canal, and being shown up a magnificent flight of stairs into rooms full of gilt and painted silks. He fell in love with it all at that moment. No sooner was his luggage put in his rooms than he went out again in the drizzle, for the rain had eased, to stroll through the narrow streets and the great squares.

What a city! From the two famous columns at the edge of the lagoon onto which the Piazza San Marco faced, he could see the Doge's Palace, the Basilica of St. Mark, the colonnades surrounding the piazza, and the campanile—a panorama of history and beauty in one sweep.

True, the great days of Venice were over. Only two or three *conversazioni*, where one could meet civilized people, were left, and only two coffeehouses were open all night. Yet it was still a wonderful, fascinating place—he would be happy there. Best of all, since nobody walked anywhere in Venice, his limp would not be so noticeable.

Next morning he went out early, and immediately found lodgings in a private house in the Frezzeria, a small alley-like street just off the Piazza San Marco. They cost only twenty francs a day, and were over the shop of a draper named Segati, with the sign of the stag—Il Cervo—over it. He was shown over the premises by the draper's wife, Marianna, and as soon as their eyes met he knew he would be stag to that doe. Marianna was twenty-one, with large, black, Oriental eyes, and regular, rather aquiline features, a small mouth, a clear, soft skin, dark, shining, curly hair, a light, pretty figure, and a sweet voice. She could sing, too, she told him—always for him the ultimate charm. She had one child. She would satisfy certain needs, and the *conversazioni* of the Countess Albrizzi, others—he would meet Alfieri the poet and Canova the sculptor there. He would have his own gondola and study Italian. He would tell Augusta all about Marianna—and all about Claire and her baby, too.

On Sunday, January 12, at four o'clock in the afternoon in Bath, Claire gave birth to a daughter, whom she called Alba while she awaited Byron's decision about a name. Byron received the news in a letter from Mary, which she signed proudly Mary W. Shelley. That, he knew, was a result of Shelley's having to face a Chancery suit to deprive him of the custody of his children by his first wife. That wretched girl, Harriet, whom he had deserted, had become pregnant by another man and had drowned herself. Her family wanted to keep her children, and Shelley wanted to take them to live with him, so he had married his mistress in order to seem respectable to the court. Harriet had had a baby soon after he left her—*his* child—and the boy would be heir to the Shelley baronetcy after Shelley's death. Mary begged Byron in her letter to write to Claire, but he would not. She was a faraway, unpleasant memory.

Now he was absorbed in Venetian life. It was a wicked place, Venice, where if a married woman had only one lover she was considered chaste, and a husband slept with anyone's wife except his own. The only thing he did not care for was the *cavalier servente* business—all that carrying of fans and twirling of shawls the wife's lover had to subject himself to. He was no good at it. His Marianna turned out to be jealous. She had torn out the hair of her sister-in-law and slapped her face when she found them together—but her husband was accommodating. Byron had plenty of other women, too, though not as many as he pretended in his letters to his friends in England. Yet he was working hard, even during the

Venetians' annual springtime Carnival. He had finished *Manfred*. In fact, he was so exhausted by the time the Carnival was over on February 18 that he began to feel that the sword was wearing out the scabbard. He wrote:

So we'll go no more a-roving
So late into the night,
Though the heart be still as loving,
And the moon be still as bright.

For the sword outwears its sheath,
And the soul wears out the breast,
And the heart must pause to breathe,
And love itself have rest.

Then illness struck after the Carnival, and grew worse. Marianna looked after him, but he found himself longing for England—longing for it, and dreading it. If only he could reinstate himself in some military or political career. He wrote to Tom Moore, his Irish poet friend: "If I live ten years longer you will see that it is not over with me—I don't mean in literature, for that is nothing, and odd though it may seem to say it, I do not think it my vocation. But you will see that I shall do something or other—the times and fortune permitting." Then he added, "But I doubt whether my constitution will hold out." After all, in ten years he would be nearly forty, and his life of constant dissipation was hardly likely to lead him to old age. He spent a terrible two weeks in bed, with a burning skin, an unendurable thirst, a continual headache, and almost no sleep—he was delirious some of the time, too. Marianna said it was an annual Venetian epidemic, and foreigners usually got it.

All he really wanted, Byron told himself, was Augusta, and she was no comfort at all. At length he rebuked her again for not writing to him. "*I* never shrank," he protested, "and it was on your account principally that I gave way at all, for I thought they would endeavour to drag you into it—although they had no business with anything previous to my marriage with that infernal fiend, whose destruction I shall yet see."

He could not know that now Augusta was completely in thrall to Annabella, and that all his letters to her went straight to his former wife. For many months Annabella and a former close friend of Augusta's, Mrs. George Villiers, had been bullying and bribing Augusta. Now she was completely in their power, beyond hope of ever again escaping. At that very time Annabella was writing to Mrs. Villiers, "She has shown me of her own accord *his* letters to her—having only suppressed them because of the bitterness to me. They are *absolute love letters*—and she wants to know how she can stop them."

Byron decided to spend the summer in the Villa Foscarini at La Mira, a pretty village about seven miles from the river mouth at Fusina on the Venetian lagoon. Marianna could stay with nearby friends, and visit him in the great boxlike mansion, and relax in its small, shady English garden. He had been there since June, and Hobhouse was with him.

He had paid a price for publishing *Manfred*. Murray had been frightened out of his wits, certain that everyone would recognise Augusta in Astarte. Sure enough, when it appeared, *The Day and New Times* published an attack on its theme of incest, and pointed the finger at him. Roundly it had declared that he had "coloured *Manfred* with his own personal features." It had reached him all too soon, and he read it at once. He had flung down the paper and shouted for Hobhouse to go riding with him.

Hobhouse and he galloped hard along the Brenta River. The sun was just setting, and they were slowing down their horses, when he noticed two very pretty girls standing in a group of peasants. One was very dark and tall, at least five foot ten inches, with a splendid figure. The other girl was smaller, but very pretty, too. To Byron's surprise the tall one called out,

"Why don't you think of us, too, with your gifts?" So, she had heard of his charities and wanted her share. "Dear one, you're too beautiful to need my help."

"If you saw my hut and my food you wouldn't say so."

"I'll come and see them tomorrow."

Next day, again at sunset, he kept his promise. The tall one, he found, was called Margarita Cogni, and the little one was her cousin—Margarita was married to a baker and her friend was single. Hobhouse liked the little one, but he was nervous and soon left the hut. The little one followed him.

"Will you sleep with me?" Byron asked Margarita.

"I don't mind making love with you, for I'm married and all married women do it. But my husband is very ferocious—he might kill me."

A few evenings later they met, and he had his way. Margarita was full of animal passion, but she wasn't jealous like Marianna. "Have all the women you want," she laughed. "You'll always come back to me." She couldn't read or write, which was another good thing. There would be no letters like Claire's from her, pestering him.

Then Marianna found out. He had visited Margarita, known as La Fornarina because she was a baker's wife, late at night while her husband was baking, and his horse neighed and gave him away. By morning Marianna was told; and by noon had stormed up to Margarita and screamed at her. He had been there, by the river, to see it all. La Fornarina was wonderfully cool. She threw back her veil, her pretty *fazziola*, and replied, "*You* are *not* his wife, and *I* am not his *wife*. *You* are his *donna*, and *I* am his *donna*. Your husband is a cuckold, and *mine* is another. For the rest, what *right* have you to reproach me? If he prefers what is mine to what is yours, is it my fault?"

Marianna's husband, Segati, at least gave no trouble. He came at weekends, to make love to another man's wife, and brought Byron all the gossip from Venice.

Byron was tiring of women and the troubles that inevitably came with them. He preferred the company of a new friend, the smooth, suave Richard Hoppner. Hoppner had been the British consul in Venice since 1814. He was the son of the famous portrait painter, and an amateur painter himself, and was married to a pretty, pleasant Swiss woman. Already Hoppner was handling all Byron's business affairs for him. Then by September he was heartily sick of Margarita Cogni and her friends at La Mira. She was, it seemed, jealous after all—and vindictive. Once she had thrown her scissors at him. She was expensive, too—she had already cost him about five hundred pounds. Then Marianna was pretending—if she *was* pretending—that she had found another lover, and was ready to throw him over. Just when he was getting over Annabella other women became a burden.

November slipped by. He had been away from England for just over eighteen months. At first no news came about Newstead, but by December he heard that the Abbey had been sold to his old Harrow schoolfellow, Major Thomas Wildman, for ninety-four and a half thousand pounds. It was a great relief. Now he could pay off the moneylenders and settle his debts. He might even settle the half-year's rent still owing to the Duchess of Devonshire, and send five hundred pounds for his Napoleonic carriage. From what remained he could arrange for a regular fixed income for himself. He was so relieved that he wrote to Shelley at once in high spirits, saying he would look after his bastard by Claire if Shelley would have the child sent to him at Venice. Shelley would be glad to be rid of the little girl—there was talk in Bath that Shelley had fathered her, and that therefore he had wanted to put her with two respectable young ladies to get her out of his house. Shelley answered at once to say that he would be bringing his family to Italy and wintering in Pisa for his health, and would bring the child himself.

In the end Byron had decided to call her Allegra, a Venetian name. Her surname was to be spelled Biron, not Byron—his legitimate daughter must not be embarrassed by her illegitimate half sister.

On January 7, 1818, Byron and Hobhouse took their last ride together on the Lido, and said farewell at midnight. The next morning Hobhouse left for England, carrying the manuscript of Byron's new cantos of *Childe Harold*. And the next day the Carnival began. Now Byron was heartily sick of Marianna and her tantrums. Worse, she had sold some jewels he had given her. He had bought them back for her, but he had not forgiven her. So now he threw himself into the Carnival, taking all the women he could persuade to sleep with him—he even found a blond, blue-eyed Venetian girl. It was a saturnalia—romance, masks, passion and pleasure—and all to forget that dreaded day, his thirtieth birthday, on January 22.

That evening Byron examined himself anxiously in the mirror. There was nothing to comfort him there. His hair was decidedly greying, and thinning, and beginning to recede. He could feel that his teeth were loose, too, though they were still white. Well, at least, he thought, his lame foot was hidden, now that he wore his trousers very long and affected great capes touching his toes—and no one noticed it at all when he was on horseback. All the same, he was filled with depression. He would go to the Countess Albrizzi's and forget his age in company.

It was midnight when he entered the Countess's salon. Almost at once he was sorry he had come—the company was boring, the usual collection of pretentious intellectuals. Then his eye was caught by an extremely pretty girl—the prettiest girl he had ever seen. Who was she? He asked his hostess, and was told that she was half-Greek, half-French, and had come to Venice from Padua for the Carnival.

Then the door opened, and another girl entered. She was

short, with auburn ringlets falling to her shoulders. She had a plump, full bust, rounded arms, and a fair, fresh complexion. Her legs were too short, and she was too broad below the waist, he thought, yet her face was pretty in a doll-like way, with its large, soft eyes and small, smiling mouth. She looked passionate, if rather naïve. He preferred the other girl.

Byron looked away to find his hostess asking him to escort the newcomer to see her Canova bust of Helen of Troy. "The Countess Guiccioli is a bride of three days," she was saying, "and very tired from two days of travelling." The little Countess could not have been more than eighteen, he decided, looking at her again.

"And this is Count Guiccioli," the Countess Albrizzi was saying.

He looked round for him. That old man. He must be sixty if he was a day. Byron bowed to him and offered his arm to the little Countess. He led her to the Canova. But she was exhausted, he could see that. She could hardly raise her eyes to the bust, and she hardly noticed him. As for him, he hardly noticed her, either. He liked women with life in them. The Greek girl was much prettier, too.

*　*　*

CHAPTER
❦ 11 ❧

On March 9, 1818, Claire Clairmont took her child to the parish church of St. Giles-in-the-Fields in London. The infant was christened Clara Allegra, and in the register the entry was made, "Clara Allegra Byron, born of Rt. Hon. George Gordon Lord Byron ye reputed father by Clara Mary Jane Clairmont." Claire had no intention of their relationship being overlooked, and had not spelled the child's name Biron.

Two days after the christening Shelley and Mary, Claire and Allegra, an English maid, and Elise, a Swiss nurse they had brought with them from Geneva in 1816, left England. After a month of travelling the party arrived at Milan. There they waited, in the hope that Byron would come for his daughter. But he would not leave Venice. Shelley gave him nine days, then wrote to him again, telling him that the little girl had arrived in excellent health and spirits, "with eyes as blue as the sky over our heads." He asked him to visit them and take her home. Byron's reply came quickly and it was sharp. He asked Shelley to send the child to Venice with a nurse. He would send a messenger from Venice to conduct her.

Claire burst into tears, and Shelley wrote again: "You write as if from the instant of its departure all future intercourse were to cease between Claire and her child. This I cannot think you ought to have expected or even to have desired. I know the arguments present in your mind on this subject; but, surely, rank and reputation and prudence are as nothing in comparison to a mother's claims." But Byron would not give way.

"Don't send her to him," Shelley urged Claire. "A Venetian at the post office told me of his terrible life in Venice. His home will be no place for her."

Then another letter came from Byron. It was gentler and promised that Claire should see her child again soon. Claire immediately recovered her spirits.

"He's not as bad as he pretends. Send her to him," she said.

So at the end of April Allegra left Milan with Elise and Byron's messenger. With them went a letter from Claire: "Dearest and best, I entreat you to think how wretched and lone I feel now she is gone, the darling bird. I have one favour to beg of you. Send me the smallest quantity of your own dearest hair that I may put it with some of Allegra's in a locket. My dearest Lord Byron, best of human beings, you are the father of my little girl and I cannot forget you."

Now Byron was installed in the Palazzo Mocenigo. He had had a painful spring because not only had he caught gonorrhea, for the first time since 1811, but both his mistresses had given him a great deal of trouble. Margarita Cogni had persuaded her husband to take an oven in Venice; and now that she was able to visit him she was creating constant friction with Marianna Segati.

He decided it was high time to move out of his lodgings. Besides, he needed more room. He had made up his mind to take one of the palaces that were so cheap in Venice, and found what he wanted at once. The Palazzo Mocenigo was the third of three palaces built close together—a fine, massive building of grey stone, dating from the great days of the merchant princes. It faced north, just beyond the first sharp turn of the S-shaped canal. One could see the Rialto Bridge from it, and the palace was only a few hundred yards from the Piazza San Marco. There were three floors above the ground floor, which opened out on to the gondola landing. On the second of the upper floors was a vast and lofty drawing room, outside of which was a fine stone balcony overlooking the canal. There were dozens of rooms, large and small, for guests, for servants —and for Allegra. Yet for all that he would pay only a pittance. He took a lease for three years at once.

Marianna had been sent away, and Margarita, he thought grimly, might soon find herself in the same boat.

On May Day Allegra and her nurse arrived in Venice. Byron's nerve almost failed him as he opened the door for his first sight of his daughter. Was this another Claire? If so, he could not answer for his feelings.

The small, self-contained fifteen-month-old creature in a long dress who stood alone in the middle of the floor looking up at him was not in the least like her mother. She was very pretty, and as soon as he spoke to her he knew that she was intelligent. Her eyes were very blue, and her hair was fair and curly. Yet as she turned her head she suddenly reminded him of his own mother. The thought was unbearable, and he repressed it. At once he wrote to Augusta to tell her of the child's prettiness, her intelligence, and her charm. "She has the devil of a spirit," he added, "but that is Papa's."

It was a pleasure, unexpectedly, to have this new toy, provided Claire and the Shelley crew were kept at a distance. Mary Shelley was having a great success with her novel, *Frankenstein*, and perhaps that would keep their noses out of his business—she would be busy writing another book, no doubt. Allegra would help him, too, to forget another blow. Lady Melbourne had died. She had been the best, kindest, ablest woman he had ever known, old or young, and a friend to the end. He had taken it hard.

So he went on with his life: daily rides with Hoppner on the Lido, and swims in the Grand Canal, and women, always women. His latest was a pretty opera singer. Then, late at night, every night, he worked at his poems, sometimes until dawn broke. Settling into the Palazzo Mocenigo took time, too.

Now he had fourteen servants, of whom Fletcher was the only one who was English. He had also supplied himself with some animals—two monkeys, a fox and two mastiffs. They lived on the chilly, damp ground floor, where he could stop and play with them on the way to his gondola. He had engaged a gondolier, Giovanni Battista Falcieri, known as Tita. Tita came of a family of celebrated gondoliers, and his father and brother served the Mocenigo family. He was a burly fellow, all muscle, and he looked ferocious. They said he had stabbed at least two men—murdered them—and certainly he looked the part, with his tasselled fez worn on one side as if in deliberate braggadocio, his shirt opened to the waist and his great arms always akimbo. Yet Byron had found him as gentle as a woman—or gentler.

Now his friends in England hardly bothered to reply to his letters. Hobhouse and Kinnaird were absorbed in politics; and even Hanson didn't trouble to send the Newstead papers for his signature.

He was eating too much again, and getting very heavy and looking bloated. The Venetian women didn't seem to mind—perhaps because he spent a lot on them. His affairs, Hoppner said, were the talk of Venice, even of the gondoliers; and the English visitors all wanted to come and gawk at him. Some of them had even bribed his servants to let them into his palace. He had actually found two of them in his bedroom once. He heard that two women had described him to Lord Glenbervie as a fat, bulbous-headed, middle-aged man, unkempt and extremely slovenly, with long locks that hung on to his shoulders, shabbily dressed and with appalling manners. Was it as bad as that? He didn't think so, and if it was it couldn't be helped.

He liked Venice, gay, cheap Venice, and he would go on living there. In two years he had spent five thousand pounds. He could have lived on a third of that if it hadn't been for the women. Even so, women were cheap in Venice, and what was three thousand or so for two hundred women of one sort or another? Two hundred? Well, that was the figure he would stick to—it was a good boast and it made his English friends jealous.

There had been one excitement in June—his swimming match with the Cavalier Angelo Mengaldo. He had been boasting, as usual.

"I swam the Tagus at Lisbon, and the Hellespont."

"And I," the Cavalier had rejoined, to his surprise, "swam the Danube, and the Beresina, under enemy fire."

"Let's have a competition, then, and see who is the better man."

"Agreed."

Alexander Scott, a good-looking young English bachelor who was visiting Venice, had joined them. The starting place was the Lido, and the finishing post the entrance to the Grand Canal. He had leapt into the water at half-past four, and swum steadily until a quarter past eight with no rest. Both he and Scott had outdistanced Mengaldo.

Suddenly Byron decided that the Palazzo Mocenigo was not the place for Allegra, and sent her to the Hoppners with her nurse Elise. Elise wrote to Claire at once. Claire received her letter on August 14, and had a fit of hysterics. Byron had given his word not to send the child to strangers until she was seven, she railed at Shelley, and it must be stopped.

Three days later Claire and Shelley suddenly left Bagni di Lucca, where they had all been staying, for Venice—a journey of well over two hundred miles. As they travelled, Claire asked Shelley again and again, "Where shall I stay? What shall we do?" At first Shelley suggested that she stay at Padua while he negotiated with Byron.

"No. No. I must go to Venice. I must see my child."

They arrived at midnight after five days of travelling, and went straight to the Hoppners. Elise woke the little girl and brought her to them. She was taller, Claire thought, and pale, and not so lively as before, but she was as beautiful as ever.

"Now, Claire," Shelley repeated, before the Hoppners, "Byron mustn't know that you're here. I hope that you'll keep the secret, Your Excellencies." The Hoppners agreed to do so.

At three o'clock next day Shelley called on Byron at the Palazzo Mocenigo, and at once told him of Claire's anxieties.

Byron listened politely but said nothing. When Shelley had finished he said, "Come, let us go to the Lido and ride."

They went in Byron's gondola, and rode along the sands. It was sunset before they left for Venice. Then, back in the Palazzo, Byron refused to let Shelley go, keeping him talking until the small hours. Claire had been waiting for Shelley since three o'clock on Sunday afternoon.

At five o'clock on Monday morning Shelley returned to Claire, spoke briefly to her and at once began a letter to Mary. Byron, he said, had offered him and his family the use of his villa, the Casa Capuccini, at Este in the Euganean Hills, not far from Venice. Allegra could visit her mother there. Mary must come to Este at once, where he and Claire and Allegra would meet her. Meanwhile the Hoppners would look after Claire and not let Byron know that she was actually in Venice. Mary *must* do as he said in order to support what he had told Byron—that Claire was staying with Mary and her children at Padua. Then Allegra could join her mother and her little friends for a summer holiday.

Next day Shelley visited Byron again and played with Allegra while he was waiting for his host. Byron had sent for the child, not knowing that Shelley had already seen her at the Hoppners, especially to show her to him.

It was on August 28 that Mary Shelley received her husband's letter at Bagni di Lucca. She was to pack and, with her two children, start off within two days on five days' travel.

Mary dropped the letter on her lap. At the best of times she would have flinched from struggling alone across Italy with two small children in the baking August heat. Shelley, she thought, had not allowed Claire to travel alone, and now she must face the dreadful journey alone with her children. Worse, the baby, Clara, who was not yet a year old, had been ill ever since Shelley had left. She was teething, she was very young, and she was not at all strong. Then travelling in Italy was bad at the best of times. Now at the height of summer, the dangers would be at their worst for travellers—fevers, unclean food and water, and the heat itself. Yet what could she do? Shelley would be angry, and Byron offended, if she refused, and she might spoil Claire's chances of ever being with her child again.

So on August 30, her twenty-first birthday, Mary Shelley packed for the journey up the Arno Valley to Florence, over the formidable Etruscan Apennines, and across the plain of the River Po, with her two-year-old son, William, and her baby, Clara.

Hardly had the journey begun than the baby, already weak, seemed to sicken. Then she had an attack of dysentery. Mary clutched her to her bosom, anxiously watching her face. There was nothing she could do but travel on and pray.

The nightmare had lasted for what had seemed an eternity. When Mary at last stumbled out of the coach at Este, Clara was desperately ill. Shelley met her in a bad temper. He had made himself sick eating Italian cakes, and was sharp and impatient, making light of the baby's illness.

As soon as they were settled in the villa Clara began to regain her strength and her colour, but it was a slow recovery. Day after day went by, and the baby was still weak and thin and feverish, a shadow of what she had been. Shelley was still impatient of Mary's worries about her. He worked hard on *Prometheus Unbound*, oblivious of everything else. At least, Mary thought wearily, the villa was a pleasure. The rooms were light and spacious, the gardens were full of fruit trees, and the vines were heavy with grapes. Beyond it was a ruined

Gothic castle, which had once been inhabited by the Medicis before they settled in Florence. Now only owls and bats lived in it.

Claire was not well either. On September 22 Shelley took her to the doctor at Padua. They had meant to ask his advice about Clara, too, for she was still weak and very thin, but they arrived late and found the doctor gone. They made another appointment for Thursday, September 24. "Now, I shall go on to Venice," Shelley said to Claire. "I want to see Byron again." He handed Claire a letter for Mary.

Mary opened Shelley's letter to her. "Am I not like a wild swan to be gone so suddenly?" it began. As she read on she realized that Shelley was demanding that she and the sick baby were to go with Claire to Padua on Thursday, meet him there and travel on to Venice. But Claire's appointment with the doctor was at eight-thirty in the morning. "You must therefore arrange matters so that you come to the Stella d'Oro in Padua a little before then—only to be done by setting out at half past three in the morning."

Once again Mary had to pack up for herself and little William and baby Clara, and follow Shelley and Claire. Shelley, she thought bitterly, had no thought for what it meant to her and them—he was simply thinking of Claire and of his friendship with Byron.

At half-past three in the morning Mary wrapped Clara as warmly as she could against the cold, and set off with her and William. Hardly had the coach driven off than the nightmare of her first journey began again. At once Clara became ill.

When Mary staggered from the coach at Padua, Clara was very ill. Mary pointed to her baby, the tears streaming down her face.

"She's dying," she sobbed to Shelley.

"I don't think much of the doctor here," he said. "We must go on to Venice." He was white, suddenly, at last, realizing the danger.

As they rattled and bumped on through the heat Mary grew more and more terrified. The tiny, shunken baby was clearly failing, her eyes rolling back in her head. Life and death, Mary knew, hung on their speedy arrival in Venice. They did not arrive until five o'clock in the evening. Looking down at her child, Mary could not be sure whether she was alive or dead. She stood, silent and miserable, surrounded by a crowd of gondoliers screaming and yelling their demands. Shelley made his choice, and instant silence fell.

In the gondola Clara went into a convulsive fit. At long last they arrived at the inn. At once Shelley left to try to contact Byron's physician, Dr. Aglietti. Mary sat in the hall, holding their child, watching her die in her arms. She had already lost one daughter. Now she was completely overcome by the horror of this new disaster. Shelley returned to find her sobbing convulsively.

"I couldn't find Dr. Aglietti," he said. "We must wait. Another doctor will come."

By now, however, there was no hope. When the other doctor came at last there was nothing he could do. Mary held her child, and Shelley watched. In less than an hour their baby was dead.

Mary was desolate. She knew that Clara need not have died. "She had a sickness babies get in Italy," Shelley said, but she did not agree. She blamed him, and was plunged in despair. She moved like an automaton, dispiritedly doing the things that had to be done. The Hoppners came to see them at once, and then did their best to fill their days. Mary clenched her teeth, cared for her son William, read, worked, and looked at the sights she was taken to, like a sleepwalker. She turned away from Shelley, physically and emotionally. He was hurt and bewildered. Byron saw her and gave her his new poem, *Mazeppa*, to copy out. She went back to Este, bearing it, and, like a silent ghost, set to work.

* * *

Byron had gotten rid of Margarita Cogni. She had quarrelled with her husband, insisted on staying in the Palazzo Mocenigo, and took to wearing hats instead of her pretty *fazziola*—scornful of it because it was the wear of the lower classes. Once he had actually thrown her out, but she returned and made a scene while he was at dinner. She had snatched the knife from his hand and cut him on the thumb. He had ordered Tita to get the gondola ready and take her home, and went on with his dinner. Then a great hullaballoo had interrupted him again. "La Fornarina," the baker's wife, Margarita Cogni, had thrown herself in the canal. But Tita had rescued her. After that she had made many attempts to return to him, but he would have no more of her.

He had refused to see Claire to the last, and in the end Shelley returned Allegra to him and went off with Mary, and little William, and Claire to Rome.

Things were tidier, financially, for Hanson had arrived at last, bringing the papers for the sale of Newstead Abbey for his signature. It had been painful. He could see himself in Hanson's eyes—sallow, bloated, with a gross body, broad, rounded shoulders, and the knuckles of his hands sunk in fat—like his mother's. He had taken the opportunity of Hanson's being there to add a codicil to his will, leaving five thousand pounds to Allegra.

Venice, or at least his way of life there, was beginning to pall. He had had another Carnival of dissipation, and now he felt ill and exhausted. He had taken up with a Venetian girl called Angelina, the daughter of a noble and only eighteen years old. He climbed regularly to her window at midnight. Then she had decided she wanted to marry him, and her father found out and locked her up on a diet of bread and water—had even sent a priest and a commissioner of police to see him. It was all too exhausting. If he hadn't feared that he was losing his attraction for women he wouldn't have started it at all. He put his fears into verse.

But now at thirty years my hair is grey—
(I wonder what it will be like at forty?
I thought of a peruke the other day)
My heart is not much greener; and, in short, I
Have squandered my whole summer while 'twas May.

Had the sword outworn the sheath at last?

Early in April 1819 he went with Alexander Scott to the Countess Benzoni's. It was about midnight, and guests were beginning to arrive after the theater. He and Scott sat on a sofa facing the door of the grand salon. As soon as they were seated the door opened again. In the doorway there appeared a small, plump girl dressed in black, with rich auburn curls falling to her splendid shoulders. She had a full bust, well-covered arms and short legs. Her face was doll-like, her eyes large and lustrous. He had no recollection of ever having met her.

As soon as she entered, Teresa Guiccioli noticed Byron. The Countess Benzoni saw their exchange of glances, and moved to Byron. It was late, the lagoon had been rough, and there were fewer guests than usual.

"Will you allow me to present you to the Countess Guiccioli?" she asked.

"You know very well, madame, that I do not want to make any new acquaintances with women—if they are ugly because they are ugly, and if they are beautiful because they are beautiful."

"Come, Byron," Scott murmured, "make an exception in a salon where beauty is not common."

"No. No."

"I insist, my lord," the Countess Benzoni persisted. He rose, bowed, and she led him up to the Countess Guiccioli.

"I present to you Lord Byron, peer of England and its greatest poet, Madame la Contessa."

Byron smiled. He sat beside the little Countess, and she

reminded him that they had met the year before at the Contessa Albrizzi's: "I was too tired to pay attention, but next day they told me I had met the famous English poet, Lord Byron."

She told him, too, that she had just lost her mother and her elder sister, and had gone to the theater with her husband only under protest. She had wept at the thought of a party where she would be among strangers, and begged to be excused. In the end she had agreed to go, but only if Guiccioli promised that they would stay for only five minutes. She came from Ravenna, she said, and Byron replied, "Ah, that is a city I long to visit, if only to see the tomb of Dante."

To his astonishment the Countess broke into a quotation from Dante.

"You are conversant with the poet, Madame la Contessa?"

"The Abbess of my convent school, the Convent of Santa Chiara at Faenza, admired him and taught me all about him and his work."

They talked happily together while time slipped by. At last Count Guiccioli came to tell his wife that the five minutes they had agreed on had long passed. Teresa Guiccioli rose. Byron whispered hastily, "I must see you again—tomorrow."

"How?"

"Won't *you* tell me how?"

"Meet me in the afternoon, an hour after dinner. Guiccioli always sleeps then. I'll come with an old gondolier, in an ordinary gondola, to your gondola. Wait for me there."

In a moment she had been swept away by her husband.

* * *

CHAPTER
❧ 12 ❧

The rendezvous was kept—and another and another. Teresa was his mistress. She was in transports of sentimentality. Byron, on the other hand, was writing with a chilly frankness to Hobhouse about her.

"She is pretty, but has no tact; answers aloud, when she should whisper; talks of age to old ladies who want to pass for young; and this blessed night horrified a correct company at the Benzoni's by calling out to me '*mio Byron*' in a loud voice during a dead silence, so that the other women stared and whispered to their respective *serventi*."

Everything went well to begin with. Fanny Silvestrini, who had been a governess in Count Guiccioli's household and was the mistress of his steward, Lega Zambelli, an unfrocked priest, was a great help. Teresa began to take long rides in a gondola with Fanny on the pretext that she was studying French. She and Byron would meet and travel together as far as the Lido to see the vivid Venetian sunsets, and to sleep together in the little house, the *casino*, he kept at Santa Maria Zobenigo. For ten days they met constantly and appeared together at the theater and in salons. Soon, it seemed, everyone except the Count knew of their affair.

Then, suddenly, the blow fell. The Count was called back to Ravenna. They must part, or Byron must follow her—as her "pretty chick," her *cicisbeo*. He did not care for that role. This Italian game was supposed to be in the tradition of courtly love. He would appear in society as the *amico*, or friend, of the husband as well as the wife, and the lady would be his *dama*, or *amica*. Such an affair was called an *amicizia*, or a *relazione*; and the husband was not allowed to be jealous. It was no light-hearted affair, however. The code was strict—stricter even than marriage. Society was more shocked by a *dama* and her *amico* who broke its rules than by the cuckolding of a husband. It was all hypocrisy, he thought, and he was caught in the spider's web.

Far worse, however, was Byron's mistrust of Guiccioli himself, now that he knew more of him. They said that this tall, fifty-eight-year-old aristocrat was the richest man in the province, the Romagna. He was certainly cultivated—a friend of the poet Alfieri, and a keen attender of the theater in Ravenna, which he had restored, largely with his own money. He had been a handsome man. He was intelligent, with polished manners, an old seducer. His family was illustrious, too.

Other things, less savoury, were said of him, however. They said he was strong-willed and horribly cunning. Politically he had been shrewd, and two-faced. When the French had occupied the Romagna he had decided to lead the *canaille* instead of losing his head to them, as he put it. So the aristocrat, part of the old order, allied himself with the revolutionary mob, his natural enemies. But when Napoleon fell and the papal regime took over, he made a point of winning over the Cardinal Legate and the Papal Court. Yet he was not trusted—after all, by his third marriage he had allied himself to one of the most enthusiastic of the aristocratic families which hated the Austrian invaders and worked for their downfall. Teresa's father, Count Ruggero Gamba, and her brother, Count Pietro, were among the keenest workers for freedom from the oppressors in Ravenna. Did Guiccioli mean to join them, or was he anxious not to throw away his great assets?

The stories of Guiccioli's private life were even more horrifying. It was said that he had assassinated two men, one of them a priest. His first wife had been a woman much older than he, Contessa Placidia Zinanni, and she had brought him a very large dowry. It was one of his pretty housemaids, however, Angelica Galliani, who had borne him six children. When his wife objected she had been sent away to a lonely country house. Then, when at last he had allowed her to return, she had died at once—after making a will leaving everything to him. She had died in agony, and there were rumours that he had poisoned her. Then Guiccioli had married Angelica, and with the help of Cardinal Malvasia—for the price of a ring—had legitimized some of his children. Yet when Angelica died in 1817 he had gone to the theater at Forli that very night, and before the year was out he was looking for a third wife for himself and a stepmother for his seven children, the eldest of whom, Ferdinando, was only twelve.

Teresa Gamba had just left her convent school at Faenza. One evening Count Guiccioli visited his old friend Count Gamba, and his daughter, Teresa, was brought out to meet him. The room was dimly lit, Teresa told Byron, and Guiccioli had taken a candle and walked round her as if he were inspecting a piece of furniture. He had closed the deal on the spot, and accepted a modest dowry of four thousand five hundred scudi.

Teresa was nearly forty years younger than her husband, but she had been ecstatically happy and in love with him for the first few months of her marriage, though she did not tell Byron that. Afterwards things had changed, but she would not tell Byron exactly what it was that Guiccioli did which she found so repellent. He had been a sensual man, she implied but she hinted too at vile and violent practices.

Well, Byron asked himself, should he follow her or not? He was afraid that she was a kind of Italian Caroline Lamb, hot-headed and with no respect for public opinion. Already she had shocked the Venetians by going into his box at the theater, full of men, to tell him of the Count's decision that they must leave Venice within forty-eight hours.

Next day Byron watched as Teresa was swept away in the

darkness, seated beside Guiccioli in a gondola. Before she went she left him the name of an obliging priest, Don Gaspare Perelli, to whom he could address letters to her in Ravenna. She was leaving Fanny Silvestrini in Venice, too, to receive her letters to Byron.

As soon as Teresa reached Ravenna she wrote passionately to him. "You are my first love," she swore. And he replied, "You will be my last passion." To Augusta, however, he wrote, "My dearest love, I have never ceased nor can cease to feel for a moment that perfect and boundless attachment which bound and binds me to you, and which renders me utterly incapable of *real* love for any other human being—for what could they be to me after *you*? My own goose, we may have been very wrong, but I repent of nothing except that cursed marriage, and your refusing to continue to love me as you had loved me. I can never be other than I have been, and whenever I love anything it is because it reminds me in some way or other of yourself. Do you remember our parting? They say absence destroys weak passions, and confirms strong ones. Alas! *mine* for you is the union of all passions and all affections, has strengthened itself, but will destroy me."

He did not give up his Venetian women—on the very night that he wrote to Augusta he tumbled into the Grand Canal on the way to Angelina's balcony, and kept the tryst in his wet clothes.

In a few days Byron heard that the Guicciolis had moved on from the Count's property at Cà Zen to an old abbey among the marshes. There Teresa had at once developed a fever and was ordered back to Ravenna. It was a forty-mile journey over bad roads. Halfway there she was seized by terrible pains. Then, with only her maid to help her, she had a miscarriage as they were halted by the roadside. She was very ill when she reached Ravenna.

When Byron heard the news he decided it was a bad time to follow Teresa. Besides, Hoppner and Scott were both doing all they could to dissuade him from leaving Venice. At least, he wrote to Kinnaird, he knew he was not the father of the lost child—Teresa had been three months pregnant when they had slept together. But he feared that he might have been the involuntary cause of the miscarriage.

On the first of June, seven weeks after Teresa had gone, Byron left Venice at last. Hoppner's clerk, Richard Edgecombe, was to look after the Palazzo Mocenigo, all the servants and the ever-growing menagerie.

Ten days later, after a pause in Bologna, where he had decided to go back to Venice and then had changed his mind again, Byron pulled up in his Napoleonic carriage at the Porta Sisi in Ravenna. He had been halted by the annual religious procession to celebrate the feast of Corpus Domini, which filled the streets. Gazing at the pavements strewn with flower petals, and at the palaces hung with brocades and tapestries, mirrors and holy pictures, he did not at first notice an extremely pretty woman who was staring at him. Then, descending from the carriage into the crowd, he asked her where the inn was. She told him.

Ten minutes later the pretty woman was with Teresa. "The beautiful man has arrived, *cara*," she said.

"I have just been writing to tell him not to come to Ravenna, Geltruda. How can he see me, ill as I am?" Still, Teresa tore up her letter.

As soon as Byron settled into his inn, he sent off a letter of introduction to the acting head of the local provincial government, Count Alborghetti. He was angry at finding that the inn was small and dirty, and was ready to return to Venice at once. But no sooner had his letter been delivered than an invitation came to him from Alborghetti, inviting him to the Count's box at the theater that evening. Byron changed his mind, wrote a note to Teresa and set off for the theater.

143

Hardly had Byron arrived before the Count came into the box. "Have you any acquaintances in Ravenna, Lord Byron?" he asked.

"Yes, I am very friendly with Count and Countess Guiccioli."

"Alas, you will not be able to see the young lady. They say she is at death's door."

At the shock, Byron forgot himself. "If she dies I hope I will not survive her," he exclaimed.

Count Alborghetti gave him a look of astonishment. At that moment Count Guiccioli arrived. He saw Byron and came over to the box.

"The Contessa—I hear she is very ill," Byron stammered.

"She *has* been very ill, but she is well on the way to recovery."

That night Byron sent Teresa another letter. This time he wrote passionately. To his amazement Count Guiccioli himself called on him the next day at the hour of the evening promenade, and took him to Teresa's bedside. Byron looked down at her as she lay pale and still, unable to speak for emotion. Teresa, too, was overcome, but they could say nothing to each other in the presence of the Count.

Byron was more troubled than ever. The situation was difficult and dangerous. Surely Guiccioli would be bound to become suspicious and try to separate them? He wrote Teresa an emotional letter: "If trouble arises there is only one remedy; that is, to go away together. For this a great love is necessary, and some courage. Have you enough? I can already anticipate your answer. It will be long and divinely written, but it will end in a negative."

Teresa was enchanted by the proposal. Her answer was long, and prettily written, and it ended in a negative.

It was a fortnight before Teresa was allowed up. Then, at sunset, she and Byron and the Count and some friends drove out to the fresh, green, sweet-scented forest of umbrella pines, full of the song of nightingales and the chirping of crickets, which stretched from outside the city to the sea and as far as Rimini. It was an evening she would never forget.

As Teresa grew stronger she repeated the experience, riding with Byron in the forest as often as she could slip away. Byron preferred their rides to meeting her in her husband's palace. They were cuckolding the Count in the great salon, after the midday meal, when the Count and his whole household were asleep. There was no possibility of bolting doors, and Byron was living in terror of a stiletto in his back or poison in his drink. Teresa, however, had no qualms.

Byron could not fathom the Count, who often called for him and took him for a ride in his coach-and-six. He was afraid, too, that Teresa was succumbing to consumption. Then he felt old and jaded, and was finding the young Teresa too sexually demanding. She expected him to make love to her every day. And once again he was spending long sessions before the mirror, worrying about his crow's-feet, his shaky teeth and his growing corpulence. He was unhappy, and in such moods he wrote sneeringly to his friends about Teresa, saying that he doubted whether she would like anything but sex for long. He even flirted with her friend Geltruda Vicari to make her jealous—and succeeded. Teresa became almost insane with anger. Yet when Hoppner suggested that she was playing with him and would make him a laughingstock, he was furious and wrote: "All I know is that *she* sought me, and that I have *had her, here and there and everywhere*, so that if there is any fool-making *two* can play at that." Yet he admitted that he had been on the point of poisoning himself when she had been in danger. Then, as Teresa grew better she grew a little fickle and it was his turn to be jealous—he was enraged if she spoke to anyone else at the theater, and he wrote her angry letters. Even he realized that he was in a hysterical state.

Teresa or no Teresa, he never forgot Augusta. She had written, at last, to say that she had a pain in her side. He was very upset. "I do not at all like it, and think of your mother's constitution," he wrote. "You must always be to me the first consideration in the world. Shall I come to you? Or would a warm climate do you good? If so, say the word, and I will provide you and your whole family (including that precious luggage, your husband) with the means." He told her about Teresa, saying he had come to Ravenna because of her: "She is pretty, a great coquette, extremely vain, excessively affected, clever enough, without the smallest principle, with a good deal of imagination, and some passion. She had set her heart on carrying me off from Venice out of vanity, and succeeded. She is an equestrian too, but a bore, for she can't guide her horse, and he runs after mine, and tries to bite him, and then she begins screaming in a high hat and sky-blue riding habit, making a most absurd figure, and embarrassing me and both our grooms, who have the devil's own work to keep her from tumbling or having her clothes torn off by the trees and thickets of the pine forest."

He confessed, too, to his flirtation with Geltruda, and to Teresa's anger. With his letter he enclosed a copy of a printed broadsheet, with a sonnet addressed by Teresa to her cousin, Countess Teresa Cavalli, on her marriage to Count Francesco Sassi. In it Teresa spoke of Guiccioli, who, she claimed, satisfied all her desires and to whom she was before God eternally linked in faithfulness. Her heart, she claimed, was cemented in its vows, was adamant, and did not yield to any force. Byron marked the passage and wrote beside it, "One hundred and fifty times." Augusta would know what *that* meant—it would make her laugh.

It was not long after that Byron decided to cut his ties with Venice. But what could he do with Allegra? Now he wished that he had accepted the offer of Mrs. Vavassour, the wealthy childless widow from the north of England, who had fallen in love with Allegra when she had seen her at the Hoppners and had offered to adopt her if he would relinquish all parental authority. He had refused. Now the Hoppners did not want her to stay in Venice during its unhealthy summer months. Mrs. Hoppner had even written to Mary Shelley that Allegra had become as quiet and serious as a little old woman, and that it pained her and her husband. Elise had gone, and one of their maids was looking after the child. They suggested she be sent to Switzerland. While he still delayed, the Hoppners themselves fled Venice, leaving Allegra with the wife of the Danish consul, Mrs. Martens, at La Mira. There at least, they said, she would have a change of air. He could not decide what to do. He would ask Teresa to decide for him.

One morning Count Guiccioli came trembling with anger to Teresa, holding out an anonymous letter. The writer had enclosed some verses which, the letter said, were being sung by boys in the street—a sonnet addressed to Guiccioli. Teresa read the opening lines.

Of lord enamoured, all the world knows,
The wife her falcon has a cuckoo made,
While still in ignorance the old bird goes
That low he now should hang his horned head.

Teresa laughed. "Surely you don't believe this?" Guiccioli said nothing and left the room. Teresa did not know what to do. But after thinking it over she decided to show the verses to Byron. He was very upset.

"Guiccioli is scornful of this rubbish. Pay no attention," she assured him. But he was uneasy, afraid the Count would take his revenge before long.

Next day Count Guiccioli announced that he was taking Teresa with him on a journey to his property in Bologna. "Don't worry," Teresa reassured Byron. "You can follow us at once."

So within a day of the Guicciolis' arrival in Bologna, Byron appeared. That evening he went with them to the Arena del Sole Theatre. The play was Alfieri's *Mirra* on the theme of incest, the love of a girl for her father. When Teresa turned to speak to him she was surprised to see the tears running down Byron's face. But he would not reply to her questions.

Byron was becoming more and more uneasy about Guiccioli. The Count was extremely polite, and left Teresa alone with Byron in his Palazzo Savioli. Byron was staying at the Palazzo Merendoni only a few doors away. When the Count went to the theater or to a *conversazione*, they spent the evenings under the trees or by the fountain in the garden. Teresa hardly went out.

Then Guiccioli showed his hand. He came to Byron with a proposal, outlining it in his most urbane manner: "I would like, my lord, to be British consul—or, if that cannot be, vice-consul—for Ravenna. I think that perhaps you could arrange that for me."

He did not say that he was afraid that the Austrians were watching him, suspicious of his changeable politics and conscious of the wealth that gave him great power. Nor did he say that he was looking for British protection in case of trouble. As Byron said nothing, he added, "I do not ask for a salary—or for any emolument at all."

"I have no power in these matters, Count."

"But you have friends."

So Byron wrote to Murray, his publisher, asking him to approach his Tory friends in Parliament with influence in the government—Croker, who knew everyone, the brilliant Canning and the rising star, Robert Peel—asking them to arrange the appointment of Count Guiccioli as consul or vice-consul in Ravenna. He had no idea that the Austrian police were investigating his own movements, and had been examining his correspondence ever since the incident involving Polidori in Milan. Now every move he made was noted by the Bologna police. He was thinking of other things—of going to South

America, or perhaps back to England. Douglas Kinnaird had been elected Member of Parliament for Bishop's Castle. Why should he himself not do something about reform at home?

Towards the end of August Teresa left Bologna with Guiccioli to visit some of his properties between Bologna and Ferrara.

Byron was overcome with a feeling of despair—of utter desolation. His life seemed futile, and he himself of importance to no one. Teresa had left him the key to the garden of the Palazzo Savioli. Wandering alone there, he found himself bursting into tears. Teresa made no demands on him, financial or otherwise, except sexual ones. And the *cicisbean* existence he led with her filled him with increasing shame.

He wandered into Teresa's rooms and picked up the fat little volume she often read. It was Madame de Staël's *Corinne*, in small print and bound in purple plush. He had often teased her about her passion for this sentimental novel. Now, however, he took it out into the garden and wrote on a blank page.

"My dear Teresa, I have read this book in your garden. My love, you were absent, or else I would not have read it. It is a favourite book of yours, and the writer was a friend of mine. You will not understand these English words, and *others* will not understand them, which is the reason why I have not scrawled them in Italian. But you will recognize the handwriting of him who passionately loved you, and you will divine that, over a book which was yours, he could only think of love. In that word, beautiful in all languages, but most so in yours—*amor mio*—is comprised my existence here and hereafter. My destiny rests with you, and you are a woman, seventeen years of age, and two out of a convent. I wish that you had stayed there, with all my heart—or at least that I had never met you in your married state.

149

"But all this is too late. I love you, and you love me—at least you *say so*, and *act* as if you *did* so, which last is a great consolation in all events. But *I* more than love you, and cannot cease to love you.

"Think of me sometimes, when the Alps and the ocean divide us—but they never will, unless you *wish* it."

* * *

CHAPTER
❧ 13 ❧

Allegra arrived in Bologna before the end of August. She stood before him, this two-year-old lonely child who had no playmates. He was surprised at her self-control.

"Well, Allegra?"

"*Buon dì*, Papa."

He found that she still could not pronounce her r's, like him, and that she still frowned and pouted as he and Augusta did. He wrote to tell Augusta and added, "Blue eyes, light hair growing darker daily, and a dimple in her chin, a scowl on the brow, white skin, sweet voice, and a particular liking for music, and for her own way in everything—is not that B. all over?"

Not long after Teresa returned with Guiccioli. He called on her at once.

"My husband has agreed that you can move into our palace, with all your furniture," she said joyfully. "There's a vacant apartment on the ground floor."

"Is that wise?"

"Oh, yes. He's quite happy about it."

In two days he was installed. Now he could watch Allegra playing by the fountain in the garden, admired and spoiled by Teresa and her servants. Guiccioli was all smiles, too, apparently blind to Byron's private meetings with Teresa. It was not long, however, before he was summoned to the Count's apartment.

"I have a favour to ask of you, Lord Byron."

"I'll be glad to do anything I can for you, my dear Count."

"I want you to lend me some money."

"Indeed. How much would you need?"

"In English money, a thousand pounds. I will pay you interest of five percent."

"Very well."

He had been surprised into agreeing, but he was angry. The Count was letting him sleep with his wife for a price. Next morning he went to Insom, his banker in Bologna, and told him the story.

"He is not acting in good faith, my lord. You will never see that money again if you lend it. He's relying on your not being able to sue him for it."

"What shall I do?"

"You could say you haven't sufficient funds in your bank."

The Count received the information icily. Next morning Teresa told Byron that he had lost his temper and blamed her. Teresa had burst into tears, and was full of rage at her husband.

It was Teresa who made the next move. After her meeting with Byron she told Guiccioli that she had had another relapse, needed Dr. Aglietti's care, and must go to Venice.

"Lord Byron is returning there, and can escort me."

"That will never do." Guiccioli was clearly angry at the thought.

"Why not? I *must* go with Byron."

Suddenly Guiccioli gave way. "Well, if you go with him you must travel in my coach-and-six, and your maid and the oldest servant in our house must go, too. Also you must promise that you will stay in the apartment in Venice which I will order Lega to prepare for you."

"Very well."

So by mid-September Byron and Teresa left for Venice. Byron was in his Napoleonic carriage, its green paint now marred by several chips. It was heavily laden with his traveling bed, his books, his servants—and his little daughter. It lumbered on in the dust behind Guiccioli's coach-and-six, and Teresa was ecstatic, delighted when they stopped together to rest and stay at the same hotel. For Byron, however, it was tiring when Teresa insisted on his walking up a bad road to visit Petrarch's house and tomb—all the more so because he was suffering from corns. He said nothing, and Teresa did not guess. Together they admired the frescoes which had been painted by Laura, looked at the chair in which the poet had died, and saw the embalmed body of his cat in a niche above a door. They wrote their names together in the visitors' book, drank water from the fountain, and walked down again to their carriages.

Next day was less happy. They had put up for the night at an inn at Padua, and the same evening the Countess Benzoni and her *cavalier servente*, Beppe Rangone, arrived at the inn on their way to stay at a summer villa. The Countess lost no time in speaking her mind to Byron.

"We fear you don't understand what you're doing," she said. "You don't realize what Guiccioli is like—jealous, devious, capable of anything. Don't you agree, Beppe?" The dark young man with the bright brown eyes nodded earnestly.

When they left Byron went to see Teresa. "You see what it will be like in Venice. There's too much gossip already," he said.

"What are we to do then?" Teresa was growing hysterical. "Shall we fly together to the ends of the earth? You said that was what you wanted."

The silence was painful. At length Byron said, "That wouldn't be prudent. Let's wait and see."

So they journeyed on to Venice. They stopped for the afternoon at Byron's summer house, the Villa Foscarini on the banks of the river Brenta at La Mira, where he had once met Margarita Cogni. Teresa was enchanted with it, walking in the English garden and along the great avenue of plane trees running beside the water's edge, and admiring the view from the windows of the boats and the other summer villas. Allegra played beside the toy lakes and bridges in the garden. Not until evening did they travel on to Venice by gondola.

Next day Teresa wrote to her husband to propose that, since Dr. Aglietti had examined her and ordered no drugs but had suggested another journey and a change of air, she should be allowed to go with Byron to Lake Garda and Lake Como. She added that Byron sent a message that his English friend was going to present a petition about the vice-consulship, and do everything possible to obtain it for the Count. She did not say that she was not living in the Palazzo Malipiero, as she had promised, but in the Palazzo Mocenigo—with Byron. Lega Zambelli, however, reported that to the Count at once.

By the time the Count's answer came, to their amazement agreeing to the journey, Teresa had moved to La Mira with Allegra and Fanny Silvestrini. It was convenient for Byron to visit her there. Besides, as Teresa told Byron, she was suffering from piles and a suspected prolapse of the uterus. Life would be more restful there for her than in Venice for the time being.

Teresa's father, Count Gamba, was far from happy, however. When Teresa wrote to him that she was at La Mira with Byron he flew into a rage and ordered his carriage at once to take him from his country house at Filetto to see Guiccioli at Ravenna. The fifteen miles of travel there seemed interminable to him.

"How dare you let my daughter go back to Venice with a man like Byron?" Gamba shouted at Guiccioli. "Have you thought of the gossip? Her reputation will be ruined."

"I'll go for her as soon as I can."

Gamba wrote to Teresa, too. He was sure she was innocent, he said, but the world would condemn her. Above all, she and Byron must not go to the lakes together. Teresa replied lovingly, but she did not promise to leave Byron, or to return to her husband's apartment in Venice. She agreed only to remain at La Mira until Guiccioli came to collect her, and not to go to the lakes with Byron. She was bitterly disappointed.

So they stayed at La Mira, and there Byron told Teresa his version of the story of his marriage and separation. He was the victim, he was ignorant of the real causes of the separation, and he had tried again and again to find out what they were, without result. He wanted her to believe the best of him, yet his heart, he felt, was no longer with Teresa. Now he was dreaming of going to Venezuela and settling there, either on land he was allowed to buy or as a tenant—without Teresa. He might even become a citizen, if possible. Allegra would soon be three, and he would take her with him. He would write to Simon Bolivar, who had been a hero to him since he had liberated Colombia and Venezuela from Spanish despotism. He was bitter that of the last, best ten years of his life nearly six had been spent out of England. Now, once again, he was not rising until two in the afternoon. Then he would breakfast lightly and sit in the garden reading, talking and playing with Allegra. At sunset he rode along the Brenta with Teresa, and in the evenings he made love. In the early hours of the morning, however, he was writing *Don Juan*.

They had been at La Mira for a little over a fortnight when the poet Thomas Moore arrived. As Byron took the hand of the small, dumpy man with the mop of curly hair and quizzical features, he saw once again the shock in the eyes of one who had known him years before. "Yes, I am changed," he said.

"A little," Moore replied. "We all have. But you are still a very handsome man."

Moore did not seem to care much for Teresa. Still, Byron was very happy to see his old friend, and insisted that he should stay, not at the Hotel Gran Bretagna but at the Palazzo Mocenigo. That night they groped their way through the dark on the ground floor, trying to keep clear of angry dogs and vicious monkeys, until they reached Moore's bedroom.

It was not until Moore's last night, however, that they had an evening of the kind they had so often enjoyed in the past. "The Contessa has given me leave to make a night of it," Byron crowed. "We'll go to the opera, and then have supper afterwards at a café."

Before dinner Byron read Moore what he had written of the third canto of *Don Juan*. At three o'clock in the morning he left Moore at the door of the Palazzo Mocenigo, and departed for La Mira. Teresa was expecting him.

Twelve hours later Moore arrived for dinner at La Mira on his way to Padua. Byron met him at the door. As Moore entered the hall he spoke to Allegra, who had just returned from her walk with the nursemaid.

"What a beautiful child, Byron."

"Do you suffer from the paternal feeling, Moore? I've not the least feeling of it."

"I don't believe you," Moore scoffed.

Before dinner Byron left the room. He returned with a little white leather bag.

"Look here, Moore. This would be worth something to Murray, though you, I daresay, wouldn't give sixpence for it."

"What is it?"

"My life and adventures. It's not a thing that can be published during my lifetime, but you may have it if you like. There, do whatever you like with it." He added, "The life is memoranda, not confessions. I've left out all my loves, but put in a detailed account of my marriage and its consequences—as true as I can make it, for I suppose we're all prejudiced."

Moore took the bag. After dinner he departed, bearing it.

He could not conceal it from himself. He was bored, with his life and with Teresa. She cost him nothing, always refusing gifts or money, but she was a strain emotionally as well as sexually. He wrote to Kinnaird, "I never offered her but one present—a brooch of brilliants—and she sent it back to me with her own hair in it. I shall not say from what part, but that is an Italian custom. I have not had a whore this half-year, confining myself to the strictest adultery." When he fell ill after having been caught in a sudden rainstorm, she hurried to nurse him in the Palazzo Mocenigo, watching constantly by his side. He was grateful, but he felt shackled.

On All Saints Day Count Guiccioli arrived without warning. He disembarked from his gondola at the palazzo with his son, Ferdinando, and several servants. Gamba and he had decided that if he stayed with Byron it would help to control the gossip, which was now widespread, in Venice. As soon as Byron was well enough to see him Guiccioli called on him.

"As far as I am concerned you are welcome to Ravenna and in my palace, Lord Byron. But Count Gamba is most disturbed at the gossip. I don't want to upset the Gambas, so I must ask you not to return to Ravenna—and please say nothing of this to the Countess Teresa."

Byron did not find it too difficult to give his promise to Guiccioli.

Next Guiccioli went to Teresa. He handed her a sheet of paper, in silence, and left the room. Teresa glanced at it and flung it to the floor. She thought for a long time. Then she took the paper to Byron and read extracts from it to him.

"These are promises I'm supposed to make—'Indispensable Rules' he calls them—about my behaviour when I return to him. There are seventeen of them."

She read, " 'Let her busy herself with those household matters which are within her competence. Let her offer suggestions, and ask advice, but not give orders.' And 'After our drive together, in the early part of the evening, reading aloud before dinner, then together to the theater, then conversation, and to supper and bed together.' He dares to give me orders about my toilette. And, of course, he says, 'Let her receive as few visitors as possible.' "

"What will you do?"

"I have prepared my own indispensable rules, and he shall have them tomorrow. Here they are.

" 'To get up whenever I like.

" 'Of my toilette I will not speak.

" 'In domestic matters to be absolute mistress of all that is within a lady's province.

" 'To dine together as usual, but to spend the time of your rest as I please, even if it were in pulling the donkey's tail.

" 'But all this would not be enough to live together peacefully etc. if you should refuse to grant me the following:

" 'A horse with everything necessary for riding.

" '*To receive, without discrimination, any visitors who may come.*' "

Byron took no part in the battle between husband and wife. But he wondered that Teresa seemed to have so little fear of her menacing husband. She was insisting on Byron's going to Ravenna with her, while Guiccioli was insisting that he should not.

Then Guiccioli searched Teresa's room and found a letter from Count Gamba giving his daughter advice on how to placate her husband in his angry moods. There was another terrible quarrel.

Finally Guiccioli gave Teresa his ultimatum.

"You can decide whom you prefer, me or Byron."

"Byron," Teresa said at once.

Guiccioli went to Byron and told him of his wife's decision.

"I'll speak to her for her own sake," Byron said. He went to Teresa and took her hand. "It's impossible. You must go back to Ravenna. I'll try to come and see you there."

Teresa wept and stormed. At last she said that she would agree, but only if Byron gave his word that he would come. She went to Guiccioli and told him what she had told Byron. Guiccioli came to Byron again, and Byron saw, to his surprise, that he was weeping. Was it from frustration or anger? He said that he would take his wife back if Byron would help him persuade her.

"If you abandon your wife, I'll take her," Byron said. "It's my duty. But if, as you say, you'll live with her and love her as before, I won't bring any more disturbance into your family. I'll go away—across the Alps." He was still suffering from fever and ague. It was all a severe strain.

At last, after ten days of argument about the conditions, Teresa was ready to go back to Guiccioli. Now, Byron wrote to Hobhouse, he would have to leave Italy, for he couldn't form another liaison without making Teresa seem despised and abandoned. He had left England because of his own wife, and now he must leave Italy because of another man's wife.

Then, finally, Teresa departed for Ravenna.

Byron had ordered his packing to begin, when Allegra fell ill with malaria. He could not set a date for his departure for England. Teresa took a good deal of calming, and it was difficult by letter. He had not told her that he was not coming back to her and was returning to England. Her letters were growing more and more desperate as she noticed that he said nothing about joining her.

It was nearly the end of November before Dr. Aglietti said that Allegra was well enough to travel to England. Byron could no longer defer telling Teresa of his decision. He did not know that Fanny Silvestrini had been listening at the door when he and Guiccioli had spoken, that Fanny had already warned Teresa of his promise not to return to Ravenna, and that Teresa felt she had been betrayed. Now, at last he wrote to her, "I am going *to save you*, and to leave a country which, without you, has become insupportable. Farewell. In that one word is comprised the death of my happiness." She could show that about. It would save her pride—and his, perhaps.

He wrote to Augusta, too, telling her of his scene with Guiccioli, and that he planned to set off for England as soon as Allegra was better. Even before his letter arrived in England, however, Augusta had heard from Hobhouse that he meant to return. She had been thrown into a state of hysteria, and written to Hobhouse that the less said of Byron's return the better—and ordered Hobhouse to burn her letter at once. As soon as Byron's note arrived Augusta sent it to Annabella. "You must decide," she wrote. Annabella decided. Byron must not associate with his sister. He was clearly unreformed. "It can scarcely be doubted," she ended, "from the whole series of his correspondence that you are his principal object in England."

For his part, Byron was feeling great relief at the thought of escaping from his amorous difficulties. He expressed his sentiments in verse.

> *When lovers parted*
> *Feel broken-hearted,*
> *And, all hopes thwarted,*
> *Expect to die;*
> *A few years older,*
> *Ah! how much colder*
> *They might behold her*
> *For whom they sigh . . .*
> *You'll find it torture*
> *Though sharper, shorter,*
> *To wean, and not wear out your joys.*

He was working on *Don Juan* again, and had written more than a hundred stanzas in a few days and nights. Murray wanted to apply to the Lord Chancellor for an injunction against a publisher who had pirated the first two cantos, but Byron forbade it. Shelley had lost paternal control of his children because he had written *Queen Mab*. If Eldon, the Lord Chancellor, pronounced against him, Byron might lose Ada entirely to Annabella. Murray, he said, could have his copyright fee back if he wanted it.

Now there was nothing to stop him going, but still he did

not go. Everything was arranged, and Hoppner would look after his affairs, shutting down everything when he had gone. There was always an excuse—Allegra's health, if all else failed. Once everything was packed up, all his boxes were on the gondola, and he had even put on his gloves and his cap and taken his cane. Then, suddenly, he exclaimed, "If the clock strikes one before everything is ready I won't go today." Five minutes later the clock struck, and he went back into the palazzo.

The next day a letter came from Count Gamba. Teresa was ill at Ravenna. No one knew what was wrong with her, not even the doctors; but she was in such a state that he, her father, begged Byron to come to her. Her husband had agreed because of her illness—they feared consumption. He, Count Gamba, swore that there would be no further scenes between them—he would guarantee it. Byron would not be compromised in any way.

Byron wrote to Teresa at once. Love had gained the victory, he said. He had not been able to summon up resolution enough to leave without at least seeing her once more. "On *yourself*, perhaps, it will depend whether I ever again shall leave you." He sent the letter by courier so as to get it to her as quickly as possible. If he had not been so lazy, he thought regretfully, he would already have left Italy.

As soon as she read his letter Teresa began to recover. Byron, however, was still in no hurry to leave. Ten days passed before he started. Now, it was true, he had to make new arrangements for all his servants.

Not until four days before Christmas did Byron finally set off. He arrived in Ravenna on Christmas Eve. The smiling Teresa, her father, her husband, and her friends, all welcomed him. She was happy and triumphant. Her *amico* had come home. As for Byron, he could think of nothing but the Christmas he had refused to share with Sir Ralph and Lady Milbanke and Annabella, the Christmas just before his marriage, which he had spent with Augusta at Six Mile Bottom. He was very tired, and stale. He passed for a happy and successful lover. Yet he had wanted to leave Italy, and had meant to do so. Now he was in Ravenna—and at the urging of Gamba and Guiccioli. Guiccioli, too, had not only asked him to come, he had insisted on it. Here he was, caught in the trap of *serventism*, this Italian social custom of accepting a lover as a part of the domestic establishment, with no escape that he could see.

*   *   *

CHAPTER
❧ 14 ❧

It was as he had feared. From New Year's Eve on, Teresa paraded him at balls and receptions as her *amico*, seeming to glory in the scandal. She was jealous, even of his wife, and fickle, and childish, and wayward. Even worse, he found her disingenuous and evasive. Hardly a week had passed before things began to go wrong between them. He felt she was subjecting him to slights, and that she was conspiring with her husband's friends to humiliate him. He wrote long, bad-tempered letters to her, and she was angry and resentful. Before January was half over he was ready to leave Ravenna.

At first his search for a suitable house there had been fruitless. Then Guiccioli offered to rent him the empty first floor of his palace. Byron liked the heavy stone building, facing one of the narrow streets not far from the magnificent Basilica of San Vitale, but he suspected that Guiccioli was hoping to catch him and Teresa committing adultery in his own palace. Teresa insisted on his accepting. However, he refused to enter the palace until a maid whom Guiccioli insisted should serve Teresa was dismissed. Teresa dismissed her. Then Guiccioli heard that Byron had interfered, and asserted that he was master in his house and the maid must stay. So Byron refused to visit Teresa while the maid remained. In the end Teresa had her way, as usual, and Byron moved in with the maid still there, with all his servants, and his animals, and Allegra. At least they had a lookout when Teresa slipped into his apartment, one of the two black pages whom Guiccioli dressed in Oriental costumes with pistols and daggers in their belts. The other was Guiccioli's spy. When Guiccioli sent the maid away for a while, Byron was able to resume his visits without appearing to have given way. Yet Guiccioli refused him a receipt for the hundred pounds he borrowed to engage Madame Pasta for the theater, so that he could take all the credit. This was another quarrel, which made it difficult to maintain the role of friendship. Byron felt it was all low and degrading. Yet he had already veered from his desire to return to England. Hobhouse was in prison for his libel on the Prince Regent. Scrope Davies had escaped to Bruges owing debts of twelve thousand pounds. His friend Dallas, who had made seven thousand four hundred pounds from the sale of Byron's copyrights and his personal generosity, had asked for more money and called *him* ungrateful. Once again he was sick of England and the English.

Now the only thing Byron took undiluted pleasure in, apart from his writing and his riding, was Allegra. She was, he declared, as obstinate as a mule, as ravenous as a vulture and as vain as a peacock, but she was very pretty. Teresa and the servants still spoiled her disgracefully, and encouraged her to have her own way. Teresa had even driven with her down the Corso in her coach-and-six at Carnival time, preceded by outriders with blue and white feathers in their caps, as part of the cavalcade. Claire was upset at his having taken Allegra to Ravenna, where she could get no news of her, and bombarded him with demands to see her. She wanted to set out to fetch her.

"I beg you to remember," she wrote, "that I did not part with her at Milan until I had received your formal and explicit declaration that I should see my child at proper intervals. Nearly two years have now elapsed since I had that pleasure, and no time could be better than that of our visit to the Baths of Lucca, which are so good for the health."

He did not reply. Then he wrote sneeringly to Hoppner about the Shelleys' ill luck with their children. "Have they reared one?" he asked, remembering that they had lost their third child, the boy William, in Rome, where they had gone after visiting him at Venice. "The child shall not quit me again to perish of starvation and green fruit, or be taught to believe that there is no deity. Whenever it is convenient, her mother can have her with her; otherwise no." Claire wrote and wrote, each letter more wretched than the last. In the end she wrote in her diary, "A brutal letter to Shelley from Byron," and she did not write to him again. She had given up hope.

Suddenly, at the beginning of April 1820, Byron received an urgent note from Teresa. A servant had told her that early that morning, before she awakened, her husband had broken open her writing desk and gone through all the papers in it. Fortunately there had been nothing compromising. "Why?" Teresa asked Byron, and answered herself. "I think his friends taunted him about you—they want him to get you out of Ravenna." Byron had been expecting trouble. But Teresa had told him that the Count was happy as long as she read to him and slept with him now and then.

"I must go away," Byron said. "It won't do to compromise you and embarrass your relations."

"You don't love me!" Teresa cried. The tears were flowing again.

"I do. But if you come with me you'll be unhappy and compromised. With your husband you'll be respectable and respected, if not happy."

"Let me leave the Count. Then I can try to get a separation."

"No. Speak to your father first. If it ends with a separation we can make our decision then. But don't forget, I can't marry you." Then he added, "You must return any letters and gifts of mine you have to avoid Guiccioli's getting hold of them."

"You *want* to leave me. You don't love me. You want to get rid of me!" She behaves worse than Allegra, Byron thought disgustedly.

They knew that Guiccioli was paying servants and work-men to watch them, to write statements, and to sign affidavits about what they saw. He was gathering evidence, they were sure, so that he would not have to return Teresa's dowry or make her an allowance in the event of a separation. Eighteen of his servants were watching them. Yet whenever Guiccioli went to the theater Teresa joined Byron in his rooms. Her footman, Luigi Morelli, stood guard outside the house. They were entirely in his hands.

At last Byron said, "All right, a separation is inevitable. Don't stay with him. They are saying in Ravenna, I hear, that he shouldn't have tolerated our affair for a year, and then suddenly behaved like this. Even the law is against him. He condoned the affair."

"My relations are against him too," Teresa said. "They say it's ridiculous of him to complain of being cuckolded at sixty when other husbands are cuckolded at twenty." Teresa was laughing, to his relief.

Even while Guiccioli was trying to get Byron to leave he was still attempting to extract money from him. Then he produced every argument he could think of to persuade him to go.

"You *must* go away," Guiccioli insisted. "Everyone thinks so. You shouldn't stay and cause trouble in a family. You should use your influence to make her give you up and love her husband again."

"How can I do that?" Byron asked.

"And you should persuade her to find another *amico*—an Italian," Guiccioli persisted.

"You don't want a separation?" Byron asked.

"No, I don't want to lose the woman. I don't want to disgust my relations. I certainly don't want to pay her an allowance. Why should I? I've done nothing wrong. Above all, I don't want to cut the figure of a complacent cuckold. True love is conjugal love. You should make her see that."

166

At that very moment Teresa was speaking to her father, Count Gamba.

"There are things I couldn't tell you before, Papa. I don't like to tell you about them now." Then she told him. As Count Gamba listened he cried out in horror, jumped to his feet and strode about the room, gesticulating. With her head low Teresa told him, explicitly, of Count Guiccioli's sexual habits and of the violence to which he subjected her when his will was thwarted.

"He's a pervert, Papa, and a sadist."

"You should have told me all this long ago. Much as I regret your relationship with Lord Byron I will no longer oppose it. And I will challenge Count Guiccioli to a duel."

"No, Papa, not that."

"I can do nothing less in honour."

Count Gamba went home, and at once applied in his own name to the Pope for the separation of his daughter from her unnatural husband. He wrote: "In the short space of one year the *cavaliere* has behaved so strangely, and has heaped so many insults upon his unhappy bride, that it has become wholly impossible for her to live any longer with so exacting a husband, and she is obliged, in the opinion of the whole city, to seek a complete separation. In this state of affairs the petitioner humbly appeals to your Holiness, beseeching that the *cavaliere* Guiccioli may be ordered to pay a suitable allowance to his wife, the aforesaid daughter, in accordance with the position of her husband, in order that she may live suitably, as befits her birth and position."

He sent his petition through Teresa's maternal grandmother, Cecilia Machirelli Giordani. She was a personal friend of Pope Pius VII, and would be able to speak to him of the intimate details he could not bring himself to write.

While they waited for the Pope's decision Byron and Teresa continued to meet in secret. Then they went too far. Teresa ordered a blacksmith to change the lock on the door leading into Byron's bedroom, because Guiccioli had a duplicate key. The Count was out but returned unexpectedly before the new lock had been put on. At once the page who spied for him told him what was going on. Guiccioli walked up the stairs and ordered the blacksmith to replace the old lock. At the sound of the hammering Byron and Teresa appeared on the other side of the door. Guiccioli stared at them. Teresa said nothing to explain her presence in Byron's bedroom. After a while her husband went away without a word. To Byron his silence was more menacing than words. When Count Gamba had challenged him to a duel he had ignored that, too.

At last Byron wrote to Teresa, giving her the promise he had always refused her before: "He may abandon you—but I *never*. My love, my duty, my honour, all these should make me forever what I am *now*, your lover, friend, and (when circumstances permit) your husband." If any way could be found to dissolve his marriage he would marry her, it was true. But in Italy there was no possibility of divorce. The promise was a compliment, no more. Teresa was delighted. She wrote on the letter, "Promise!!!! To be my husband!!" Then she put it away among her treasures.

The weeks went by, and still there was no edict from the Pope. At last, on July 6, 1820, Byron wrote to Hobhouse: "When the Pope has decided on Madame Guiccioli's business I will tell you whether I can come to England via Switzerland or not. I can't settle anything till I know the result." If the Pope ordered Teresa back to Guiccioli he would leave at once.

That very day the Pope sent his decree. He granted Teresa her separation from Count Guiccioli on the grounds that it was no longer possible for her to live in peace and safety with her husband. The decree went straight to Countess Cecilia Giordani at Pesaro, and she forwarded it to Ravenna. Teresa was to return to her father's house, and Guiccioli was to give her an allowance of a hundred scudi a month—about a thousand pounds a year—to be paid to the Cardinal Legate for her. She had nothing more to fear from Guiccioli, she thought.

Count Gamba had informed Teresa secretly of the Pope's decision. Now, he said, she must make her escape. She must meet him in her carriage outside the city the next afternoon, and be taken to his country house at Filetto. The Cardinal Legate had promised not to inform Guiccioli of the Pope's decree until she had gone, so as to avoid any violence from him and the consequent scandal.

Teresa was frightened during her last day at the Palazzo Guiccioli. It was obvious that Guiccioli was suspicious. She herself was deeply upset, knowing that she and Byron were together in the same palace for the last time, yet she had to behave as if everything was as usual. Guiccioli, she soon discovered, had given orders that none of the horses were to be used that day. Teresa watched him nervously during their midday meal, but he behaved impeccably. He helped her to food from the dishes the servants passed round, and made conversation with her. He, too, was anxious that everything should seem normal.

After the meal Teresa slipped out and ordered Luigi Morelli to hire a coach. Two hours later he returned to tell her it was waiting some distance away. Teresa could do little more than press Byron's hand before she stole out of the Palazzo Guiccioli—alone, except for her maid and Morelli. They had not gone far on the road to Filetto when they sighted Count Gamba and transferred to his carriage.

That night, after two years of married life, Teresa slept again in her father's house. Byron's last words, she told her father, were to warn her not to go out alone, and to promise that he would send his cook, Valeriano, after her. He and Morelli, he hoped, would be able to act as her bodyguard. Guiccioli was not a man with whom anyone took risks.

*   *   *

The two lovers were separated, and had been for over a month. Byron continued to live in Guiccioli's palace, partly out of braggadocio and partly in order to repay himself the hundred pounds he had lent to Guiccioli by living rent free. Guiccioli sent him a formal notice to leave. He ignored it. Count Gamba did not want him and Teresa to meet, but she slipped into the palace to meet him now and then, dressed as a servant.

Now he had found a villa near the Casa Gamba at Filetto, where he had installed Allegra and her nurse, from which he was able to make easy, unobtrusive visits to Teresa—the Villa Bacinetta. He had taken his time, continuing to write *Marino Falieri*, or excusing himself because of Allegra's second attack of malaria. He had even thought of going to England, at Hobhouse's request, to vote for Queen Caroline, who was on trial in the House of Lords because her husband, the new king, George IV, had forced his ministers to bring in a divorce bill in the hope of ridding himself of her. Now he was seeing Teresa and her family again.

Byron was spending as much time with Pietro Gamba as with Teresa. He went riding and shooting duck, snipe and woodcock with him. But, above all, he talked about the heady politics of the Italian states with him. Byron was greatly taken with the tall, gentle, good-looking fellow with bushy eyebrows, so hotheaded for revolution. He had a better sense of humour than his little sister, and he was sincere, loyal and spirited. He was modest, too, and candid, but very impractical. Pietro had brought news of the ridiculous bloodless revolution against the Bourbon tyranny in Naples. It was all over, and the cowardly Ferdinand I, King of Naples by grace of the Holy Alliance and Austrian power, had provided a constitution. That had encouraged the secret societies plotting revolution throughout Italy. Byron felt, at last, that he had found something worth doing, a means of using his energies to fight against oppression, and perhaps make a name for himself. At once he joined the Turba branch of the Carboneria, in which all his best friends were active; Count Ruggero and Pietro Gamba and Ruggero's nephew, the Marchese Antonio Cavalli, were among the most ardent. He began to attend its secret meetings in the forest or in a guardroom. In some moods he liked their rituals and passwords; in others he felt cynical and contemptuous of their foolish melodrama. But he was stirred by their passion for the cause of liberty. He longed to escape from his life of the boudoir and play a hero's part.

Byron was still at the Palazzo Guiccioli when the Count's eldest son, Ferdinando, fell ill. Byron did not send his sympathy, though he liked the boy. He had often ridden with him and Teresa in the pine forest.

Then Ferdinando died. Teresa at once wrote to her husband to send her sympathies, and warned him not to go to Milan in case of reprisals because of the recent uprising, though he had taken no part in it. She wrote to tell Byron what she had done. Byron said to Pietro, "Tell her that she should decide whether she wants me or Guiccioli."

For two weeks Byron did not visit Teresa or write to her. Then he wrote coldly that she did not need his letters since she was writing to her husband, or his company since she had been to Ravenna and had not let him know. He felt that he did not understand the Italians after all, and least of all Teresa.

His thoughts turned to Augusta, and he wrote to her again. Ada was nearly five years old, he said, and he had been almost as long out of England. "And *you*? What have *your* five years done? Made your house like a lying-in hospital. There never was such a creature, except a rabbit, for increase and multiplication. In short, we are five years older, in fact, and I at least ten in appearance." He closed, "I have got a flourishing family, besides my daughter Allegra. Here are two cats, six dogs, a badger, a falcon, a tame crow, and a monkey. The fox died, and a civet cat ran away."

Teresa too was miserable and frightened. Byron constantly postponed his visits to her. Suddenly she went to her father.

"Papa, I cannot bear it. You must take me back to Ravenna."

"You must be prudent, my child."

"I must see Byron, and he does not come here."

"The best way to make sure you will never see him is to let him be caught visiting you."

"I *must* go, Papa."

"Very well. If you insist."

So Teresa arrived in Ravenna. By the time she came, however, Count Alborghetti had informed Byron that he was being watched by spies, not only as a potential political hothead but as the lover of the Countess Guiccioli. "The Countess may be shut up in a convent," Alborghetti warned him. "Tell her to be very careful."

One evening, early in December 1820, at eight o'clock, Byron was getting ready to visit Teresa in her father's house. Suddenly he heard a shot, then several more. Shouting to Tita, he ran downstairs and out into the street. There, lying on the ground, he saw Luigi Dal Pinto, the commandant of the local troops. He had met him often at *conversazioni* and had liked him. He was a brave but unpopular officer. Byron knelt down beside him, surrounded by a silent, menacing crowd. An old gun lay beside Dal Pinto, and he could see that he had been wounded in several places.

"Tita," Byron called. "Come and help me, and get two men from the crowd to lend a hand. Carry this poor devil upstairs to my quarters."

As they carried the wounded man upstairs he cried out, "*O Dio!*" and then "*Gesù!*" By the time they laid him on the bed they saw that he was dead.

"Why was he killed?" Byron asked. "Why?"

There was no answer. The corpse remained on the bed.

Then a lieutenant of the local troops arrived and sat on duty beside it, smoking his pipe. He stayed there all night.

Next day Count Gamba came to see Byron. He told him that the Carbonari disapproved of his behaviour, which they regarded as treacherous to their cause. Dal Pinto had been executed by their orders. He and Pietro had had to work hard to preserve his standing with their leaders and it would not survive any more such incidents.

Now, in his despondency and uncertainty about the future, Byron wrote again to Annabella. He reminded her of the request he had made in his farewell letter of Easter Sunday, 1816, that she be kind to Augusta. Annabella wrote the last letter that she would ever write to him: "The past shall not prevent me from befriending Augusta Leigh and her children in any future circumstances which may call for my assistance. I promise to do so. She knows nothing of this."

Byron received her note before the end of the year. Three days after Christmas he replied: "I acknowledge your note, which is on the whole satisfactory. The style is a little harsh, but that was to be expected. As to Augusta, she knows as little of my request as of your answer. Whatever she is or may have been, *you* have never had reason to complain of her. On the contrary. You are not aware of the obligations under which you have been to her. Her life and mine, and yours and mine were two things perfectly distinct from each other—when one ceased the other began—and now both are closed. She and two others were the only things I ever really loved. I may say it now, for we are young no longer."

* * *

CHAPTER
🌿 15 🌿

The year 1821 began badly for Byron. As usual he was miserable at the approach of yet another birthday, this time his thirty-third, with nothing he considered worthwhile achieved. Besides, the Austrian army, bent on quelling the uprising in the southern kingdom of Naples, had moved sooner than expected, crossing the Po early in February. The plans laid by the Carbonari in Ravenna—to stage an uprising themselves in their province, the Romagna, in concert with insurgents from Naples—were foiled. Now there was nothing they could do but harass the troops as they advanced towards Naples.

Then, less than a week later, the Austrian government in Ravenna suddenly issued an order that everyone found with concealed arms would be liable to severe penalties. Two days later Byron came home after his evening visit to Teresa to learn that a great heap of arms had been thrown into the palazzo. Without warning, his friends, the patriots, at Pietro Gamba's instigation, had returned the arms with which he had supplied them, at their express request and at his own risk and expense. Byron had been so angry that he hit the crow with a stick when he found it stealing the falcon's food.

In his personal financial affairs things were going badly, too. He had lost his lawsuit to recover the profitable coal mines in Rochdale in Yorkshire which had been leased illegally by his ancestor, the "Wicked Lord." He had no confidence that his appeal would be successful. Worst of all, although Teresa and he were together again and happy enough, since they saw each other every day, he felt she had been wrong to leave her husband and blamed her for it in his heart. She had deprived him of the freedom to act as he pleased. For once the annual New Year's Carnival gave him no pleasure.

Realizing that he might at any moment be involved in a bloody revolution, Byron decided that he must make some provision for Allegra. He would put her in a convent.

Teresa chose the convent, San Giovanni Battista in Bagnacavallo, about twelve miles from Ravenna on the road to Bologna. It had been recently opened as a school for girls between seven and eighteen, and the best families of the region were sending their daughters there. Allegra was only four, but the nuns had agreed to take her. Her nursemaid packed her little dresses of muslin and cotton and velvet, her caps and gloves, a string of coral and a silver spoon and fork, and her underclothes and bed linen. The steward, Lega Zambelli, bought furniture for her bedroom and had it packed up. Then Teresa presented her with a little waxen statue of the Madonna dressed in puce-coloured silk, with a golden crown on her head. Allegra was ready to go. Byron did not inspect the convent himself, and he did not take Allegra there. He left that to Pellegrino Ghigi, his banker. On the first of March he said good-bye to Allegra, and Ghigi and Lega set off with her for the convent. There Lega paid for her first half-year's tuition, and then they left her, to a new life among strangers.

Byron wrote to Shelley and told him what he had done. As soon as Shelley received his letter he wrote to Claire in Florence, where she had moved from Pisa. Claire was upset and angry. She wanted Allegra to have an English education, she replied, and she did not want her brought up as an Italian and a Catholic. She begged the Shelleys to help her get her child out of the convent, and to see that she was given back to her. She wrote to Byron, too. Byron replied to Shelley that he had never meant to give a bastard child an English education: "Abroad, with a fair foreign education, and five or six thousand pounds for a dowry, she might marry very respectably.

In England the dowry would be a pittance. I am determined that she will be a Roman Catholic." He was not a Catholic himself, he thought, but he was far from being a typical English Protestant bigot, and had always had a genuine respect for the Mother Church. Besides, his putting Allegra in a Catholic convent, and making a Catholic of her, would probably do something to reconcile Teresa's devout grandparents to her friendship with someone they mistrusted because he was a Protestant; they had a great deal of influence in the family.

He sent his peer's gown to the convent to be made into dresses for Allegra and her dolls.

In March 1821, the Greek war of independence had erupted. In May Byron heard of it, and his hopes stirred again. At last the Greeks had taken to arms to express the resentment of centuries against the domination of a cruel and despotic Islamic empire. Now, Byron felt, there might be some role of major importance for him there. On his thirty-third birthday, in January, he had written:

> *Through life's road, so dim and dirty,*
> *I have dragged to three-and-thirty.*
> *What have these years left to me?*
> *Nothing—except thirty-three.*

Here was his opportunity to set that right. In March, too, the Neapolitan army, strong in numbers but weak in discipline, had met the Austrian army in the plain of Rieti, and fled almost before a shot was fired. Now he felt nothing but contempt for the Italians—let them stick to making operas and macaroni. He would look towards Greece.

Early in May Byron turned down another proposal from Hoppner to take Allegra to Switzerland, this time to put her with the family of a Protestant clergyman. Byron replied that, had he known of it before, he would have agreed, but now he would leave her in her convent, where he believed she was happy and healthy. Teresa, too, was anxious that he should leave Allegra in the convent.

Now the government in Ravenna was trying to make life difficult for him. First, Tita of the great beard was arrested because of a fracas with an officer named Pistocchi. They drew knives and pistols but never came to blows. Yet Tita was ordered to the frontier, while the officer was set free. Tita would lose his employment and be left with a stain on his character.

Even more annoying, Teresa had objected to Byron writing *Don Juan*. She had read an article in the Milan *Gazzetta*, and been upset by its attacks on his morals. She had demanded that he stop exposing himself to such criticisms. "Very well," he said at last, "I promise you not to write any more of *Don Juan* until you yourself authorize it." He resented it. *Don Juan* had come to mean a great deal to him. He had absolute confidence that he had found a way of expressing, lightly and cynically, his attitude towards life, which perfectly suited him. He had successfully resisted Murray's qualms about the poem, and Shelley had expressed the greatest admiration for it. He suspected that Teresa only wanted him to stop writing this offensively unromantic odyssey because women disliked love poetry which was not sentimental. At times he found himself almost disliking her for what she had done.

In July the blow they had long expected fell. Pietro Gamba was returning from the theater, when he was suddenly arrested and conducted to the frontier. There he was ordered to leave and remain in perpetual exile as a leader in the plots against the state. The next morning police arrived to search his rooms. Luckily Teresa had been warned, and she had destroyed all his compromising papers. "But the government knew all about his activities as a leader of the Carboneria," Byron said to her. "This was inevitable. It's lucky he wasn't cast into a dungeon and tortured."

Byron was convinced that Count Ruggero's turn would come next, and that it was all part of a plot to get rid of him. The authorities knew that if her father was exiled Teresa would have to follow him by the terms of the separation, and then he, Byron, would follow her. Indeed, Count Ruggero was ordered to leave within twenty-four hours.

"You will have to go with him," Byron said.

"How can I? I *will* not leave you in danger in Ravenna."

"By the terms of the separation you must live with him."

"I will not go."

So Count Ruggero left her in Ravenna while he went to Filetto to arrange his affairs. Then Byron wrote to him asking him to leave Teresa in Ravenna until he and Pietro were sure they could have asylum in Tuscany.

The day after, Pietro and his father went to Bologna and then travelled on to Florence. Byron was working hard to get them recalled, but nothing had any effect on the authorities. Not even a letter to the Duchess of Devonshire, now living in Rome and a friend of the Papal Secretary of State there, did any good. He would always wonder whether his unpaid rent on her house in London had anything to do with that. At least he was able to bribe Count Alborghetti to get Tita released, but that was all he achieved.

Then, to crown it all, Guiccioli made a hostile move. He had noted Teresa's contraventions of the separation order, and now he tried to force her either to return to him or face the threat of being shut up in a convent for violating its terms. Count Alborghetti at once sent a family friend to warn Teresa of her danger.

"You *must* go!" Byron insisted.

"It's all a lie."

"No. You must go."

She grew hysterical. "I won't. I can't leave you."

"I'll come. I'll take your whole family to Switzerland—yes, I promise. But you must go."

Teresa had left, after delaying as long as she could. When she reached Bologna, however, where friends of the Gambas were waiting to take her on to Florence, she refused to go on. Byron, she wrote, must either let her return or meet her at Bagnacavallo. She accused him of trying to get rid of her, and the more he begged her to proceed the more certain she was that she was right. She was in a terrible state. All day she stayed indoors, remembering Byron's handsome face, his musical laugh, and the charm that drew everyone to him, and reliving their happy hours together. She stayed for eight days. Not until the beginning of August did she at last cross the Apennines and join her father and her brother in Florence. Byron breathed a sigh of relief. Now at last he could settle down and enjoy a respite from the strains of this demanding relationship. He needed a rest.

The summer wore on, but Byron did not leave Ravenna. He wrote Teresa that he was trying to get the exiles recalled and pardoned, and was busy helping Count Ruggero's family and the families of the other exiles. Count Ruggero had left a family of young children behind, including an infant of two. Byron was depressed by the death of Napoleon, too. He was attracted by the idea of publishing a newspaper with Thomas Moore in England. He would go to Teresa, he decided, in his own good time and not be hurried. Besides, he was waiting for Shelley's long-delayed visit.

Disturbed by news of the exile of the Gambas and the imminent departure of Byron and Teresa, Shelley had set out on the day after Teresa left. He was anxious to see how Allegra was, and to find out what would be done for her if Byron left for Switzerland or anywhere else. He spent the first night at

Leghorn, where Claire was staying, and next day rowed with her on the bay. He left without telling her where he was going; she would have insisted on going with him. He had travelled all night in a little open carriage to Bologna. Then he went on at once to Ravenna, and arrived at ten o'clock at night.

Byron welcomed Shelley warmly. Three years had gone by since they had met at the Palazzo Mocenigo in the autumn of 1818. Byron was full of praise for *Adonais*, which Shelley had sent him. Shelley was impressed by the improvement in Byron's health and way of life, but he did not say so. They sat up until five o'clock in the morning talking.

Day after day Shelley stayed on at the Palazzo Guiccioli, waiting for an opportunity to visit Allegra at her convent. Byron always found some excuse to defer it, and sent him off instead with Tita to see the Basilica of San Vitale, the tomb of Theodoric, and the church of San Appollinare. He did not want to let Shelley go—he had seen very few Englishmen for almost two years in Ravenna, and he had disliked those he met. They rode together in the pine forest; Shelley fitted in with Byron's routine, rising late, and talking until four or five o'clock in the morning, without protest. He himself got up at noon and wrote letters, or strolled about the palace, staring at the growing menagerie—eight enormous dogs, three monkeys, five cats, an eagle, a crow, a falcon, five peacocks, two guinea hens, and an Egyptian crane. They all walked about the palace, which re-echoed with their battles. If Byron was very late Shelley strolled about Ravenna, looking at monuments. Byron questioned him closely about Tuscany and possible places to live there, though he was still thinking of taking a villa on Lake Geneva.

"Have you forgotten the English with their spyglasses? And the narrow-minded Swiss?" Shelley asked.

"Count Pietro Gamba is very anxious to live in Switzerland.

He says it is the only country in Europe where he and his family can still breathe the air of freedom."

"Don't go there. Come to Tuscany."

"Well, you write to the Countess Guiccioli. See if you can persuade her."

Shelley was full of admiration for *Don Juan*, and disappointed to hear that Byron was no longer adding to it. He was not so happy when Byron told him that Murray had offered Moore a thousand guineas for his memoirs, on condition that he would edit them if he survived Byron. "I might even have them published in my lifetime," Byron said.

Next day Byron told Shelley that he had decided to go to Pisa. "Write to Mary, and ask her to look out for a house for me—a large and magnificent one," he asked.

Not until August was half over had Shelley been allowed to go to the convent at Bagnacavallo to visit little Allegra. Now he waited in the Mother Superior's office until Allegra was brought in to him.

The small creature who entered, holding the hand of a sister, was more serious than he remembered—too serious for a four-year-old child. He was distressed at the sight, though she looked pretty and cared for. Her thick golden hair hung in large curls. Some nun had taken loving care of her appearance.

"Go to Mr. Shelley and curtsey to him," the nun encouraged her. Allegra at once moved to him and curtseyed gracefully, but she was still very shy.

"I will leave you alone together, and she will be more at her ease then, I expect," the nun said. As soon as the door closed Shelley knelt before Allegra.

"Don't you remember me?"

"Yes, I do." She was still very quiet.

Shelley drew her to him and petted her, stroking her hair.

She softened and warmed to him at once, snuggling her face into his neck. Shelley drew a little package from his pocket. "Look what I've brought you from Ravenna," he said, unwrapping it.

Allegra seized the little box he offered her eagerly, and opened it. She drew out a gold chain with a little locket. "Put it on for me, please," she begged. Shelley fastened it round her neck. Now she was all smiles. She turned to him and asked, "Do I look pretty?"

"Yes, you do. *Very* pretty."

There was no trouble from then on. Allegra chatted vivaciously, too much so, Shelley thought, for a child.

At last the time came for him to go.

"What shall I say to papa?" he asked her.

"Che venga farmi un visitino e che porta seco la mammina, That he must come and pay me a little visit and bring my little mama with him."

He would not deliver *that* message to Byron. Poor Claire. The visit had saddened him. The child was well treated, but her mind was uncultivated, and her vanity and her temper were unchecked.

As soon as he got back to Ravenna Shelley did his best to persuade Byron to take Allegra with him to Pisa. He warned him about Italian convents: "Dreadful things have happened in them." Byron said nothing. He looked offended and stubborn.

Next day letters came for Byron from Teresa. She said she would give up all idea of going to Switzerland if Byron would come to her. She had written to Shelley, too, imploring him not to leave Ravenna without Byron. Shelley could not wait until Byron decided to uproot himself. But he wrote to Mary immediately, suggesting that they should stay in Pisa instead of going to Florence. He toyed with the idea of asking Leigh Hunt to join them with his family. He was growing excited at the prospect of forming a circle of like-minded spirits, with

Byron and Byron's Italian friends, and with their own friends.

When Shelley left Ravenna he took a reassuring letter from Byron for Teresa, and one for Pietro. He stopped at Florence on his way to Pisa, and called on Teresa. Teresa liked him at once, and when he left she begged him to find a house for her father and brother in Pisa.

It had taken Shelley only a day or two to find a house for Byron and one for the Gambas.

Byron's house was the Palazzo Lanfranchi, which had been the home of the Lanfranchi family but which was now owned by a Madame Felichi, from whom Shelley had leased it. It faced on the street following the right bank of the Arno, and behind it was a pleasant little garden surrounded by high walls. It had been well restored by the architect Gherardesca, and the interior was very fine.

So at the beginning of September 1821, the Gambas moved to Pisa, and took lodgings in the Casa Finocchietti on the Lungarno. After three weeks they were able to move to the house which Shelley had found—the house of the Parra brothers, also on the Lungarno. They had been given only temporary passports in Florence, and were aware that the authorities in Pisa were watching their movements. They grew even more nervous when several of their friends from Ravenna and Faenza who had been active in their nationalist revolutionary Carboneria movement also arrived in Pisa. They went out very little.

Shelley was busy, and he was elated at the prospect of forming his circle. He wrote to Leigh Hunt, inviting him to come to Italy and join in editing a literary paper, to publish original work and to share the profits. He added that he was only the link, and that, although Byron did not yet know it, *he* had no intention of sharing the profits. He signed the contract for the Palazzo Lanfranchi, on Byron's behalf, for four hundred pounds a year, and wrote at once giving him instructions for bypassing Florence, where Claire, who was still at Leghorn, was expected to return at any time.

Shelley realized that he had to face breaking the news to Claire that Byron was coming to Pisa. Byron had left England on April 25, 1816. Claire had last seen him in October of that year. Now once again, years later, she might well meet him despite his determination to avoid her.

Teresa was nearing a breakdown, convinced that Byron would never come. Still he did not leave Ravenna. There was always something, he persuaded himself, to delay him. Once, indeed, there was a real difficulty. The Ravenna carriers were expensive, so Byron had asked Shelley to send eight wagons from Pisa to collect his belongings. Somehow or other Pietro also managed to send eight wagons. Sixteen wagons would have arrived if Shelley had not hurried to Florence to intercept the second caravansary. Then the wagons did not reach Ravenna until the permit for entering Tuscany had expired. Everything had to come to a halt while Lega wrote for a renewal.

When the wagons arrived at last, Byron's whole household was in chaos, the packing conducted in dust and noise with a great deal of shouting and swearing. And now Byron was talking of going to Pisa only for the winter.

At last the packing was done. There were hardly any beds left to sleep on in Byron's apartment in the Palazzo Guiccioli. Still Byron did not leave. Still he sat up every night, writing into the small hours and sleeping late into the day. He was still in Ravenna at the beginning of October, excusing himself by saying that he had a slight incipient, intermittent fever.

As always, when he was unhappy his thoughts turned to Augusta. For the first time in months he wrote to her, reminding her that their father had run off with a married woman:

"So you see that I have closed as Papa began, and you will probably never see me again as long as you live. Indeed, you don't deserve it, for having behaved so coldly, when I was ready to have sacrificed everything for you. It is nearly three years that this liaison has lasted. I can say that, without being so furiously in love as at first, I am more attached to her than I thought it possible to be to any woman after three years— *except one, and who was she? Can YOU guess?*" If his wife and Guiccioli should die, he added, he and Teresa would probably have to marry—"though I would rather not, thinking it the way to hate each other."

He did not know that, to add to all her other troubles, Augusta's second child, her namesake, was developing signs of insanity and would soon have to be cared for away from home at a cost of two hundred pounds a year, a sum the Leighs would find it hard to provide. Already they had been forced to sell Six Mile Bottom at a poor price to avoid Colonel Leigh's going to a debtor's prison. Queen Charlotte was dead and had left Augusta spacious apartments in St. James's Palace, and a pension of seven hundred pounds a year for her and her husband for as long as either of them survived, but Leigh was as spendthrift as ever.

Still Byron delayed. First, there was a rumour that the exiles were to be expelled from Tuscany. Then the Pope issued an encyclical against the Carbonari, threatening to excommunicate all those who remained in it. Those who had already left it were allowed to return to their homes on payment of substantial sums and with declarations of abject penitence. Would the Gambas give in? At length Byron discovered that they would not. So now there was no hope of their returning to Ravenna with dignity. Still he stayed on, riding, swimming and waiting in the empty apartment, now so bare of furniture, since it had all been sent ahead to Pisa, that Lega was sleeping on straw. Almost two months had gone by since his promise to Teresa to join her.

At last Byron sent Lega on with the grooms and carriages, but he did not move. Shelley wrote saying that his house was ready and his furniture arranged, and that Leigh Hunt was planning to come to Italy in November. He asked for a date when he could expect him. Teresa, he said, seemed fearful that he would never leave Ravenna. He asked, too, what Byron was doing for Allegra. Byron had said only that he would not, for the present, remove Allegra from the convent.

Only the nuns at Bagnacavallo seemed to believe that Byron was leaving Ravenna. The rumour had reached them, and Marianna Fabbri, the Mother Superior, wrote to him. She was sorry to hear that he was leaving Ravenna, and invited him to visit his daughter before he went. On the opposite side of the sheet containing the nun's letter, Allegra had written to her father, too, in Italian. Her letter had been written on carefully drawn lines in a large copybook hand.

"My dear Papa," Byron translated. "It is fair time, and I would very much like a visit from my Papa, as there are so many things that I want. Won't you please your Allegrina who loves you so?"

Byron threw the letter down. He felt angry and disappointed. She only wanted to see him in order to get things for herself. He did not reply to the Mother Superior or to his daughter, and he did not go to see her.

It was only a letter from Samuel Rogers, who was touring in Venice, suggesting that he visit Byron in Ravenna, which made him move at last. He could not be put up in his empty quarters. He suggested that they meet in Bologna and cross the Apennines together.

So at last, at the end of October, three months after Teresa had left Ravenna, in the dark of early morning Byron's heavy Napoleonic carriage rattled through the silent streets of the medieval town which he had entered nearly two years before. Count Alborghetti, whom he had paid so highly for information, and many members of the families who had enjoyed his charity, stood at their windows watching him go. To his banker, Pellegrino Ghigi, so used to performing all the tasks he avoided, Byron left the care of a goat with a broken leg, an ugly dog, a heron, a badger on a chain, two old monkeys—and Allegra.

That afternoon, as the carriage bowled along the road to Bologna, Byron nodded drowsily. The noise of an approaching carriage roused him, and as he raised his head he saw a familiar face—it was Lord Clare, his favourite fag at Harrow. They had not met for eight years. The carriages drew up, and the two men leapt out. They stood on the public road, staring at each other, smiling and laughing. Then they embraced, wordlessly, both of them extremely moved. Byron could feel Clare's heart beating against his chest. Then they returned to their carriages.

That night Byron wrote in his journal: "We were obliged to part for our different journeys—he for Rome, and I for Pisa; but with the promise to meet again in the spring. We were but five minutes together, and in the public road; but I hardly recollect an hour of my existence which could be weighed against them."

After that Byron and Rogers travelled together over the Apennines. They arrived in Florence and put up at a little inn. Next day Byron went with Rogers to Santa Croce. He stood, looking bored, before the tombs of Machiavelli and Michelangelo; but before Galileo's he said, "I have a pleasure in looking upon that monument; he was one of us."

"One of us?"

"One of the nobility."

Florence was full of the English. Every morning there were English carriages at the door of the inn. When, on the morning of November first, Byron emerged to start for Pisa, every window of the inn was open and filled with faces watching him set off. He left, scowling.

As the carriage lumbered towards Pisa Byron composed a lyric.

Oh! talk not to me of a name great in story;
The days of our youth are the days of our glory . . .
Oh! Fame! if I e'er took delight in thy praises,
'Twas less for the sake of thy high-sounding phrases,
Than to see the bright eyes of the dear one discover
She thought that I was not unworthy to love her.

It was just beyond Empoli, about thirty miles from Florence, that Byron's caravan of carriages passed the public coach from Pisa. In it was a dark-haired girl, who started and peered out at him. Claire Clairmont was on her way back to Florence. Oblivious, Byron rolled on to Teresa's arms.

* * *

CHAPTER
❦ 16 ❧

All had gone well. Byron was delighted with Pisa. The Palazzo Lanfranchi was lighter and brighter than the Guiccioli palace in Ravenna, and he was enchanted at being able to pick his own oranges in his garden in November. Only the noise of the traffic on the street alongside the Arno in front of his palace was a nuisance.

Then he liked the Shelley circle. Now it was Teresa who saw hardly anyone, and whose few acquaintances spoke a foreign language. He saw her once a day; but he was seeing a great deal of Shelley and his friends. Closest to Shelley were Edward and Jane Williams, who had come to Pisa the previous January on Thomas Medwin's invitation and now lived with their two young children in the same large house as the Shelleys. Thomas Medwin, who was Shelley's cousin and had been at Eton with him, had come to Pisa to be with him. He had served with Williams in the Eighth Dragoons in India; so when the good-looking, rakish half-pay lieutenant with literary leanings had run away with a brother officer's wife, Medwin had invited them to come to Pisa, where life was not only pleasant but very cheap. He and his mistress were known as Mr. and Mrs. Williams. Jane Williams was pretty, with large eyes, a smooth forehead, a sweet mouth and long, curling ringlets. It was not only the men who liked her, however. She and Mary Shelley had a good deal in common.

Then there were the other lovers, George Tighe and Lady Mountcashell. Lady Mountcashell had left her husband, an Irish earl, about eight years before, and was living with Tighe in the Casa Silva. They were known as Mr. and Mrs. Mason. She was a strong-minded, intelligent woman, and had known Mary Shelley's famous mother when she was a governess in the Irish household. She and George Tighe had two daughters. Tighe himself was an expert on growing potatoes—he was known as "Tatty" Tighe in Ireland.

There was John Taaffe, too, an Irishman of good family, who had also fled to Italy after a love affair but without his mistress. He had abandoned her in Edinburgh and formed a new liaison with a Madame Regny. He had lost his position in charge of the Regny stables, and now spent his time writing a commentary on Dante and doing his own translation of the *Divine Comedy*. Byron, he hoped, would help him to get them published. Everyone was careful not to mention the secret marriage he had made at Pisa, on an English ship, for his wife had died soon afterwards.

Thomas Medwin himself had returned to Pisa simply in order to meet Byron. He was full of stories of India, and he also had literary ambitions. There was Captain John Hay, too, an old friend of Byron's who had recently arrived in Pisa. It was company in which Byron and Teresa could feel at ease in their anomalous situation.

All the men visited Byron almost daily, and dined at his table as often as they were asked. Shelley usually left early, but the others stayed till two or three in the morning. Shelley and Williams even left their families on Christmas Day to join Medwin and Taaffe at Byron's table, abandoning Mary and Jane to a lonely Christmas. That day Shelley and Byron made a vow. The first to come into his estate would give the other a thousand pounds. Byron could hardly wait for Lady Noel's death, or Shelley for his father's. All the men were under thirty except for Byron and Taaffe, who were both thirty-three. Now everyone was waiting for Leigh Hunt to arrive. Shelley had furnished the ground floor of the Palazzo Lanfranchi for him, and Byron had paid for it.

Not everything was perfect, however. Byron had a shock when he heard that the conceited Dr. Polidori had committed suicide with an enormous dose of poison because of a gaming debt. He was worried about Ada, too, since he heard that she had a violent temper, and he was always afraid that Annabella would prejudice her against him. Then Claire never ceased to implore him to bring Allegra to Pisa. It was annoying also that he had been refused permission by the governor to set up a rifle range for his pistol practice in his garden. He had to make arrangements with some friends of Shelley's doctor, who lived outside the city walls. Almost every afternoon he and his friends rode out to practice pistol-shooting at the Villa la Podera, a pretty farmhouse with a vineyard and a garden in Cisanello, about two miles outside Pisa by way of the Porta alle Piagge. It was there that he had found Maria, a beautiful dark peasant girl. In no time he had adorned her plump arms with bracelets in return for favours received. Teresa was suspicious and jealous, and she and Mary took to riding or walking to meet him on his way back to Pisa. He had no idea how Teresa had learned anything, and he did not greatly care. Now she was becoming less and less important to him.

Then, in January 1822, a new friend arrived to join the circle. Edward John Trelawny had come to Italy on purpose to meet Shelley and Byron. Trelawny was a tall, piratical-looking Cornishman with short, curling raven hair and a beard, expressive eyes under overhanging brows, a hooked nose, curling lips, and a daredevil smile of great charm. He was all but illiterate, but he told wonderful stories—about his unhappy childhood; his boyhood service in the Royal Navy and the ill treatment received from its sadistic naval officers; his desertion in India; the privateer who put him in command of his vessels though he was still a boy; his fights against Malay pirates while flying the French flag; the prizes he sailed into the harbours of Mauritius; his visits to the hillside estate of De Ruyter, the leader of the privateer band; his Arab disguises;

and his Arab bride, and her death and cremation on the sands. (He never mentioned his disastrous marriage at twenty-one, and the scandalous divorce which had followed after his wife had eloped with their fellow lodger.) Byron did not believe half of his stories, but Mary Shelley drank them all in. Byron believed it was all a deliberate impersonation of his "corsair," and he declared that Trelawny slept with the poem under his pillow. All the same, when Trelawny began to encourage Shelley and Williams to have a boat built and spend the summer on the Bay of Spezia, Byron was enchanted with his idea. "Get a yacht built for me, too, Trelawny," he urged him, "and find me a house near the sea to sail her from."

So by February 1822, Trelawny's friend, Captain Daniel Roberts, was giving instructions for a vessel to be built in Genoa. She was to have an iron keel, copper fastenings, a high and roomy cabin, and there was to be no expense spared to make her luxurious. There were to be four guns with brass swivels. To begin with, Trelawny had estimated a hundred pounds or so. Soon the cost shot up. On the other hand, the boat meant for Shelley and Williams grew more and more modest. Soon she had shrunk from thirty feet to seventeen or eighteen feet.

That February news came of the death of Bryon's mother-in-law, Lady Noel. She had died in January at the age of seventy-one. Byron at once went into deep mourning, and ordered all his servants to wear black. Then he awaited the decision of the arbitrators as to how the Wentworth estates, which Lady Noel had inherited from her brother, Lord Wentworth, and which he was told were worth about ten thousand pounds a year, were to be divided. He named Sir Francis Burdett, the radical Member of Parliament and a friend of Hobhouse, to represent him, and asked for ten thousand pounds' insurance to be taken out on his wife's life, since on her death the estate would go elsewhere. Then, for the first time, he signed himself Noel Byron—writing to Douglas Kinnaird, "since it must be so, *Noel* Byron." He expected a fixed income to be awarded to Annabella out of the annual rents, with all the rest coming to him.

Week after week went by while he waited impatiently for news. He would have been concerned about more than money if he had known what Claire was up to. Still desperately worried at his not having brought Allegra with him, or even removed her from her convent when he left Ravenna, she had at last persuaded Tighe to make a secret trip to Ravenna and Bagnacavallo to find out all he could about the convent and Allegra's treatment there. He had brought back disturbing stories about the fevers which came from the marshes of the Romagna, the terrible poverty of the nuns, the austerity of their lives, their refusal to have fires in the winter, and the wretched food supplied to their pupils. Now Claire could never look at a fire without suffering agony for her child. She had begun to make plans for rescuing Allegra, while still beseeching Byron to put her with some respectable family in Pisa or Florence or Lucca. No answer came from him, and she wrote again, pleading for a chance to see Allegra before leaving for Vienna to join her brother and look for work there. She received no reply to that letter either. Byron was very busy with plans to produce *Othello*, with himself as Iago, while trying to soothe Teresa, who was deeply offended at not being in the cast since she could not speak English.

Then Claire arrived in Pisa. She went to Shelley and said, "We must steal her from that terrible place."

"You're exaggerating," Shelley said. "And Byron *must* not know that you are here."

"You must help me. You *must*." She broke down. So, at last Shelley went to Byron and said, "Please do something to ease her mind, Byron."

Byron shrugged impatiently. "Women can't live without making scenes!"

Shelley went back to his apartment and found Lady Mountcashell and Tighe there, visiting Mary.

"I could have knocked him down with pleasure," Shelley said. "He looked positively malicious when I told him how ill and miserable Claire is." Then he added, "It's foolish of me to be angry. He can no more help being what he is than that door can help being a door."

"You're quite wrong," Tighe replied. "If I were to horsewhip that door it would still be a door. But if Lord Byron were to be horsewhipped he'd become as humane as he is now inhumane."

"I want to break away from him," Shelley said. "But I mustn't, for Hunt's sake. When the new journal is established I'll do it. He's a great poet, but a petty, paltry human being."

"And Claire?" Mary asked.

"Try to calm her. Have nothing to do with these mad plans for abducting Allegra."

So life went on much as before. Byron had another shock when Hanson told him that Lady Noel had left his portrait to Ada on condition that it was not given to her until she was twenty-one. He was certain that Annabella was behind this decision, and was actively poisoning his child's mind against him. He wrote at once to Hanson, instructing him to find out what legal right he had to direct her education.

Then, suddenly, a letter came from Guiccioli, asking Teresa to return to him. "It's the allowance," Teresa said calmly. "He doesn't want to pay it. He'll have a very firm answer from me."

It was a Sunday towards the end of March. Byron, Shelley, Trelawny, Captain Hay and Pietro Gamba had ridden out for their pistol practice and were returning to Pisa. They were about half a mile from the city gate when they saw John Taaffe, the Irishman and lover of Madame Regny, coming towards them, walking his horse to cool him down. Taaffe turned round, remounted and rode on with them. Now they were riding four abreast. Taaffe was on the left next to the ditch. Then came Byron, Shelley and Trelawny, almost filling the road. Hay and Pietro and Byron's courier, Giuseppe Strauss, brought up the rear. Teresa and Mary Shelley were driving in Teresa's carriage some distance ahead, on their way home after meeting Byron and Shelley. Byron's coachman, Vincenzo Papi, was driving the carriage, and Teresa's servant, Antonio Maluccelli, was riding behind it.

They were only a quarter of a mile from the city gate, when a horseman suddenly galloped up from behind and thundered between Taaffe and the ditch. Taaffe's horse reared with fright, whinnying, and bumped into Byron's mount.

"Did you ever see anything like that?" Taaffe shouted to Byron, struggling to control his horse. Byron at once galloped off in pursuit of the rider. The others galloped after him, except for Taaffe, who was still trying to calm his horse. Shelley caught up with him first, and saw a solid-looking man in a dragoon's uniform covered with gold braid and with epaulets. At thirty paces from the gate the man had to slow up, and Shelley spurred his horse past him and blocked his way.

"What do you want?" the man shouted.

"Please explain what you mean by your behaviour," Shelley replied in Italian, politely but firmly.

The dragoon shrugged and tried to ride on. Now Byron and the others had come up, and they quickly surrounded him. Byron did not notice that the soldier was not an officer but a sergeant-major in the Tuscan Royal Light Horse. "Why have you insulted us?" he shouted. A stream of Italian came from the dragoon. "This fellow's damned insolent," Byron called to Trelawny, reaching into his saddlebag and drawing out a visiting card. There was a soldier standing nearby, and he gave it to him to hand to the dragoon.

"*I* haven't got a card, but my name is Masi, and I'm ready to fight you all, one at a time."

"Right," Byron replied. "I challenge you to fight me to-morrow."

"And I do the same," Trelawny cried.

Captain Hay was trying to attract Byron's attention, calling out, "My lord, he's not an officer. You can't fight him. Let him go."

No one listened to him. They were overexcited. While they were all issuing their challenges Taaffe came up, but stayed in the background. He had remained behind to pick up his hat, which had fallen off when his horse reared, and brush the dust from it in case Byron and the others laughed at him. He watched as his friends, all on horseback, jostled Masi. Then he saw Pietro Gamba strike Masi across the chest with his riding crop, shouting "*Ignorante!*"

"You're all lunatics!" Masi shouted. Turning his horse, he galloped towards the gate. Then he wheeled back and called, "If I liked I could draw my saber and cut you all to bits, but I'll arrest you instead!" He shouted to two old soldiers standing at the gate, "Arrest them all!"

Byron threw his head back and laughed loudly, "Arrest us, indeed! Let's ride on."

Byron spurred his horse through the gate. The others followed, but only Byron and Pietro got through. Trelawny, Shelley and Hay found Masi and two foot soldiers blocking their way. Masi was slashing wildly to right and left with his saber. Trelawny managed to parry a few blows, then ducked away, untouched. Suddenly Shelley rode between him and Masi. Masi rushed at him and knocked him from his horse. Shelley lay on the ground, unconscious. At once Masi turned to Captain Hay, who was holding up a walking stick for protection. Masi's saber cut the stick in two and slashed Hay's nose badly. As Hay put his hand to his face he could see Strauss being beaten by one of the foot soldiers with the hilt of his saber.

Now Byron was galloping down the Lungarno, calling to Pietro to ride on and send Lega Zambelli to the police to report the incident. Soon he passed the carriage with Teresa and

Mary in it. Papi touched his cap with his whip as Byron went by.

Pietro galloped on, found Lega standing in front of the Palazzo Lanfranchi and sent him off. Next Strauss arrived at the palazzo and staggered inside. As Byron arrived Strauss, looking distraught, came out again and thrust a black sword stick at him. Byron seized it and started back to look for Trelawny, Shelley and Hay. Strauss followed, more slowly, and Tita, armed with two cavalry sabers, ran after Byron.

At that moment the carriage arrived, and Teresa jumped down and ran up the stairway of the palazzo screaming, "Oh, God! Oh, God!" Mary stayed behind in the carriage, calmly ordering Maluccelli to take the news to the Williamses. "Say we may not be able to entertain them to dinner this evening as we promised, but that I'll let them know," she ordered.

Meanwhile, after a short gallop, Byron had met Masi. Masi at once put his hand on his saber.

"Don't draw!" Byron shouted. He half-drew his sword stick to show he was armed.

"Are you satisfied now I've beaten you all?" Masi cried.

"No. I still want satisfaction. What's your name?"

"Sergeant-Major Masi." He rode very close, caught Byron's hand and held it so tight that Byron could not draw his sword. They rode on together, like that, towards the Palazzo Lanfranchi. A great crowd had gathered before it. As they came up Tita arrived, pushed between the horses and seized Masi's bridle. He offered Byron a saber.

"No, Tita. Release the soldier's bridle."

Masi kicked his horse and galloped past the palace, keeping to the river side of the roadway. It was growing dark, and Byron lost sight of him in the crowd. Then, as Masi passed the palace, Byron heard someone shout, "No! No!" as a man with a lance suddenly ran from the steps. It was Vincenzo Papi, Byron's coachman. Masi had already passed, but Papi lunged at the sergeant-major from behind. He yelled, "I hit him! I hit him!" Byron saw Masi reel in his saddle and clap a hand to his right side as his horse galloped on. A hundred yards farther on, his *casque* and *berretta* fell off. He swayed in the saddle, crying out, "I am killed!" Byron saw Masi fall from his horse to the road in front of a café. Then he saw him struggle to his feet, making a great effort, and stumble into the café. There was no sign of his assailant.

At last Byron returned to the Palazzo Lanfranchi. Trelawny and Shelley arrived from the opposite direction, helping the wounded Hay, who was spitting blood. Byron found Teresa still hysterical and almost in a state of collapse. He spent an hour trying to soothe her and help Hay, and then decided to take her to the Shelleys' house since it was near that of Dr. Vaccà, Shelley's doctor. As they were leaving, Tita came to report that Masi was badly wounded. Somehow he had made his way to a jeweller's house, had collapsed and been carried to the hospital. Byron at once sent Taaffe to give an account of the affair to the provincial governor, Viviani, before other stories reached his ear. Then he and Teresa went to the Shelleys' apartment. The Williamses were still waiting there. Teresa could hardly stand. Shelley was sick and faint from the blow he had received, and Byron and Pietro were shouting explanations to the Williamses. Only Mary Shelley was still calm, looking coolly and philosophically at it all, as if she were at a play.

They all waited for the doctor, but after a while a messenger came to say that Dr. Vaccà could not be found. A few minutes later a surgeon named Foscarini arrived. By then Teresa had gone into convulsions. "She must be taken home and bled," Foscarini decided. "Immediately."

So Byron, Mary and the surgeon went with Teresa in the carriage, with Papi on the box. As soon as they arrived Teresa was bled. After that she seemed quieter. Byron left with Mary and the surgeon, and went back to the Palazzo Lanfranchi.

There he found the men of the party reassembled. Taaffe was soon back, too. He had failed to see the governor, but made his report to a Captain Bini. He said gloomily that he had heard that the sergeant-major could not live through the night.

"You go, Shelley," Byron said. "Take Pietro and Hay to the governor's palace, and make a full report. I'll stay behind. It's very important that we should be the accusers and not the accused." Hay's nose was still bleeding, but he went. They were back within the hour. They had done as Byron had asked, but they were not at all happy about it. The gathering did not break up until eleven o'clock that night.

Next morning Byron was up early for once. He immediately sent Dr. John Todd, an English doctor in Pisa who had attended Hay, to offer his services to Masi at Byron's expense. Taaffe had brought another report that Masi's wound was not serious. By two o'clock, however, they heard that Extreme Unction had been administered to the dragoon. Everyone in Pisa was waiting for him to die.

Byron and his friends held another conference.

"We must draw up a deposition," Shelley said, "signed by us all, and give it to the police."

So they drew it up. Then Taaffe refused to sign it. "I had nothing to do with the fighting at the gate," he said. "I can't swear to what I didn't see."

The others signed and agreed to draw up individual depositions as well. They were all very angry with Taaffe, but tried not to show it.

At four o'clock Tita came to say that word had gone round that the dragoon was dying. At half-past four all the men armed themselves with sword sticks and pistols, mounted their horses amid a large crowd pressing close to the doors of the Palazzo Lanfranchi, and went off for their usual ride. Byron had decided that they must not appear to be frightened.

Things were no better the next day. All over Pisa people

spoke of nothing but the wounding of Sergeant-Major Masi. Dr. Vaccà had heard his story from Masi himself, and he took a serious view of the matter. "Masi is better," he said to Shelley, "though he is not out of danger. But it's a bad lookout for Lord Byron and his friends. The authorities won't like it."

They consoled themselves that the police had so far only required the deposition and Strauss's evidence, and had released Strauss since he had been near Byron at the time of the wounding. Byron began distributing alms before his palace in the hope of creating a less hostile attitude in Pisa.

The month of March was nearly out, and Masi's condition was still poor, when Trelawny, Shelley and Williams called on Byron to find that the police had arrested Tita and Papi.

"So they've discovered that it *was* Papi who wounded Masi," Trelawny blurted out.

"For God's sake say nothing of that," Byron begged him. "Tita was released, but like a fool went back to make his deposition armed to the teeth—stiletto, pistols and all. Now they're both in prison, Tita for illegal possession of firearms. I've sent Tita a twelve-course dinner to share with the other prisoners."

Byron was agonized that reports harmful to his reputation would reach the English press. He wrote to Edward Dawkins, the British Chargé d'Affaires in Florence, giving his side of the story, and ordered copies made of the Englishmen's depositions to go with his letter.

Next day Papi was released. At once he altered his appearance as much as he could to avoid recognition. Everyone was still very angry with Taaffe for not submitting a deposition. He was staying away from the Palazzo Lanfranchi. But that day Byron decided that he must be made to write his account, and demanded it. Taaffe produced three closely written pages in Italian. He claimed he had not been insulted by the dragoon, only taken aback by his suddenly galloping between the riders, and that it was Byron who had started all the trouble by pursuing Masi, which had incited the others to follow. Byron was furiously angry, and Williams agreed with him. "Jane has christened him False Taaffe, after Falstaff," he said. But no one smiled.

That day, too, Teresa's servant, Antonio Maluccelli, was arrested. After giving very confused testimony, he was also imprisoned. At least the dragoon was on the way to recovery, to everyone's relief.

Byron was determined, however, to get some personal vindication. The fact that Taaffe had sent his deposition to Dawkins did not help matters. "Everyone will blame me for it all if it is not cleared up," he insisted. "We must get a clear statement to England of what happened before the papers print a lot of scandalous stuff. And Dawkins is the right man to do that." But no appeals to Dawkins produced the report, and he told Byron crisply that if he wanted to bring an action against Masi he could consult a local lawyer. It was all Williams could do to get Byron to speak to Taaffe at all, and Trelawny and the Shelleys would have nothing more to do with him.

At the beginning of April Captain Hay left for England. Medwin had already gone. The Shelleys and the Williamses were talking of leaving for the summer. Byron himself decided to rent a house at Montenero near Leghorn for the season, and was due to arrive there on the first of May. The once-happy Pisan circle was growing smaller, and soon, it seemed, there would be no one left.

Nagging troubles pursued Byron in other directions. Hanson had failed to insure Annabella's life—her health was, it seemed, considered poor. He wrote bitterly to Hobhouse, "Must I be reduced to marrying a rich woman if she dies? My greatest obligation to her is that she has prevented me from marrying."

Then worse news came. The arbitrators had decided that

Annabella was to have half the net proceeds of the Went-worth estate—a mere five thousand pounds a year after deductions—largely on the grounds that she had to pay for Ada's maintenance. Byron was cruelly disappointed. Still, the two and a half thousand pounds a year which would come to him would double his yearly income. At once he sent Leigh Hunt the two hundred and fifty pounds he was begging for, though Shelley had already sent him a hundred and fifty pounds. He grudged it, however. Now he was no longer a spendthrift. He would, he thought, have to provide for himself, for Allegra, perhaps for Teresa and her family, and very likely for Augusta and all her children, including his own Medora.

The only bright spot for him was that at last he had persuaded Teresa to release him from his promise of the summer before to give up writing *Don Juan* until she asked him to resume it. He was beginning the sixth canto, and he could forget his troubles as he sat up late at night describing Don Juan's tribulations. He was to be bought in the slave market at the behest of an infatuated Sultana, and smuggled into the harem disguised as one of the wives to share a bed with the desirable Dudu. He was thoroughly enjoying himself in that at least, and writing well.

At last Byron had been allowed to pay Tita's fine for illegal possession of firearms, and he was released. But then the Pisan authorities at once took him back into solitary confinement, and recommended to the governor that he should be sent into exile. Byron immediately wrote hotly to Dawkins. Then the examination of the principal witnesses began at their own houses.

For five hours Mary and Teresa were questioned. Teresa went too far. "I can't swear, Your Honour," she said, "but I believe it was Mr. Taaffe who wounded the dragoon."

Mary was shocked but said nothing. Both she and Teresa

knew very well that it was Papi who had thrown the lance at Masi.

Next it was Byron's turn, and then Trelawny's. Captain Hay, who had actually been wounded and who was one of the most important witnesses, could not be questioned, since he had already gone. The Cancelliere Lapini, who had come to question Byron, approached him with a mixture of fright and awe. He had heard that Byron had murdered one of his mistresses and had half her skull mounted as a drinking cup. His relief at Byron's scrupulous courtesy was painfully evident.

Now everyone waited to see what would happen next. The affair was the most serious of all for the Gambas. There was, they knew, every possibility that they would be exiled from Tuscany.

* * *

CHAPTER
❧ 17 ❧

In the midst of the Masi difficulties Claire Clairmont arrived in Pisa. The Shelleys had invited her to spend the summer with them on the Bay of Spezia, and she had decided to put off going to Vienna. Her mind was still full of plans for abducting Allegra.

"If I go to the convent with a forged letter from Byron," she said to Shelley, "I can take her away and bring her here. You *must* help me."

"You can never get Allegra by such means—or any means. He has her in his power, and he is inflexible."

Claire seemed to weep all day, and she never ceased to plead with Shelley; but he would not change his mind. He insisted that Byron was not to be told that she was in Pisa. She saw only the Williamses and the Masons and Trelawny, and they kept the secret.

None of them knew that Byron had had disturbing news of Allegra. Ghigi, his banker, had written to Lega Zambelli to say that Allegra had had a slight fever for several days. "I have sent Dr. Rasi to attend her," he wrote, "and will report again in a few days, as to how she is progressing." Three days later Lega had another letter. The doctor, Ghigi said, had ordered Allegra to be bled because he thought she showed symptoms of consumption. That letter disturbed Byron when Lega brought it to him.

"Send a courier at once for more news, Lega," he ordered, "and ask the nuns to call in Professor Tommasini of Bologna if they think it necessary."

He told only Teresa of the child's illness, however, and charged her to tell no one else about it.

Very soon another letter came from Ghigi. The doctor had spent a night at Bagnacavallo and had ordered two more bleedings. Ghigi himself had visited Allegra frequently at the convent. "There is hope," he wrote, "that Allegra can be kept out of danger, but I assure you that she has been ill, dangerously ill." He added that he was sending Dr. Rasi to her again, with orders to remain with her until she was on the way to recovery. "I last saw her myself on Thursday, April 18th," he wrote. "She seemed better. She was talkative, and begged me to bring her some cheese. She was in her little bed in a fine room, surrounded by three doctors and several nuns. They are doing everything they can for her. If there is any fault, it is of too much care, not too little."

That letter was sent on April 20 by special messenger, and it reached Lega in a couple of days. On its heels came one from the convent. "The little Allegra," Lega read, "suddenly took a turn for the worse. She was stricken with a convulsive catarrhal attack, and, a little after ten o'clock, she died." There was a letter from Ghigi, too, to Lega. The nuns were devastated, he wrote, and had left it to him to make arrangements for the disposal of Allegra's body as her father wished. He had ordered the small corpse to be embalmed and put in a lead casket inside a wooden coffin. He asked Lega to choose the best time to break the news to Byron. He told him, too, that the Mother Superior had written in her records, "The late Mademoiselle Marie Allegra Byron, sent to the Convent of the Capuchin Nuns of St. John the Baptist in Bagnacavallo at the tender age of four years to be educated in the Catholic religion, confirmed the 17th September 1821, by Monsignor Prienne, Bishop of Faenza, died in the said convent on the 20th April, 1822, at ten o'clock in the evening. Her extraordinary qualities of heart and mind, her rare talents, and the lovableness of her character will make her long remembered by all those who had the happiness to know her, and especially by the nuns, whose delight she was."

One of the sisters, Ghigi said, was confined to bed with grief after Allegra's death, and the nuns had consoled themselves by saying that she was too intelligent to live. They had never, they declared, had such a gifted pupil.

When Ghigi's letter arrived for Lega, he hurried to Teresa and handed it to her. When she had read it he said, "Will you tell the lord Byron for me, Madame la Contessa?"

Teresa nodded and went at once to order her carriage.

When Fletcher came to tell Byron that Madame la Contessa had arrived at the Casa Lanfranchi, Byron knew at once that she must have had word about Allegra.

"Admit her, Fletcher."

She came in, her face grave.

"Byron, I have something to tell you."

"It is about Allegra."

"Yes. I must warn you that Allegra is not going to recover."

"You mean, Teresa, that she is dead?"

She was silent for a long time. Then she nodded.

"I understand. Don't say any more." He had gone very white, and staggered, feeling for a chair, and sank into it. He did not weep, he who was so easily moved to tears, but Teresa was shocked by the look on his face.

For an hour Byron sat without moving with Teresa beside him. She tried to comfort him, but he did not speak to her. At last he said, "Leave me alone," and she went away.

Sitting alone, Byron blamed himself for having ignored the advice of Shelley and of Hoppner not to leave Allegra in the convent, but he made up his mind to keep his reactions to himself. When at last he got to his feet, it was to go to his desk and write to Murray, asking him to arrange for Allegra's coffin to be laid in the little tall-spired church at Harrow, so full of memories of his boyhood.

Next day Teresa called on him again. She was full of dread

as to how she would find him. Now he seemed calm and resigned. "She's luckier than we are," he said. "Besides, she would never have been happy because of her position in the world. It's God's will. Let's not speak of it again." From that day he never mentioned Allegra to Teresa again. Underneath, however, he was tortured. She had never seemed important to his happiness. He remembered his impatience when she was ill-tempered or greedy, and how anxious he had been to send her away from him. Now he was sorry that he had not taken her to the convent, or visited her there as she had written to ask him. He had almost hated her when she reminded him of Claire or of his mother. He had enjoyed her prettiness and her cleverness less and less, and had disliked her more and more. He had resented it, too, that she had enjoyed all that he would have preferred to give to Ada. His little bastard had driven in his carriage, and had sat on his knee when he felt like caressing her. But it was Ada's birthday that he had noted in his journal, Ada's miniature which stood on his writing desk, and, always, it was Ada and her future that he spoke of—never Allegra's. Now he felt that he could not live without her. His grief was great, almost as great as that he had felt for Edleston, his deepest love, whose death had stricken him at Newstead Abbey at the time of his mother's funeral.

At last he nerved himself to write to Shelley and give him the news, saying that the blow had been stunning and unexpected, that he did not feel he had anything to reproach himself with, that her death had been natural and inevitable, and that nothing could have been done to prevent it.

Byron had still no idea that Claire was near him. When Shelley received the news she had gone with the Williamses to look for a house near Spezia.

Claire returned on the twenty-fifth of April. Shelley did not dare to tell her what had happened while she was near Byron, for fear of what she might do. "Trelawny," he said, "you and Mary must take her away. Say you have heard of a house—

anything. Settle for the best unfurnished house you can find, and Jane and Edward and I will pack up the furniture and follow. Don't bring her back to Pisa."

Next day Shelley and the Williamses followed. Trelawny and Claire had hired the Casa Magni, near Lerici, and they all moved in. Then Trelawny left for Genoa to see to the building of the boats, and, in due course, to bring Byron's boat to Leghorn.

Neither Shelley nor Mary knew how to break the news to Claire. Three times Shelley went up to her, intending to speak, and three times he walked away without doing so. Mary, too, tried to tell her, but her courage failed her also.

At last Claire realized that something was wrong. They had finished their light midday meal, and she had gone to her room. Mary and Shelley were alone, once again conferring as to what it was best to do. Suddenly Claire appeared.

"Tell me what it is. It is Allegra, isn't it?"

They nodded, without speaking.

"She is dead, isn't she?"

Mary ran to her and held her in her arms; but Claire broke away. She gave a scream, and fainted. Mary slapped her cheeks, and Shelley ran to get some water. They helped her to her room. "Leave me," Claire said, and they went.

Next day Shelley wrote to Byron: "I will not describe her grief to you. You have already suffered too much." He wrote only, he said, to send Claire's last requests to Byron. She wanted to see the little body in its coffin before it was sent to England, and she begged for a portrait of Allegra and a lock of her hair, however small.

Byron sent the portrait and the lock of hair by Shelley's messenger. He had, he said, ordered Allegra's body to be sent to Leghorn. Unknown to Shelley, however, Claire had been writing to Byron. She rehearsed his whole conduct towards her and Allegra, and accused him of cruelty. He had promised her, she said, that she would see her child frequently, and that she would not be given to strangers before she was at least seven, and that he would look after her himself and love her. All those promises had been broken, and her child had been murdered. He was, she declared, deformed in body *and* mind.

Byron sent Claire's letter to Shelley at once. Shelley apologized for her, and said that he had succeeded in dissuading Claire from going to see Allegra's body.

Now Byron was determined to put the whole thing out of his mind. He announced Allegra's death to his friends in England in a brief, unemotional sentence, expressing no sorrow. When the priest Fabiani, and his friend Baldini, came to Pisa after leaving Allegra's embalmed body at Leghorn, and came at Ghigi's request to give him a full account of Allegra's last illness, he refused to see them. They were very upset, and Ghigi was ashamed for him. Ghigi wrote to Lega that they had returned to Bagnacavallo greatly mortified. "I too," he wrote, "blush to think that one day it will be known that they were refused admittance. I am prepared to believe that my lord is very sensitive and deeply grieved, but I also recognize that every man has his own self-respect, and sorrow must not make one forget one's manners towards others." Byron did not even pay the bills which Ghigi sent to him for his daughter's medical care, and when he heard that the embalming had been expensive he refused to pay for it. Ghigi, ashamed to put off the creditors any longer, paid all the bills himself, and waited, in vain, to be repaid.

On the night on which Byron learned of Allegra's death he was informed that Tita had been ordered out of Tuscany. "The Great Beard," as he was known to his jailers, had been given fifteen days in which to arrange his affairs, but had been refused a safe-conduct pass through Florence. Byron applied for permission for Tita to stay with the Shelleys at the Casa Magni, but that was refused. Angrily, Byron told Dawkins that if he had not already rented two houses and had other business on hand, he would leave Pisa at once.

Tita was confused. "Where am I to go?" he asked his captors. "I must stay with Lord Byron, for he bought me. He paid my father for me, and still gives him money every year." But at the end of the month he left prison, in a carriage hired by Lega, with two troopers. On his last day he had given a final feast to all his fellow prisoners, with hired plate and silver candelabra paid for by Byron. That night he was locked up in the Palazzo di Giustizia in Florence—it was only a change of prisons. At once he was ordered to shave off his huge beard.

"Will it be given to Lord Byron?"

"No."

Tita shaved off his beard, in tears. Then he wrapped it carefully in a sheet of paper, and put it inside his shirt. The transformation was dramatic. The prison officers with him burst out laughing. The formidable Tita now seemed a fat, mild man of the greatest benevolence. That night he was given permission to go to Lucca. "From there," Dawkins said to him, as he gave him his papers, "you can make your way to the Shelleys at Casa Magni. It is all arranged."

But Teresa's innocent servant, Antonio Maluccelli, was still in prison.

"He is being held as hostage for our conduct," Pietro said.

"You must leave Pisa," Byron urged him. "Come and stay quietly in my summer house near Leghorn till all this blows over."

"Whenever you're ready to go, we'll come."

Yet Byron stayed on in the Palazzo Lanfranchi, ignoring the danger to his friends. He was still there after the middle of May. He was too depressed, and too lazy, to move. Then he was still determined to press on with the case against Sergeant-Major Masi, even though Hay and Trelawny had gone, so that it could be established that it was the dragoon who had been to blame. He pressed Shelley hard, through Lega, to give evidence to support the prosecution. He could not understand why Shelley, who had been badly hurt by the dragoon, did not want to follow it up.

"He's suffered enough for his rashness, poor fellow," Shelley said. "Besides, I don't want to come back to Pisa." There was no shifting him.

Even Byron could not wait for the decision of the court. Not until two months after the affray had taken place was judgment given—that there were no grounds for holding Tita Falcieri or Giuseppe Strauss or Antonio Maluccelli on criminal charges. By then Byron had moved most of his household, and that of Count Gamba, to the Villa Dupuy near Leghorn. There the Gambas would be out of the way of the spies at Pisa, and Teresa could enjoy the sea bathing Dr. Vaccà had recommended for her nerves. Strauss and Papi were given permits to join Byron. Everyone believed Byron had bribed the officials to secure his servants' acquittal.

Everything, it seemed, to do with the Masi affair was concluded. It was not, however. Suspicion and enmity in Tuscany had been inflamed against Byron and his friends, and had not subsided. The Masi affair had done a great deal to break up the Pisan circle. After Shelley's departure it no longer existed.

* * *

CHAPTER
❧ 18 ❧

Byron and the Gambas settled at once into the Villa Dupuy at Montenero near Leghorn. The house was low and rambling with salmon-coloured walls. It stood on a slope, and, looking through the olive trees across the blue sea, they could see the white houses of Leghorn about four miles away.

There Byron quickly regained his spirits. Kinnaird had written that he had at last succeeded in insuring Annabella's life for ten thousand pounds, and that he had transferred forty-six thousand pounds from government stock to a mortgage paying four and a half percent. Both Byron's present and his future would be better provided for. He had put Allegra's death behind him, leaving to Teresa all the details of shipping her body to Murray in England. He would spend hours simply looking at the Mediterranean, or relaxing in the evenings with Teresa in the garden among the sweet-scented roses, heliotrope, tuberoses and jasmine, and watching the lights of the fishing boats out in the bay. He played at draughts with her, too, and she let him win, even when she saw that he was cheating.

One day early in June, Lord Clare, his friend of his days at Harrow, with whom Byron had had such an emotional encounter on his way to Pisa, arrived to visit him. It was an enchanted day. They parted affectionately, and as Byron watched him drive off in his carriage, he said to Teresa, "I have a presentiment that I shall never see him again."

There was one great drawback to their paradise. One of the terms of the lease had been that there must be a constant supply of water to the house and stables. Yet, in that exceptionally hot summer, the water supply gave out, and every drop of water had to be fetched by mule from a spring over a mile away. Byron complained to Dupuy, his landlord, and offered him fifty scudi to take the rest of the lease off his hands. Dupuy refused, and Byron engaged Frederigo del Rosso, a well-known lawyer, to help him rescind his contract. It was annoying—and would be expensive.

Far worse, however, was the aftermath of the Masi affair. The Gambas were now in peril of being ordered out of Tuscany, and it was very doubtful whether any Italian state under the Austrian heel would take them in. Once again Byron was thinking of going to South America, this time with Teresa and her family. His admiration for the liberator of Colombia and Venezuela had flared up again; and he decided to call his new schooner the *Bolivar*. He had wanted to call her *The Countess Guiccioli*, but had abandoned the idea because he feared it would compromise Teresa and annoy her father. Now, it seemed to him, there was something symbolic in the change.

Meanwhile, at Lerici, fifty miles up the coast, Shelley's boat had arrived from Genoa. Their first sight of her had been a shock, for the name *Don Juan* had been painted on the mainsail. When they had decided to share the costs that name had been chosen for her. But then Shelley had taken on the entire expense of building her, and he had chosen the name *Ariel*. Byron, they realized, had been offended, and had told Roberts to paint the old name on the mainsail. Shelley and Williams unbent the mainsail, and sent for help. Nothing had any effect on the paint. In the end they had to cut the piece out. Shelley shrugged his shoulders and decided to use the name *Don Juan* after all, but Mary was very angry. At any rate, she said, they had escaped the vulgarity of having it painted on the sail, like a coal barge. Then, at last, Shelley and Williams could enjoy their boat. They were delighted with her. "She sails like a witch," Williams exulted.

It would be a month before Byron's schooner would be completed at Genoa. She was costing more and more, and the authorities were alarmed at the thought of the two two-pound cannons which were to be mounted on her—they would have been even more concerned if Byron had held to the original plan for four cannons. The Governor had already given orders that Byron was not to be allowed to moor her offshore, but must keep her inside Leghorn harbour and conform to the sanitary laws. Byron had no suspicion how awkward these orders would be making life for him when his ship was finally ready.

At last, late in June, the *Bolivar* was handed over to Byron in Leghorn.

"She is fast *and* safe," Trelawny said proudly.

"She's damned expensive. And do we really need five able seamen?"

"We do. When will you sail in her? We should take a cruise."

"Not today."

Every day, Trelawny found, it was "not today." Byron always had some excuse. He took little interest in the ship. "I'm a landlubber," he said at last. "All those sea terms in my poems—I looked them up. I hardly know the stem from the stern, and I don't know the name, or the use, of a single rope or sail."

So the *Bolivar* remained tied up at the dock while Byron stayed at the Villa Dupuy. Shelley stayed at Lerici, determined not to renew his close contact with him, all the more so because Claire, ill and miserable, was living at the Casa Magni.

At the beginning of July Leigh Hunt arrived in Leghorn. He went to Trelawny, who showed him the way up to the Villa Dupuy. It was an extremely hot day, and Hunt, streaming with sweat, trudged the four miles to the villa. There he stopped for a moment, mopping his brow and hating at sight the salmon colour of the villa's walls. No one, it seemed, noticed the little, shock-headed Englishman approaching. But as he came closer Hunt was struck with astonishment at the scene before his eyes.

There seemed to be a violent quarrel in progress in front of the house. Two men were shouting and gesticulating at each other. Suddenly a third man came running out of the house, and one of the other men drew a knife and struck the newcomer in the arm. Blood dyed the light shirt he was wearing. Then another man emerged. Was it Byron? Hunt wondered. Yes, he decided, but a Byron grown very fat. Reluctantly, Hunt approached him.

"Go inside," Byron said abruptly. "I'll be with you shortly."

Hunt made his way inside the house, and climbed a flight of stairs. He opened a door and walked into what seemed to be the drawing room. A long time passed before Byron came to join him.

"There you are, Hunt," he said casually. "The fracas is over." He explained that Papi had refused to bring water from the spring and had quarrelled with the cook, and then when Count Pietro had intervened, had stabbed him in the arm. "My man Fletcher has gone for the police," he said.

Hunt looked out of the window. He could see Papi glaring upwards, and he felt frightened. He turned away to see a plump young woman, with a flushed face and with her red hair streaming in disorder, waving her arms at Byron and addressing a stream of Italian at him. Then the young man who had been stabbed came in with his arm in a sling. Hunt was upset and miserable. The whole thing, he thought, was foreign and frightening, and Byron looked as foreign as any of these gesticulating Italians.

"I'm going for my ride now," Byron said. "Are you coming, Pietro?"

"*Sì, sì.*"

Leigh Hunt trailed outside after them. As they came out

Papi ran to them, weeping and obviously begging for forgiveness. He covered Byron's hands with kisses. Hunt had just enough Italian to understand what Byron was saying.

"I forgive you," he said, "and so does Count Gamba and the Contessa Guiccioli, but you will have to go. The police would make you go, in any case, and Fletcher will be arriving with them at any moment."

Then Byron turned to Hunt. "Your quarters are in Pisa, at the Palazzo Lanfranchi," he said. "Everything is ready for you and your family. No doubt Shelley will take you there."

He and Pietro Gamba mounted and rode away. Hunt was left, alone, standing before the house. The great Lord Byron, he thought bitterly, has lost his manners with his looks.

The Tuscan government had already decided to expel the Gambas and their servants before news of the latest incident reached Florence. An order had already gone out exiling Count Ruggero and Pietro, Antonio Maluccelli and Giuseppe Strauss, the courier. At the beginning of July the Gambas appeared before a tribunal in Leghorn, and were informed that they must leave Tuscany in four days.

"They're trying to get rid of me by exiling your family," Byron said to Pietro. "Why don't I load everyone, servants and all, into the *Bolivar* and head for Genoa?"

Pietro looked unhopeful.

"Well, I'll send a note at once to the governor of this city, asking for a delay in your exile so that I can arrange my affairs and go with you. I'll say I don't want to stay any longer in the kingdom of Tuscany, where my friends are persecuted."

He did so at once. He gave no thought to Hunt and his family, who were entirely dependent on him. Then, when a letter arrived from Shelley, saying that Dr. Vaccà had examined Marianne Hunt and that she had no more than a year to live, he said impatiently, "They'll have to go back, that's all."

* * *

At last the answer came from Florence. The Gambas had been granted an extension until July 8. Byron wrote to Dawkins at once, asking for temporary asylum for them at Lucca. He was leaving the whole matter of the Hunts to Shelley, insisting that he must settle them into their apartments in the Palazzo Lanfranchi and look after them.

Shelley, however, was having a difficult time at Lerici. In the middle of June Mary had lost a baby in a massive hemorrhage which had lasted for seven hours. Shelley had succeeded in saving her life by sitting her in a bath filled with ice, but she was still terribly weak and unable to leave the sofa on which she lay all day. Besides, their relations were still far from good. Mary disliked the Casa Magni and Lerici, despite the beauty of the bay, and detested the local people. She did not want Shelley to leave her. But he felt he had to go. At last, on the first of July, he held to him their little boy, Percy Florence, the only child left to them, who had been born five months after William's death, kissed Mary, and set off for Leghorn. He and Williams would sail there in the *Don Juan,* and he would leave her there and go overland to Pisa to see the Hunts.

Byron and Teresa had already arrived in Pisa. Byron was staying at the Palazzo Lanfranchi, and Teresa at the house of the Parra brothers. They began to prepare for their departure from Tuscany. Meanwhile Count Ruggero and Pietro Gamba remained at Montenero. If Byron were not allowed to stay in Genoa, or in Lucca, he was determined now to go to America. He was very put out to find the Hunts settled into the Palazzo Lanfranchi just when he wanted to move out of it, and appalled at Marianne Hunt's sickness and at the six dirty and ill-behaved children who were swarming everywhere. At first he refused to speak to the plain, stiff-backed Mrs. Hunt. Then, when he decided to speak to her after all, she was rude to him. "What do you think, Mrs. Hunt," he greeted her jovially one morning. "Trelawny has been speaking against my morals."

"It's the first time I ever heard of them," she replied vindictively. He would not, he thought, forgive her for that.

The subject of money was always between them. Not only had Hunt used up the four hundred pounds which had been lent to him, he was actually in debt. Yet Byron would not discuss his prospects. All he would do was offer Hunt the copyright of *The Vision of Judgment* for the first number of his journal.

When Hunt grumbled to Shelley, just arrived from Leghorn, Shelley said bitterly, "He's only given it to you because he hasn't been able to find anyone to risk publishing it, because of its attack on George the Third. I *must* get an explanation from him about his intentions. I wish I could help you, but I haven't the money." He was getting more and more anxious to return to his sick wife.

July 8 was drawing closer. Soon the Gambas must leave Tuscany. No answer had been received to Byron's appeal to Dawkins to get them temporary asylum at Lucca.

Then, at last, on July 7, Shelley left for Leghorn. From there he and Williams, and the ship's boy, Charles Vivian, would sail for Lerici.

Next day Count Ruggero and Pietro Gamba arrived in Lucca themselves, to make their own pleas for temporary asylum. To their surprise they were granted it at once.

Byron was thankful for the respite—even from Shelley. He settled back into his old routine with relief. Then Teresa and her servants arrived and took up residence in the Palazzo Lanfranchi. Now Byron had ceased to worry about Teresa's not following the rules of the Pope's decree. He had just heard that Guiccioli had at last succeeded in getting the Pope to rescind his earlier decree and suspend her allowance. His intention, the Pope said, was to persuade the imprudent young woman to give up a life which she boasted made her happy. And now Marianne Hunt refused to speak to Teresa when their paths crossed. She held her head high and sniffed loudly as she walked past her. She clearly meant to demonstrate her disapproval of Teresa's morals.

On July 11 Trelawny arrived at the Palazzo Lanfranchi from Leghorn. He brought disturbing news.

"I saw Shelley in Leghorn on the evening he left you, the seventh," he said to Byron. "Next morning I went to see him and Williams and the boy off in the *Don Juan*. There was a thunderstorm, and they couldn't start out." He paused.

"Yes?"

"Well, about noon the sky cleared, so they cast off and made sail for Lerici. That was about half-past twelve or one o'clock. I started to sail out of the harbour with them in the *Bolivar*, but the port authorities boarded me and said I'd get forty days' quarantine if I went out without port clearance. I had to go back."

"Well?" Byron was impatient.

"About three o'clock Captain Roberts saw a heavy squall coming up from the northwest—he was still on the mole, you see. He was anxious about the boat, so he got permission to go up the tower with his telescope to see if he could see the *Don Juan*. He did. She was about ten miles away, off Viareggio. There seemed to be a lot of wind, and they were taking in their topsail. Then he lost sight of them in the rain that came with the squall."

"Go on, Trelawny. Go on."

"When the squall had passed Roberts looked again. He expected to see them on their way back. But there was nothing to be seen. We've waited for news for two days. We've talked to all the fishermen who were at sea at the time and were hit by the same squall. We've found out nothing—nothing at all. So I came to you, hoping there would be a letter from the Casa Magni. But I met Hunt on the stairs, and he told me there hasn't been one."

"My God, Trelawny, you don't think—" Trelawny was surprised at the effect of his news on Byron. Shelley and he had not been at all friendly of late. Yet Byron was devastated. At last he said, "Tell Hunt to write to Shelley at the Casa Magni, asking for news."

"He's doing that now. He's asking him to write to say how he got home, since there was bad weather after he sailed on Monday, and we are anxious."

At noon the next day at the Casa Magni, Mary Shelley and Jane Williams opened Hunt's letter and read it. They looked at each other in horror.

"We must go to Leghorn at once," Mary said.

"You aren't well enough for that. You are still very weak from the miscarriage."

"It can't be helped."

They left their three children in Claire's care and caught the coach to Pisa.

At midnight Mary and Jane arrived at the Palazzo Lanfranchi. They did not know that Byron was in Pisa, and they had come to ask Hunt what he had heard. They knocked at the great door, and after a while Teresa's maid appeared.

"Is Lord Byron in Pisa, then?" Mary stammered.

"Si, signora."

"We want to speak to Signor Hunt."

Signor Hunt was in bed, but Byron was awake. The maid left, then returned to take them to see Byron. Mary staggered up the stairs, and Teresa came smiling to meet her. *"Sapete alcuna cosa di Shelley?"* Mary stammered "Have you any news of Shelley?" Teresa shook her head. Byron had said nothing to her of Trelawny's fears.

Both Byron and Teresa were shocked at Mary's appearance—she looked, they thought, like a ghost. But she would not listen to their pleas to rest. She and Jane went on at once to Leghorn in a hired carriage to see Captain Roberts and Trelawny.

At two o'clock in the morning the two young women arrived in Leghorn. They waited until six o'clock, sitting up in an inn, then went round all the other inns until they found the one where Captain Roberts was staying. Then they asked to see him. They looked fearfully at the hardened old sea dog.

"Don't you think the boat may have been driven over to Corsica-—or perhaps a long way up the coast?" Mary pleaded.

Captain Roberts did not have the heart to tell them his worst fears.

"Yes, perhaps," he said gently.

Then Roberts took them to Trelawny, now back in Leghorn after his visit to Byron. Trelawny at once took charge of the search. He sent couriers to inquire from tower to tower along the coast whether there had been reports of anything unusual. When Mary and Jane left Leghorn at nine o'clock he went with them. They stopped at Pisa to get Byron's permission to use the *Bolivar* for a search all the way up the coast, then went on to Lerici.

When they came to Viareggio they heard that a little dinghy and a water cask had been found five miles away.

"There was a boat and a water cask aboard," Mary said. "But they might have been thrown overboard in the storm, mightn't they?"

Trelawny went back with them to the Casa Magni and stayed the night. He was very gentle with them both, and the next day he told them that he would stay on and help them. Meanwhile he reported anything he heard to Byron at Pisa. The *Bolivar*, with Roberts in command, was following the coastline, and Byron and Hunt had joined the search on land, making inquiries along the coast.

On July 16 Captain Roberts wrote from aboard the *Bolivar*, "A boat came off and informed me that two bodies had been thrown ashore three or four miles above Viareggio. By their description I think it poor Shelley and the sailor boy. The third body has not yet been found."

As soon as they had Roberts's letter Byron and Hunt set out to make inquiries on the spot; but they found that the sanitary authorities had already covered the bodies with quicklime and buried them in the sand.

Two days later another body was washed ashore near Viareggio. This time the news came quickly to Trelawny, and he arrived there in time to see the corpse just before it was buried on the beach. It was badly disintegrated, but Trelawny was in no doubt. In one of the pockets of the jacket was a book, *Lamia and Isabella*, open as if it had been put away with the poem half-read. Roberts had been wrong, and this was Shelley. Trelawny went off to break the news to Mary and Jane.

When it was done he said, "Hunt told me that Byron said that if the worst happened he would put you both up in the Palazzo Lanfranchi."

Mary shook her head. "We'll go to Pisa," she said, "but we'll stay in our own house and not with Lord Byron."

Mary had decided that she wanted Shelley buried in the Protestant Cemetery in Rome beside her little son, William. There was no question of permission being granted to take Shelley's body to Rome, because of the sanitary regulations. Trelawny appealed to Dawkins for help, and permission was granted to cremate Shelley's body and remove the ashes for burial in Rome.

"I'll do everything necessary," Trelawny said to Mary. "Leave it to me."

He gave orders to an ironmonger for an iron furnace about four and a half feet long by eighteen to twenty inches wide, with a rim of three or four inches and four legs. He also ordered a lead casket enclosed in oak to hold the bones and ashes.

Nearly a month after Shelley's body had been found Trelawny loaded the furnace on the *Bolivar*. The next morning he sailed up the coast and anchored off Viareggio. The casket had been delivered to Byron by a guard of the sanitary corps, and he was to bring it to the shore in his carriage. That day Trelawny spent a long time gathering firewood.

Early the next day Trelawny went to the place on the beach where Shelley had been buried in the sand. Four men had come with him to superintend the disinterment—two dragoons and two sanitary officials. The soldiers found the three bleached sticks which were marking the place where he was supposed to have been buried, and dug, but found nothing. They chose another place, dug, and again found nothing.

It was more than an hour before, at last, a spade struck the skull.

"There! Pull him out!" Trelawny cried, his voice loud on the quiet beach.

The men brought boathooks and dragged the body to the surface of the sand. Hunt and Byron arrived with the casket at that moment. Hunt stayed in the carriage, but Byron came down to the beach. He stared down at Shelley's corpse. The limbs were separated from the body, the clothes were black, and the body itself was rotting and stank. Trelawny was looking for the book to take away as a souvenir. Nothing was left of it but the leather binding.

Byron was moved at the sight. "Are we all to resemble that?" he asked in horror. "Why, it might be the carcass of a sheep for all I can see." He pointed to Shelley's handkerchief. "An old rag retains its shape longer than a dead body. What a nauseating, degrading sight."

"And he wasn't thirty," Trelawny said.

They gathered the limbs, one by one, and put them in the furnace. Then they loaded the furnace on two poles and carried it to Trelawny's pile of firewood. Trelawny set fire to it, and the flames leapt to a tremendous height. The heat was fierce and overpowering. Trelawny and Byron kept throwing incense, salt, sugar and wine on it. They seemed to make it even fiercer.

"Keep the skull, Trelawny," Byron said. Trelawny put on his leather glove and tried to snatch it from the flames. None of the flesh on it had been consumed. As he laid his hand on it, it broke into fragments. Trelawny held it for a moment, looking at it. It was very thin, and very small. Then he threw it back on the fire. Suddenly he began to chant an incantation: "I restore to nature through fire the elements of which this man was composed, earth, air and water. Everything is changed but not annihilated. He is now a part of that which he worshipped."

Byron said wryly, "I knew you were a pagan, Trelawny, but not that you were a pagan priest. You do it very well."

Soon Byron found that the sand was so hot that he could not stand on it without pain to his bad foot. He stayed for a moment longer, gazing at the pyre, with its green and blue and white flames, on the desolate shore with the mountains in the background and the sea before it. Then he went down to the sea, stripped and swam out to the *Bolivar*, anchored a mile and a half away. The soldiers and other men had gone; and now Trelawny stood alone on the beach, watching the great fire. It burned fiercely for three hours. It was nearly four o'clock before the body was consumed; but the heart would not burn, though it was in the hottest part of the coals. They waited for another hour, adding fuel all the time.

"It's no use," Trelawny said at last to Byron. "It won't burn." He sprinkled the heart with water, then took it in his hand to examine it. As he picked it up he cried out. It had burned his hand badly. An oily fluid was still running from it.

"It must be preserved," Trelawny said.

At last Hunt had come down to the shore. "Give it to me," he said. Trelawny handed it to him.

Trelawny scraped the ashes together, put them in the casket and sealed it.

Soon they were in the carriage, with their macabre cargo.

"Let us go to Viareggio and dine," Byron said. "We'll drink to Shelley's memory."

They went to the inn in Viareggio and dined, and drank heavily. They spoke of Shelley, and of Williams, and drank to them; but no one mentioned the ship's boy, Charles Vivian. Then they ordered the barouche to drive them to Pisa. The carriage bowled at top speed through the Pisan forest. They sang, they laughed, they shouted. They felt an immense gaiety, and a guilty relief. Shelley and Williams were dead, but they were alive.

* * *

CHAPTER
❧ 19 ❧

The house in Genoa was ready—the large Casa Saluzzo in the suburb of Albaro, with a garden full of palm trees and a fine view over the harbour. There was space enough to put up the Gambas, too, and it cost only twenty-four pounds a year.

Yet Byron put off moving on one excuse after another. First it was that he was badly sunburned after the cremation on the sands; then that his money had not arrived from England; then that he must clear up the disputes about the Noel estates first. The problem of the Hunts and their awful children—their yahoos, he called them—irritated him. But far worse was the problem of Teresa, and what was to happen to her if he went to America—or Greece. Once he had sent for a notary to make a will so as to leave her provided for; but she had grown hysterical at the mere thought of it. "Do you think, Byron," she had cried, "that the sacrifices I have made for you can be paid for with money?" And she had wept, "I can't bear to think of you dying before me!" So he had abandoned the idea.

Now September of 1822 was nearly half over, and Mary Shelley and Jane Williams had already gone to Genoa. Soon Jane would sail for England. Claire was living in Pisa, but at last she was getting ready to join her brother in Vienna. Byron was alone with Teresa on the upper floor of the Palazzo Lanfranchi. He never spoke of his impending departure from Italy, but Teresa seemed to suspect it. Suddenly she had aged ten years. At times she looked positively old, at twenty-three. Sometimes he tried to be kind to her, sitting with her under the orange trees and calling her his *piccinina*. But he was bored with her and often showed it. He had grown lazy, too. Now he never rode, and of course he never sailed in the *Bolivar*. He starved himself until he was skeleton-thin, and drank a pint of gin every night.

Teresa noticed the change in him when Hobhouse arrived in Pisa with his two sisters. It was the first time the two friends had met for over four years. Teresa was cut to the quick when Byron embraced Hobhouse, weeping, and she and Hobhouse hardly tried to conceal their jealousy of each other. She did not know, however, that when Byron took Hobhouse for his first ride in months, and took shelter from a thunderstorm in the vineyard where he and his friends had practised their pistol-shooting before the Masi affray, Byron had made no bones about his affair with the dark young woman with the bracelets. Hobhouse waited, alone, while they disappeared, not displeased to have evidence that Teresa was not in sole possession of Byron after all. After five days Hobhouse and his sisters left. For Byron it had been a pleasant visit, but things had not been quite as they were before.

After Hobhouse's departure Byron went back to scraping together every penny. He tried to sell the surplus ballast of the *Bolivar*, left behind by Trelawny, and decided to lay up the ship herself, grudging the cost of maintaining her. He even dismissed two of her sailors, and made them turn in their clothes. He looked longingly at the *Don Juan*, which had been found and raised and brought ashore, dreaming of raising money on her, but he had no share in her. Captain Roberts had salvaged some of the things found in her, and had turned over most of them to Byron. He had left the letters and private papers and Williams's journal with Leigh Hunt. When he had glanced through them he had been shocked by the many vituperative remarks about Byron.

It was not until September was nearly over that Byron left

for Genoa in his Napoleonic coach, with the three geese he had meant to eat on Michaelmas Day, for luck, swinging in a cage behind it. He had been too softhearted to slaughter them. Two more carriages followed him, and Hunt and his family came in a fourth as far as Lerici. Byron was thankful to say a farewell, however brief, to him and his unceasing demands— now ingratiating, now insolent—for money. He was in a thoroughly bad temper at Hunt's latest efforts to squeeze more from him. Everything, he felt, had gone wrong. Even the bust of himself he had commissioned from Bartolini had been a disaster.

At Lucca, where the Gambas had been living on sufferance from day to day, Pietro and his father joined the caravan. The servants and Byron's freight were coming from Leghorn in a felucca—men, women, dogs, monkeys, and all their paraphernalia. For years he had not sold or given anything away, so there was a great deal of rubbish being shipped in the felucca.

It was very late at night when Byron's carriage with his cackling geese finally halted in the yard of the Casa Saluzzo. The Hunts, at least, would not be living with him—they would share the forty-room Casa Negroto with Mary Shelley when they arrived. All that was left of the Pisan circle was now at Albaro.

In Pisa, when Byron left, the spy Torelli, employed by the Austrians' puppet government in Tuscany to watch him, wrote in his diary: "Lord Byron has finally decided to leave for Genoa. It is said that he is already tired of his favourite, the Guiccioli. He has, however, expressed his intention of not remaining in Genoa, but of going on to Athens in order to make himself adored by the Greeks."

Time had gone by, but things were the same. Byron hardly spoke to Mary Shelley without wounding her, and Trelawny found it harder and harder to get money from him to keep the

Bolivar afloat. By the end of the year he had saved three thousand three hundred pounds from his annual income, sold five horses, finally laid up the *Bolivar*, and dismissed some of his servants. He was determined to live on a thousand to twelve hundred pounds a year, and had worked it out that with nearly six and a half thousand pounds from the Wentworth estates and his government bonds he would have between nine and ten thousand pounds by the end of 1823. He had even taken on the household accounts, settling them up daily. The result was a startling saving in money. "Trelawny," he said, "money is the only true and constant friend a wise man puts his trust in."

Now Byron wanted to buy an island in the Greek archipelago, or something in Chile or Peru. Every day he discussed some new scheme, but so far not one of them had come to anything. Soon Trelawny grew tired of it all, and went off on a hunting expedition; and Byron went back to *Don Juan*. He enjoyed taking the innocent young Moslem girl, Leila, to London with Don Juan and, through his eyes, pillorying the English society he understood so well and now hated so much.

By December 1822, Byron had finished the twelfth canto. He had written, too, to invite Augusta to join him somewhere in Italy or France. If she had come, he would have abandoned his other plans, he was sure, but she had not replied. He still had no suspicion that his letters to her went straight to Annabella, and that Augusta had become completely subservient to her.

The winter was cold and miserable in the great stone house with its high ceilings and its marble floors. Now things were even worse between Byron and Teresa—he could see that he gave her pain, but he did not want to do anything about it. He was aloof and detached. She was not even allowed to visit him except by invitation. He ate alone, and the two households were entirely separate. Only when it was fine did they walk together in the garden, with the geese cackling about their feet. "You are twenty-three," he said to her once. "I am nearly thirty-five—and I feel seventy."

Teresa wanted a more active life, but now he was averse to any exercise at all. Once, on a very hot day, she persuaded him to walk down the hill of Albaro to the seaside. The path was rough. On the shore he was well and lively, but going home he seemed exhausted.

"You look ill, Byron *mio*."

"Yes, my foot is hurting me—it is excruciating. You can't believe how much I suffer sometimes from the pain." He told her how when he had been a schoolboy at Harrow, he had gone to London to ask a surgeon to amputate his foot. The surgeon had refused to perform the operation. "So I gave up the idea," he said. Teresa threw her arms about him, weeping, and for a few minutes they were close again.

Teresa fitted into his routine as best she could. She saw him when he wished, usually for an hour or two in the evening. When she was able to sympathize with him she felt better. So when gossip about Allegra's funeral got into the newspapers and the *Morning Herald* complained that he had asked for a plaque bearing the words *Hic Jacet, Here Lies*, to be placed on the wall opposite the pew where Annabella often sat, she was able to comfort him. He had had no idea, he wrote furiously to Murray, that his wife ever went to Harrow Church. It did not look, in any case, as if Allegra would be allowed to lie in the church.

Byron was upset, too, when news came that Claire had lost her place as a governess in Vienna because of rumours about her affair with him. Lady Mountcashell at once appealed to him to give Claire some of the money he would have spent on her child, but he wrote her a caustic letter, refusing to give Claire anything. His hatred of Claire was even greater than before. He offered to lend Mary Shelley money to give her.

"More than that I won't do," he wrote. Mary did not reply; and she sent Claire fifteen napoleons from her own pocket, though she was herself hard pressed for money. Shelley's father had offered to provide for her son Percy, but only if she would give him up entirely. Byron had advised her to accept the offer. She had refused it and was bitter against him. Byron was still convinced that Mary longed for him to be more than a friend to her, but he found her prim and cold.

He was growing more and more cruel to Teresa. When he went out at night she worried about him. Then, when he came back he would write her a note, but he would not see her. When her younger sister Carolina died suddenly in Ravenna, he wrote her a few words of condolence which he might have sent to a stranger. Now he flinched from her tears and from her hysterical outbursts.

There were times when he felt almost suicidal—especially when things seemed to be going wrong about the sale of the only part of the Rochdale property which was not involved in lawsuits. His literary work was bringing him little or nothing now. Till recently he had been averaging two and a half thousand pounds a year.

The mirror gave Byron no comfort either. There was too much silver in the silky chestnut curls, and his hair was rapidly receding. At least, he comforted himself, he was very thin. Now he weighed under a hundred and forty pounds. It was the only thing he was really pleased about.

But at last things were moving on. He had actually written to Hobhouse to say he would go to the Levant in July if the Greek provincial government wanted him to; and he had spoken to Edward Blaquière of the London Greek Committee, and to Andreas Luriottis, a delegate from the Greek government, when they called on him on their way to the battlefront. He had asked his banker, Charles Barry, to find him a ship to take him to Greece. He would, he decided, sell his Napoleon snuffbox to raise money for an expedition. Yet he still said nothing to Teresa of all the plans which were now going forward.

By May Byron was entirely absorbed in his Greek plans. Watching him, Mary Shelley decided that he would go, because he hated Genoa, because Pietro was half-mad with joy at the idea, and because he loved Greece, noble, long-suffering Greece, cradle of liberty, fountainhead of poetry and truth. He would go, too, because his pride would be flattered. "Will you go with him, Trelawny?" she asked. "Teresa Guiccioli is an obstacle, but he seems to be making nothing of that."

"Yes, I will go," Trelawny replied.

Soon Byron was made a member of the Greek Committee in London, the organization of exiled revolutionary opponents to the rule of the Turks and their English radical friends. Shortly he received a letter to say that the committee was delighted with his offer to go to Greece. He replied at once that he wanted to go in person, at least to collect information about the military disposition of the occupying Turkish forces and the condition, and military requirements, of the Greek insurgents. He emphasized that he had already travelled in Greece and was familiar with Italian, which was widely spoken there.

Still he said nothing to Teresa, and she was agonized by his silence.

Lady Blessington had arrived in Genoa, and Byron was spending a good deal of time with her and her husband, the Earl of Blessington, and with the handsome, twenty-two-year-old Count Alfred D'Orsay, their travelling companion. Lady Blessington was at thirty-three a year younger than Byron, and at her loveliest. She had endured a brutal and poverty-stricken childhood and girlhood; her father had literally sold her, at the age of fifteen, to a Captain Farmer in Ireland, and, it was said, she had never recovered sexually from that experience. She had left him at once, and when he died soon after, had married the Earl. The portrait of her by Sir Thomas Lawrence had been the sensation of the Royal Academy Exhibition of 1821, and ever since then she had been known as "the most gorgeous Lady Blessington." She had taken London by storm with her beauty, grace and brilliance. Now this lovely woman, with large, dark eyes under well-marked brows, a tender mouth, and beautiful hands, took Byron into her small circle and charmed him. Byron liked Lord Blessington, her rich, indulgent husband, who had taught her all the graces lacking in her childhood, and, best of all, he liked Count Alfred D'Orsay, a beautiful boy and a dandy.

For her part, Lady Blessington had been more anxious to see Byron than Genoa itself. Hardly had they arrived in Genoa than she and her whole party drove to the Casa Saluzzo to call on him. Byron was polite, but Lady Blessington was disappointed. Here, she found, was no Childe Harold and no "corsair," only a flippant, awkward, undignified man—not at all what she believed one of birth and education should be. She disliked his old-fashioned clothes, which no longer even fitted him, and she thought his tastes vulgar and ostentatious. She filled her diary with details of her disappointment—his receding hair, his excessive thinness, his self-consciousness about his lameness, his effeminate voice and accent, and his overly frank and indelicate conversation.

Then, a few days later, news of the death of Blessington's son came, and Byron called on them to help console the Earl. He was kind, and understanding, and gentle. Lady Blessington seemed to be talking to a different man, and now she gave him a warmth which she had not felt before. Soon Teresa was convinced that Byron was in love with her and began to make scenes. Sometimes he was tender to Teresa, and sometimes he was cruel. Once he asked her to sit for a miniature for him, and she wept. Yet the next day, when she tried to follow him into the garden, he told her to leave him alone.

* * *

At last Byron told Pietro to prepare his sister gradually for their departure for Greece. Pietro went in to see her.

"Teresa."

She stood up, hearing something she feared in his voice.

"What is it? Tell me. Quickly."

Pietro told her. It was not tactfully done. Teresa screamed and fainted.

When she had recovered Pietro was more gentle with her, but he had more blows to deliver.

"Listen, my little sister. Papa has been recalled from exile. He would like to go back to Ravenna. There is the house and the family—"

"Of course."

"But you must go, too."

"What do you mean?"

"It is not only the Pope's decree. Your husband will forgive you, he says, if you come back to him and give up Byron."

"Never!"

"What if I told you—?"

"What?"

"That Lord Byron thinks it is the best thing—"

"He could not do that to me."

"—the best thing for you, little sister. He says so. He has shown me letters to his friends, in which he says he will try to persuade you to go back to Ravenna."

"I won't go. I want to go to Greece with him. He cannot be so cruel."

Pietro said nothing.

"He wants to be rid of me, is that it?"

She went to Byron, but he would not discuss it with her. "You must go to Ravenna, Teresa," he said. "It's the best thing." She could get nothing more from him. Then he said, "I have a presentiment that I shall die in Greece. What would become of you then? Go back to your husband."

234

Teresa did not answer. Then, suddenly, he said, "Will you sell me your Arabian horse Saracen to take with me?"

"My beloved Saracen!" She was aghast. Then she said, "You could not ask anything from me I find harder to give, but yes, if you want him. How could I refuse you?"

Sadly, she left the room and went back to her apartment. That night a letter was brought to her, and she tore it open quickly. Then she dropped it to the floor. Before she went to bed alone she wrote in her diary, "A letter from Byron saying that he cannot afford to give me more than eighty pounds for Saracen. I paid a hundred guineas, and would rather lose two hundred than part with him. How strange, to beg and entreat me for this horse, and then name a smaller price than he cost me!"

Byron's avarice was growing noticeably in other directions. He had offered the *Bolivar* to the Blessingtons, and had haggled over the price. In the end they paid him only four hundred guineas for her, so he had lost six hundred guineas on the deal. Then he removed the cannons, which had been sold with the ship. He was mean now even about small things. When the day came for the Blessingtons to leave Genoa, he presented them with a cameo pin of Napoleon's as a souvenir, and asked for one from them. The next day, however, he repented of his generosity and wrote to Lady Blessington, asking her to exchange the cameo for a gold chain. Trelawny, now living in Florence after putting a tombstone over Shelley's grave in the cemetery in Rome, was full of scorn for him. He himself was idle, with nothing to do but make love by writing letters, long, ardent and misspelt, to Mary Shelley, Jane Williams, and Claire Clairmont all at once. Only Claire, in Vienna, took him seriously. "Can you support me?" she wrote to him. No, he admitted, he had only five hundred pounds a year. He longed for adventure in Greece, and was impatient of Byron's delay.

By mid-June Barry, the banker, had chartered the hundred-

and-twenty-ton *Hercules* for two months for two hundred and thirty pounds. She would be available as soon as she was back from a trip to Leghorn. The time for departure was very near. Trelawny left Florence at once for Genoa, and arrived with a black American servant who spoke French and Italian, and could cook and groom horses, and two Hungarian cavalry horses he had bought from an Austrian colonel. He did not like the *Hercules*. Nor did he like the young doctor, Dr. Francesco Bruno, whom Byron had just engaged for his expedition.

Byron was making other preparations. He had ordered uniforms in scarlet and gold for himself and his immediate staff to wear when they landed on the shores of Greece. He had also had three helmets made. Pietro Gamba's was of green cloth, shaped like a shako, with a figure of the goddess Athene on the front on a base of brass and black leather. For himself and Trelawny there were two Homeric helmets, heavily gilded, with great plumes. Under the plumes were engraved his coat of arms and his motto, *Crede Byron.*

Now Byron was infuriated with Mary Shelley as well as with Hunt. Hunt was pestering him for money to pay for her journey to England, and for fifty pounds with which to get his family to Florence, as well as to be let off his debt of two hundred and fifty pounds for the voyage out from England. He even asked Byron to pay the hundred and thirty pounds he owed his brother.

Teresa was miserable at Byron's quarrelling with Mary Shelley. Mary had been kind to her. She wrote to her, asking if she could help, but Mary was too proud to accept. "If Byron will make the advances, I will accept them," she replied. No word came from Byron.

At last Count Gamba's passport to the Romagna had come. He was determined that Teresa should return with him to Ravenna. "It's the only way to get back your allowance from Guiccioli," he insisted. Teresa became hysterical at any men-

236

tion of going. "I will stay *here* until you return," she declared to Byron.

Byron gave in. He tried to arrange for her to go into the Convent of the Visitation at Nice. Then Teresa found that it was a cloistered convent, and that she would not be able to bathe in the sea every day. Next Byron recommended her to the Countess d'Yson, a friend of the British Minister. The Countess made her excuses. He even wondered whether the Blessingtons might not give her a home, but abandoned the idea. Teresa was too jealous of Lady Blessington for that to be a success.

"I can't do any more," he said to Teresa. "You must go with your father to the Romagna."

Neither her outbursts nor her long, miserable letters had any effect on him. He replied only, "You must go. There's no help for it." Sometimes, if she was calm, he became a little romantic. He swore to return to her, and half-believed he would. Teresa tried to believe his promises; but she was sure she would never see him again. Now he wanted to make his expedition merely a reconnoitering one. He decided that, if he did not feel like staying, he would return and bring back facts for the Greek Committee. Then at least they would know what supplies to send and to which faction among the insurgents.

The months were going by and still he did not leave, but Teresa took no comfort from the delay. Early in July she went to Mary Shelley for comfort. Mary was out. On her return home she wrote her a note, "Perhaps it was better for you, my dear, that we did not see each other. My company was never worth much, and now must be unbearable. My feelings cannot be described, and at best can only arouse compassion."

As she was writing Byron came in. He was holding a letter.

"Ah, you are writing to Mary. Would you enclose this,

please, for me? It is on business. Send my greetings to her, and say I've no feeling of enmity towards her."

Teresa wrote on, "I fear that the letter I enclose may distress you. I dare not open it. But Lord Byron's tone as he gave it to me made me anxious. Yet I *must* send it. Now he has gone back to his own room—and he, too, is very sad. What a world, my God!"

Byron had cut down the sums of money Hunt was demanding as far as he could—he was giving him thirty pounds instead of fifty for the move to Florence. Now he offered Mary a loan to take her and the Hunts back to England. His letter asked her how much she wanted. But Mary had already appealed to Trelawny, and he had given her all that she asked. "I don't want your money," she wrote in reply, "because you offered it ungraciously, and without any apology."

At last Byron had fixed the day for departure—the twelfth of July. But when the twelfth dawned there was no wind. The sailing was put off till the next day. Byron did not go to Teresa. She sat, alone, on her sofa all day while he received visitors. She wrote again to Mary Shelley, "I have not seen Lord Byron at all today, but I have just heard from Lega that perhaps he will not get off tomorrow. Only a few hours more! Yet since that moment I have breathed a little more freely."

Next morning, however, Byron was ready to leave the Casa Saluzzo. "I shall sleep aboard and sail tomorrow morning," he said to Teresa. "I shall stay with you from three o'clock until five this afternoon. I've asked Mary Shelley to come to you at five."

He sat, half-impatiently, holding her hand, while Teresa wept silently. He felt more like her father than her lover— exhausted by her emotion and anxious to get away. The two hours seemed very long to him, and very short to her.

As five o'clock struck, Mary arrived. Byron stood up at

once. Mary held out her arms and Teresa ran to them, racked with sobs. Mary held her in silence, knowing that there was nothing she could do or say to console her.

That evening, after Mary had gone, Teresa sat alone. At last she picked up the little notebook in which Byron had kept his accounts since 1819, the year she had met him, over four years ago. As she opened it and looked listlessly through its pages, a mournful sound came through the open windows. She picked up a pen—"I hear a flute," she wrote in the book. "What sadness fills me! God help me!"

Next morning Barry, the banker, helped Teresa to her father's carriage. He offered her his sympathy, but she was looking at the sky and trying to guess the direction of the wind for Byron's voyage. She looked at Barry with despair. "He is carrying away my whole soul," she said. "There is no comfort for me."

The small vessel was fully loaded. In addition to the crew there were Byron and Trelawny, Pietro Gamba, the young Dr. Bruno, and half a dozen servants. There were livestock— four of Byron's horses and one of Trelawny's, the bulldog Moretto, and a huge Newfoundland dog called Lion, which a retired naval lieutenant, Edward le Mesurier, had just given Byron. There were arms and ammunition for their own use, and the two two-pound cannons from the *Bolivar*. There were enough chests of medicine to supply a thousand men for a year.

Barry would be selling Byron's furniture, his books and three of his carriages. He would be looking after the three geese he had brought from Pisa, too. It was unlucky, Byron felt, that he had not been able to bring himself to slaughter them at Michaelmas, but it was done and could not be un- done. He was pleased at any rate to be carrying with him ten thousand Spanish dollars in cash, and bills of exchange for forty thousand more.

By ten o'clock they were ready to sail. But the sea was glassy and calm. Everybody went ashore. Hardly had Byron landed than he met Barry. "The Countess Guiccioli has already left," Barry said. "We won't go to the Casa Saluzzo, then," Byron replied. "We'll go to the Villa Lomellina instead, at Sestri. I used to ride there with Lady Blessington." So he and Barry, Pietro and Trelawny had a picnic of cheese and fruit in the garden of the villa.

Again they slept on board ship, and again, the next day, there was no wind. The day after that they weighed anchor at daybreak, and were towed out of the bay by several American boats. Yet they made hardly any way. The sun was very hot and the Italian crew was merry, but Byron sat silent and apart. Suddenly, at midnight the wind rose. It grew fresher. They shortened sail. The Italian crew were panic-stricken and took refuge below. Then the horses began to rear and kick down their stalls. Trelawny and his black groom tried to make the damage good, while the wind grew stronger and the seas rougher. Then Trelawny went to Byron.

"We must bear up for port, or lose our cattle."

"Do as you like."

So they made towards port again. It was a rough passage back, but at length they anchored once more in their former berth. Then, at last, the wind died down, and the crew crawled back on deck. Byron had stayed all night on deck, and he and Trelawny laughed at them.

Trelawny remained to superintend the repairs of the damaged stalls, but the rest of the party went ashore. This time Byron climbed the hill to the Casa Saluzzo with Pietro. "Where shall we be in a year's time?" he asked sadly. He did not say what he was thinking, that he would not be going on the Greek expedition even then except that he knew that Hobhouse and the other members of the Greek Committee would laugh at him if he did not. He had said so to Barry when he had seen him for a few moments at the harbour; but such sentiments were not for Pietro's ear.

Now there was no turning back. The weather was splendid. Everyone re-embarked. The only delay was caused by the *Hercules*, which made little more than twenty miles a day. They took five days to reach Leghorn, eating and sleeping on deck for the most part.

Back in Genoa Mary was writing bitterly to her friend Jane: "His unconquerable avarice prevented his supplying me with money, and a remnant of shame caused him to avoid me. They sailed together, Lord Byron with ten thousand pounds, Trelawny with fifty, and Lord Byron cowering before his eyes. The Guiccioli has gone to Bologna. He talks seriously of returning to her, and may if he finds nobody of equal rank to be got as cheaply. She cost him nothing, and was thus invaluable." She remembered the Christmas Day wager which Byron and Shelley had made; and that Byron had never given Shelley the thousand pounds to which he was committed when Lady Noel had died.

Teresa was in a state of breakdown, and the farther she travelled the more distressed she grew. As she journeyed on to Bologna beside her father, she was still writing in the little notebook. Now she wrote, "I feel the pain growing more acute with every step which brings me closer to Bologna—my God!"

Just before the carriage drew up in Bologna she wrote again, "I hoped to have the strength to bear this misfortune without dying. But the pain grows worse every moment, and I feel as though I *am* dying. Send after me, Byron, if you want to see me alive. Oh, that I might flee madly, and come to you, at whatever risk."

She did not know that he had left the tress of hair, her parting present to him, in his desk at the Casa Saluzzo.

*　*　*

CHAPTER
❧ 20 ❧

It had been a pleasant voyage, all nine days of it. Byron spent most of his time alone in his cabin, reading Swift or Scott, or writing letters, and lived on old Cheshire cheese and cider or ale. Now and then he boxed with Trelawny or engaged in target practice with him. They lashed a duck or a goose in a basket, with only the head and neck sticking out of it, hoisted it to the main yardarm, and took aim. That prevented the blood and brains from splashing on the deck— they were carried out to sea.

Byron hated doing it. When he had shot an eaglet on the shore of the Gulf of Lepanto in Greece in 1809 and had seen the poor wounded thing on the ground, he was appalled. He had tried to nurse it back to life, but it died. He had sworn then never to shoot another bird. He hadn't kept that vow. He had shot duck and snipe and woodcock with Pietro in Italy, and he could not face the scorn he knew he would see in Trelawny's eyes if he refused to slaughter the ducks and geese. At noon every day, if it was calm, Trelawny and he jumped overboard and swam. The crew said there were sharks in those waters, but they didn't let that deter them. The voyage wasn't uncomfortable. Tita and Lega and Fletcher looked after them, and he persuaded Trelawny to let him have his black servant.

He became friends with James Hamilton Browne on the voyage, too. The burly Scotsman had been dismissed from British government service in its Ionian Islands protectorate because he was pro-Greek, and the government wasn't prepared to commit itself to the rebel cause against the Ottoman Empire—it was too early for that. Browne had asked to join their expedition at Leghorn. He would be useful, for he spoke both Italian and Romaic. Byron had talked too much to him, of course, and too frankly as usual. Browne had been embarrassed by his confidences about Annabella and about his love affairs. He had even told him that there were those who said that the Greeks might make him their king, and that he would accept if the offer were made, for he believed he would make a good king. Well, he did believe this. But Browne had given him good advice. He suggested that they should go to the Ionian island of Cephalonia instead of to Zante, which Edward Blaquière, the agent and emissary of the London Greek Committee, had recommended, because the British resident in charge there, Colonel Napier, was a philhellene.

He stayed aboard the *Hercules* in the harbour of Argostoli, the island's capital. Napier was away, to his regret. As a pro-Greek he could be helpful, though it was important not to embarrass him, since it was his duty to preserve strict neutrality for Britain, in the war, for his protectorate.

The news that Napier's secretary, Captain Kennedy, gave him was dismal. There was political dissension among the Greek insurgents. Their war against the forces of the Turkish government in Greece was almost at a standstill. The Turks had full command of the seas, while the miserable Greek fleet of armed merchant vessels was blockaded in the islands off the east coast on the other side of the Morea peninsula. Then, Prince Mavrocordatos, who had been elected the first president of the new, liberated Greece, and who had later assumed the office of Secretary of State, had been so alarmed by the threats of Theodore Kolokotrones, the great soldier who had set himself up as leader of a rival political war party, that he had resigned his office and fled to the island of Hydra. Byron was infuriated to find that Blaquière, having persuaded him to come to Greece with all urgency, had not waited for him.

He ought to have been available to give him first-hand news, but he was already at Corfu, on his way to England. Byron dispatched a boat to Corfu at once. Then he wrote to Marco Botzaris, who was in charge of the Greek forces which were engaging the Turks in the mountainous region of Acarnania in northwestern Greece. It cost him a great deal to hire a small boat to run the blockade with that letter.

He was pleased to find a host of wild Suliote warriors, refugees with their families in Cephalonia since their exile from their homes on the cliffs of southern Albania in 1822. They would make a fine bodyguard for him, he decided at once, and put forty of them on his payroll. Their weather-beaten faces and muscular bodies made a strange contrast with their dirty white, skirt-like *fustanellas*, especially to Western eyes used to seeing only women in skirts. Trelawny and the captain of the *Hercules* disapproved, and vigorously, and Pietro was sure that many of them were neither Suliotes, nor even Greeks. But he had his way.

Captain Napier was back in Argostoli. He made it clear that he liked Byron, and Byron responded, of course. It was a pleasant life—he could ride, and swim, and dine with Napier and the other officers of the garrison. He did not feel like moving on. Pietro was clearly bored, but he ignored him.

Byron decided to go to visit Ithaca, home of Ulysses and Penelope, and the goal of Ulysses' years of struggle and adventure. He wanted to tread the earth he had trod, and remember there the story of the *Odyssey*. So one day he and Trelawny, Pietro, Dr. Bruno, Browne, and several servants rose at dawn and set off. It took them nine hours by mule in a hot sun before they reached the sea. Then they crossed the channel between the islands from Santa Euphemia in an open boat rowed by four oarsmen. At sunset they landed on the rocky shore of the little island.

It should all have been wonderful. Certainly the island did

not disappoint him. Yet it was there that he admitted to himself a truth he had been evading. He was overwhelmed by a depression so black that it seemed unendurable. He recognized that he was no longer the man who, fifteen years before, had been inspired by a burning love for Greece, and a desire to free her from her chains. The flame had died within him. Nor was he the man who had written:

> *The Isles of Greece, the Isles of Greece!*
> *Where burning Sappho loved and sung,*
> *Where grew the arts of war and peace,*
> *Where Delos rose and Phoebus sprung!*
> *Eternal summer gilds them yet,*
> *But all, except their sun, is set . . .*
>
> *The mountains look on Marathon—*
> *And Marathon looks on the sea;*
> *And musing there an hour alone,*
> *I dreamed that Greece might still be free;*
> *For standing on the Persians' grave,*
> *I could not deem myself a slave . . .*

He felt, he confessed to himself, inadequate before Napier, and before Trelawny. Trelawny was a liar, and illiterate—he was not even clean. But he was a man of action. Whether it was a question of getting a boat built, or of cremating a body, or of commanding men, he was sure of himself. But it was he, Byron, who was in command, he who must lead; and he had no heart for it. He enjoyed Ithaca like a stranger, an onlooker. He was no Ulysses, and never would be. But it was essential that no one should know how he felt. It was bad enough that he had admitted it to himself.

Ithaca was full of refugees from the Greek mainland, all in dire straits. He promised to help them. More, by the time he left for Cephalonia he had arranged with the representative of the British Resident there for a woman and her daughter to follow him. The family had once been rich, but now the two women were all that was left of it, except for a fifteen-year-old boy, Loukas Chalandritsanos, who was fighting under Kolokotrones in the Morea. They were in great distress. He would be glad to help them, in any case; but it would also create a good impression. That might be valuable.

The visit to Ithaca was over. They were on the mainland once more. They had endured a five-hour crossing in an open boat under the hot sun, and had not landed until dark. Now, exhausted as they were, they had to face a banquet in Byron's honour at the monastery on the hill above Samos across the bay, where they were to spend the night.

Byron was behaving very oddly. As the party made its way up the steep path to the monastery, it came upon some open sarcophagi. Suddenly Byron climbed into the deepest one, and lay full length in the bottom on his back, muttering. Pietro persuaded him to come out, and they went on. The monks greeted them outside the monastery, holding up pine torches, and led them inside.

The Abbot received Byron warmly. Then he led them in to the banquet. The food was delicious, but the courses seemed endless. Then, when at last it came to an end, the Abbot stood up and embarked on a long eulogy of his distinguished guest. Suddenly Byron jumped up. "My head is burning!" he shouted. "Will no one release me from this pestilential madman? He is driving me mad!" He seized a lamp and stamped out of the room, calling to Fletcher to follow him.

The Abbot stood, astounded. At length he shook his head, and tapped his forehead. Then he followed Byron, who had run into the first room he had come to. The Abbot pushed the door open further. Byron was doubled over, swearing, and shouting that he had violent pains in his stomach and his liver. The Abbot went to him and tried to make him lie down.

246

Byron at once seized him and threw him out of the room, and slammed the door.

Next Dr. Bruno opened the door. "Let me give you a pill, my lord," he begged. "It will make you better." Byron leapt at him and threw him out, too. Before he was hurled into the corridor Bruno saw that Byron had been tearing his clothes and his bedding into shreds. Outside the little crowd which had gathered could hear him still shouting and stamping.

Next Trelawny went in. He made no attempt to constrain Byron, and came out at once. "It would take ten like me to hold him," he said drily. "He won't leave a thing unbroken if he goes on like this."

Again Dr. Bruno opened the door. Byron lifted a chair and hurled it straight at his head. He fled in terror.

Then Browne opened the door, armed with a couple of Dr. Bruno's pills. This time there was silence. Then Browne came out and told Bruno he could go to bed. Byron had taken both pills and gone to lie down. His own luxurious camp bed was available for someone else to use that night. "The sun was too hot for him," Bruno said. "It has made him mad."

Next day Byron was better. He seemed to have forgotten it all. He was extremely polite to the Abbot, and as they crossed the mountains to Argostoli on muleback he sang snatches of popular songs as loudly as he could. By five o'clock they were aboard the *Hercules* once again.

It was a week later. Fletcher came in to tell Byron that a Greek boy wanted to speak to him.

"Admit him, Fletcher."

The boy came in. Byron rose, without thinking. This was the most delectable, the most ravishing boy he had ever seen; but he was dirty and unkempt.

"What is your name?"

"I am Loukas Chalandritsanos."

"I thought you were fighting with Kolokotrones."

"I heard my mother and sister were here—so I came."

"You deserted?"

The boy shrugged. Then he said, "I would like to work for you."

"Fletcher," Byron said, "ask Count Gamba to come to me."

Pietro was with him in a few moments.

"Pietro, I want this boy well dressed. Spare no expense. I will pay for it all. I want him to have a jewelled belt and a jewelled dagger. He is going to be my page—but see he is well washed!"

Now he could be happy, with this boy. He had never felt the need to be cruel to boys as, sooner or later, he was to women—any women, all women. It was boys who were cruel to him. But Loukas would be kind.

Marco Botzaris had written urging Byron to come at once, and promising to set out in two days to meet him. Three days later, while leading his band of Suliotes, Botzaris was killed by a Turkish bullet. Once again Byron relaxed into his pleasant life, far from the battlefield. The captain of the *Hercules* decided to go home to England, and not risk the capture of his vessel by the Turks. So Byron paid him off and settled at Metaxata, four miles from Argostoli. That would spare Napier any embarrassment, and it was a delightful place. The blue Ionian Sea stretched from the shore below the house beyond the island of Zante and across to the misty shape of the Morea peninsula. The house was small, and life in it was primitive and cramped, but it stood among vineyards and olive groves, and the little village of Metaxata was pretty. There was even a castle—the castle of San Giorgio—behind it. With Byron went Pietro and Dr. Bruno and Lega and Fletcher and Tita, and his forty Suliotes, who were soon to be shipped to Missolonghi, and, of course, Loukas. Pietro was more bored than ever and impatient to go. "You can see a fine picture," he complained, "but, by God, there is nothing but a picture."

On the day that Byron moved into his house Trelawny and Browne sailed for Missolonghi, in the hope of joining a brother of Marco Botzaris and his Suliotes. That night they dodged the few ships left by the Turks to guard the coast, and the next morning landed at Pyrgos on the Morea, opposite the island of Zante. From Pyrgos they would make the voyage across the Gulf of Patras to Missolonghi, where the Greek army in northwestern Greece was based. There, on the northern shore of the gulf, was the first foothold beyond the Morea, already in their power, for the Greek forces. There was their vital advance base on soil still under effective Turkish domination; and it was from Missolonghi that the final campaign of the war would be mounted.

At last Colonel Napier had retrieved their letters from Zante, where they had all been sent. There were many from Teresa, several from Barry, and one from Hobhouse, saying that the Greek Committee in London requested him to act as their representative in dealings with the Greek government, and to take charge of the proper disposition and delivery of stores, arms and other materials of war, which were sent out for the insurgent army.

Letters and emissaries from every party and faction, and from every part of Greece, were pouring in. Everyone wanted Byron's influence and, above all, his money. Byron was forced to ask Napier's advice. It was willingly given and was, despite his enthusiasm for Greek freedom, surprisingly cynical: Byron should form a European corps, but hold on to his purse and trust no one—least of all the Greeks.

Byron still wrote nothing but postscripts to Pietro's letters to Teresa, and now he wrote, "I was a fool to come here, but being here I must see what is to be done." Yet he made no move to leave, and he admitted to no one that he wished to put off going. However, the day had to come. He would have to turn from talk to action. At Metaxata he could be the source of money, and give or withhold it; and he could be the wise man, prudently refraining from action until the time was ripe. But the day must come, and soon, when he must leave for Missolonghi and assume control.

Now a number of people were arriving, inspired by the Greek cause and eager to take up arms against the Turk, or serve in some other capacity.

In October George Finlay came, fresh from his German university, on his way to join the fight for Greek freedom. Finlay was tall, rangy and intelligent—and only twenty-four. He reminded Byron of Shelley. He was brave, too, but as cynical as Napier about the Greeks. He warned Byron that he would never again see the four thousand pounds he had decided to lend them to pay their sailors. Byron assured him that he was planning to go very soon to the seat of the Greek government on the Morea peninsula. Finlay waited, and then could wait no longer. He went off, in November, for the Morea.

Soon after, Colonel Leicester Stanhope arrived as an agent of the Greek Committee in London. He had served in India in the Mahratta War, but at forty was as enthusiastic as a boy and as impractical. Both Byron and Napier set themselves to dispel his unrealistic ideas. Early in December he left for Missolonghi.

Next Dr. Julius Millingen arrived. He was twenty-three, a surgeon, and accompanied by three young German phil-hellenes. He was full of himself, with a smooth manner. He too left for Missolonghi after a while, to offer his services to the Greeks as a doctor.

Rumours, often contradictory, were reaching Byron. One said that the fleet was on its way, and that Mavrocordatos had left Hydra to join it. Another said that the executive body of the Greek government had refused to allow him to command the expedition, and that he was still at Hydra. A third said that civil war had broken out between the executive and the legislative bodies.

At last the truth came. The fleet was on its way, and had reached Kalamata on the southwestern coast of the Morea. Mavrocordatos had joined the expedition, and was on the way to Missolonghi. Byron should delay no longer.

Then Colonel Napier left, on his way to England on leave. There he would see what he could do, discreetly, to persuade the Greek Committee to organize a regular corps to help the Greeks. Byron had lost an invaluable counsellor.

Halfway through December Byron wrote a cheerful letter to Teresa. He did not mention Loukas, and he said nothing of his plans to leave Cephalonia. But now, at last, he had made up his mind to go. He must deliver the money he had promised for the fleet. He sent word to the Provisional Government that he would lend his aid, for the present, for the relief of Missolonghi. Now he was alone at Metaxata except for Pietro and Dr. Bruno and Loukas. Pietro was almost frantic, so anxious was he to go.

Prince Mavrocordatos had landed at Missolonghi. Soon Byron received a letter from the Legislative Council of the insurgents' provisional Greek government, asking him to support Mavrocordatos there. With it came a pressing letter from Mavrocordatos himself. The Turks had withdrawn their troops to the north, he said, and only fifteen hundred Albanians under Omar Pasha were left to threaten Missolonghi. Even they had withdrawn far to the north. Would Byron please come, as the saviour of Greece? The Prince was sending a brig to pick him up and take him to Missolonghi.

Byron did not intend to sail on Mavrocordatos's ship. Two days later another Greek brig appeared off Metaxata, bringing Mavrocordatos's secretary and letters urging him to come to

Missolonghi. He could sail in her if he wished. Byron sent both vessels back to Missolonghi.

But now Byron knew that he could delay no longer. He had already delayed for five months on the island of Cephalonia. At last he hired two ships and ordered packing to begin.

At Missolonghi, Prince Mavrocordatos was angry. The two brigs had returned without Byron or Byron's money, and he could not pay his seamen. He was forced to apply to Colonel Stanhope; and, with great reluctance, Stanhope lent him a hundred pounds. That would not go far. Stanhope wrote to Byron, telling him of the disappointment everyone felt at his failure to arrive.

On the day after Christmas Byron left Metaxata to go for his last ride to Argostoli. He stayed there, waiting for a breeze. Meanwhile the embarkation of men, horses and materials went steadily on. There were two ships, a light, fast *mistico* and a larger bombard ship for the heavy baggage and the livestock. Everything was loaded up within twelve hours, but the winds were contrary. For two days he and Pietro and Bruno had to stay in port at Argostoli, unable to sail. Pietro was happy, singing all day at the prospect of leaving at last for the war.

Mavrocordatos had written again from Missolonghi to say that he was sending two more vessels, which would remain under sail off Metaxata waiting for Byron.

At last the wind changed. Byron went on board the *mistico*. With him went Dr. Bruno, Fletcher, his Newfoundland dog, Lion—and Loukas. The horses, most of the baggage, all the materials sent by the Greek Committee in London, and his old favourite, the bulldog Moretto, went with Pietro Gamba, Lega Zambelli and Tita Falcieri. All the other servants, including Trelawny's black servant, were already aboard. They set sail at once.

Next morning they arrived at the island of Zante to collect

more money. Byron returned to the ship with an extra eight thousand Spanish dollars from the banker Samuel Barff. He had no difficulty in having ship's papers made out for both the *mistico* and the bombard ship, from Zante to Kalamo, one of the small British Ionian Islands close to the coast to the north of Missolonghi. If they were intercepted by a Turkish warship their passage across the mouth of the gulf towards Missolonghi would, with luck, provoke no suspicion.

At six o'clock that evening they set sail for Missolonghi. With a good wind, they calculated, it should only be a night's run.

Byron was in good heart. The sailors sang patriotic songs, and he and Pietro joined them. Soon the fast *mistico* outdistanced the bombard. They fired off pistols and carbines as they drew ahead, and signalled, "Tomorrow we shall meet at Missolonghi—tomorrow." They were full of confidence and high spirits.

* * *

CHAPTER
🌿 21 🌿

There was trouble ahead. Byron did not know that while he was at Zante the Greek sailors at Missolonghi had abandoned their posts. On the afternoon of the very day he sailed, several Turkish ships suddenly appeared off Missolonghi. At once the Greek ships at anchor cut their cables and fled, leaving the Turks patrolling the waters.

When, at two o'clock in the morning, a large ship suddenly appeared out of the darkness ahead of the *mistico*, Byron thought she was Greek. The captain, however, recognized her as a Turkish vessel, and ordered complete silence aboard. They were already under her stern, however, and had been seen, though they did not know it. Everyone froze. Even the dogs, which had been barking all night, were silent. The captain altered course sharply, and they made off with all speed. They could not understand why the Turks did not pursue them, unless it was that they mistook the *mistico* for a fire ship and were afraid of setting her alight.

At daybreak they were able to see a vessel chasing their heavy bombard ship, and another between the *mistico* and the entrance to the port of Missolonghi. Then they saw a Greek boat signalling a warning from the shore. They immediately put the helm up and made all speed before the wind along the coast away from Missolonghi, and ran into a small creek for shelter. There Byron at once landed Loukas, and another member of the crew to look after him, with money and a letter for Colonel Stanhope. "Go across country," he said to Loukas, "till you reach Missolonghi. There you'll be safe."

In his letter to Stanhope Byron reported the disappearance of the bombard ship, and asked for an escort to Missolonghi. "I am uneasy at being here," he wrote, "not so much on my own account as on that of a Greek boy with me, for you know what his fate would be; and I would sooner cut him in pieces, and myself too, than have him taken by those barbarians."

Less than an hour after Loukas had been put ashore, the Turkish ship was sighted off the entrance to their creek, but she drew too much water to enter it. The light-drafted *mistico* slipped out again and headed north along the coast. Running all the way close inshore they at last reached the harbour of Dragomestre before nightfall on New Year's Day, 1824. They were safe.

Next day Mavrocordatos's gunboats arrived at Dragomestre. The wind was unfavourable for returning to Missolonghi, so they decided to stay overnight. The captain of one of the gunboats invited Byron to sleep aboard his ship, but he refused to leave the *mistico*. Loukas had arrived from Missolonghi in one of the gunboats, and Byron preferred to be independent and take him, and Fletcher and Tita and Dr. Bruno, with him.

The following day, on the voyage back to Missolonghi, the weather was rough. The *mistico* was driven on the rocks twice. The first time they took out an anchor and hauled her off. The second time matters looked very serious. There seemed real danger that the *mistico* would be wrecked. Byron hurried to Loukas. "The water's deep," he said, "but it's not very rough. The wind's not blowing right on shore. The ship may sink, but I can easily save you and myself, too. Don't be afraid, Loukas."

Dr. Bruno was furious. He had already stripped down to his flannel waistcoat and was running about the ship in a panic. He shouted, "Save *him*, indeed! By God, save *me*!"

The ship did not sink, but the wind blew hard. They anchored for the night between two small islands off the coast.

Meanwhile Pietro Gamba was in trouble. At dawn, while

the *mistico* was scudding towards Anatolica, a Turkish frigate hailed the bombard ship and ordered her captain aboard. Pietro was terrified that the Turks would examine their suspicious cargo—horses, guns, money, a printing press, cannons, helmets with Byron's arms and name on them, and, worst of all, his own diary and Byron's correspondence with the Greek chieftains. He tied his diary and Byron's letters in a bundle weighted with fifty pounds of shot, and called Lega. "Drop this overboard as quietly as you can the moment a boat puts off from that frigate," he ordered.

At that moment they saw one of the Turks getting into a boat. At once Lega dropped the packet into the sea. Then they saw, too late, that the Turk was not coming towards the bombard. He climbed back aboard, and the frigate let her sails draw and got under way again. In the distance, towards Zante, they could see three sails—the Turk had been frightened into flight. Strangely, the captain of the bombard appeared on the poop of the Turkish vessel, and encouraged Gamba and his friends to follow. Puzzled and anxious, they obeyed.

At Patras the Turkish captain called Pietro aboard. Pietro was rowed across, bearing with him a telescope and bottles of rum and porter as presents. The Turkish captain, to his amazement, greeted him smilingly. He told him that he had been about to order the captain of the bombard to be beheaded and his ship sunk. Then he had recognized him as the man who had saved his life when he had been shipwrecked in the Black Sea. He had embraced him and taken him to his cabin instead. He told Pietro that he would recommend him to Yussuf Pasha, the Turkish commander at Patras. "He is a great friend of mine," he said. "He will let you go, I am sure."

For three days Pietro and the others waited anxiously for their papers at Patras. Pietro went shooting with his guards, and brought back some woodcocks and presented them to the Pasha, but he was far from certain what his fate would be. At last, very early on the fourth day, a messenger arrived, handed him his papers, and he was released. At noon he reached Missolonghi in the bombard ship. To his amazement he found that Byron had not yet landed. He went ashore with the others.

That night Byron's *mistico* appeared off Missolonghi. Byron decided to sleep on board. Next day would bring the moment he had dreamed of—he would land in Greece as a hero.

Next morning Byron donned his scarlet uniform and his Homeric helmet with the great curling plume, and buckled on his sword. He was pleased with his appearance. No one could see his greying, receding hair under that helmet. Then the *mistico* sailed up the lagoon towards the Vasilidi fortress, and each ship of the Greek squadron, which was lying at anchor off the castle, fired a salute as he passed her.

At eleven o'clock he landed. Crowds of soldiers, and a great number of the citizens of Missolonghi, were on the shore to see him arrive. Byron jumped out of the Greek boat which had brought him ashore, and Pietro Gamba, moved to tears, ran to meet him. The crowd shouted its delight at his military appearance. As he began to walk to the house which Colonel Stanhope had prepared for him, the batteries of the fort fired a salvo of twenty-one guns while the crowd shouted. Byron strode to the door of the house. There Prince Mavrocordatos, Colonel Stanhope and a long line of Greek and foreign officers were waiting to greet him. The crowd cheered long after he had gone indoors.

The house stood at the end of the promontory, which stretched from the marshes of the mainland into the shallow lagoon. It was large and had several sheds attached to it. Behind it was an open space. The main structure rose two stories above the ground floor. It was a strange-looking building, but there were three lookout posts, very valuable in their situation. As Byron looked over it he thought that the outlook was grim and depressing. Only from his window on the second floor was there a pleasant view. From it, at least, he could see the open waters of the gulf across the lagoon, and on clear days, he guessed, he might be able to see the mountains of the Morea, and the outlines of Cephalonia and Zante forty or fifty miles away. But the town looked depressing—marshy and poverty-stricken.

Prince Mavrocordatos was a disappointment. He had expected a tall, dashing, heroic-looking fellow. Not for an instant had it struck him that the little, squat man with the long nose, wearing round spectacles through which his large dark eyes squinted, was his long-awaited hero. *He* wore no Homeric helmet, but a small, round, soft, peaked cap, a stiff collar almost touching the ends of his moustache, and a carelessly tied cravat. He looked more like a scholar than a soldier, and fluttered like a frightened old lady. He looked, indeed, Byron thought, cunning, deceitful and cowardly, and he remembered that there were those who said that that was indeed his character. It was hard to believe him trustworthy. Yet he had sacrificed everything he had in the world to help Greece to be free —sometimes, they said, he had hardly enough to eat.

"To business," Mavrocordatos said briskly; and when he left Byron had agreed to maintain the Suliotes at Missolonghi for a year, and to take six hundred of them under his own command. Mavrocordatos had decided, too, that he, Byron, would lead a force to take Lepanto. It was the only Turkish stronghold on the northern shore of the Gulf of Corinth, which penetrated deep into the western coastline of Greece and nearly bisected the country. Capture Lepanto, they believed, and it would then be easy to take Patras on the opposite shore. Then every city in the southern half of Greece would be theirs, and they would be in a fair way to strike northwards against the remaining Turkish-held parts of Greece.

Byron was happy, playing the part of a hero in real life. Soldiers filled his house. His reception room was like an arsenal. Its walls were hung with swords, sabers, bayonets, dirks, daggers, rifles, pistols, blunderbusses, helmets, and trumpets, displayed so as to form various geometrical designs. He talked of nothing but attacks, charges, sieges, battles, ambushes and surprises, and he talked to no one but soldiers if he could help it. He was excited by their presence, by their silver trappings and their skirt-like *fustanellas.* This all seemed infinitely better to him than on his last, youthful visit to Missolonghi. That had been in 1809, with Hobhouse, as a mere traveller. In this mood he even enjoyed hardship. There was plenty of room on the second floor, which was all his, but there was almost no furniture, and he had to sit on a mattress or a cushion. Pietro had quarters elsewhere. Fletcher grumbled at the discomfort, and he and Tita did what they could for their master. Lega watched the money chests, wrote letters and helped Pietro with the accounts. Trelawny's black servant, now Byron's, was an excellent cook and a splendid groom.

It was Loukas, however, the boy he had brought with him from Cephalonia, who was his delight. Rigged out in his expensive page boy's uniform, with his dagger and his jewelled belt, he was always at his side or close by. His beauty was a constant pleasure to Byron, and he caressed him whenever they were alone. Loukas, to his surprise and pain, was cold and sulky, but time and generous gifts, he was sure, would cure that.

Now Byron was busy with plans for the attack on Lepanto. An artillery corps must be formed, and the German, English, American, Swiss and Swedish officers already on the scene would be very useful. At present they were waiting impatiently for William Parry, the firemaster, who was due on the *Anne* with men and materials for manufacturing Congreve rockets and other machines of war. Byron at once subscribed a hundred pounds for the artillery corps.

Dr. Julius Millingen, the suave young English doctor who

had passed through Metaxata on his way to Missolonghi, lost no time in coming to pay court to Byron—with an open palm. He wanted money to set up a hospital in the locality with medical stores which the Quakers had promised to send. The Greek primates had shrugged their shoulders—they were, they insisted, too poor to help. So Dr. Millingen had been reduced to opening a public dispensary for two hours every day in a house near the arsenal. Would Byron contribute? he pleaded. Not yet, Byron said. But later, he promised, he would make him staff surgeon of the artillery corps. Millingen was well qualified and would be useful.

Every day, everywhere, it was the same. They all said they had no money, and looked to him for everything. It was halfway through January before the German corps they were expecting arrived from the Morea—a mere twenty-six men, hardly a fifth of what it had been. The others were dead or had simply gone home. Byron realized that he would probably have to keep them too, for Stanhope, who had brought them to Missolonghi, as an agent of the Greek Committee in London, wanted to shrug off all responsibility for them.

Every day Byron seemed to pay out money he had little hope of ever seeing again. Desperately, he tried to make all the economies he could. He even quarrelled with Pietro when he found out that he had bought five hundred dollars' worth of cloth for his family, and swore he would never forgive him for using money that would have been useful for paying the soldiers. He was growing more and more suspicious, looking everywhere for evidence of his being cheated, fretting that Mavrocordatos had not repaid his loan to him. He was worried by the cost of keeping the Suliotes for a year, and by his promise to advance three thousand dollars by March. Yet he was willing to give the whole amount he expected to get from the sale of the Rochdale land to the cause. Kinnaird had written that the property had been sold to one James Dearden for over eleven thousand pounds.

Pietro was the same to him despite his new attitude—always adoring and loyal. He wrote to Teresa that Byron had been welcomed like a delivering angel. He encouraged her to think of meeting them in the spring, and begged her to keep calm and go out now and then to *conversazioni*, where she could enjoy social contacts in the evenings—Byron would not object, he said. Between them Pietro and Colonel Stanhope took all the routine business from Byron's shoulders. Byron would not even read official documents or business letters. Then, when Pietro and Stanhope could not cope with their responsibilities, he lost his temper and abused them. Byron seemed to regard his position, as indeed the Greek Committee in London expected it to be, as that of conquering hero and delivering angel, but his baffled supporters felt the lack of firm control and decisive leadership in him.

On the morning of January 18, 1824, Byron awoke to an ugly surprise. He looked out of his window to find that the five Greek ships which had been anchored off the shore had vanished, and ten Turkish vessels were cruising in the bay. Missolonghi was blockaded. How would Parry get through in the *Anne?*

Byron at once called his advisers together. Might they not, he asked, attack the Turks at night in small boats, damage their rigging and leave them unmanageable and likely to be wrecked on a lee shore?

"I'll volunteer," Colonel Stanhope said at once. All the others followed his lead.

"I insist only that I must be first in the field," Byron said.

"No, Your Excellency," Colonel Stanhope objected. "You are too important to risk your life." Pietro agreed warmly.

At length Byron gave way. But he was overcome by an

overwhelming depression. For a little while he had been carried away by the exciting prospect of dangerous adventure. Now he was deprived of it. He remembered, too, that he was on the eve of his thirty-sixth birthday, and that every birthday meant another year gone by without fame of the kind he longed for, not as a poet, but as a hero of national liberation, like Simon Bolivar. As usual, at such times he went to brood before a mirror. His depression deepened at the sight of his receding hair, and his moustache, he saw, was now as white as flax. It was no wonder, he thought bitterly, that Loukas did not love him—even flinched from his caresses. Thoughtfully he began to compose a poem.

> *'Tis time this heart should be unmoved*
> *Since others it has ceased to move:*
> *Yet, though I cannot be beloved,*
> *   Still let me love!*
>
> *My days are in the yellow leaf;*
> *The flowers and fruits of love are gone;*
> *The worm, the canker, and the grief*
> *   Are mine alone! . . .*
>
> *But 'tis not thus—and 'tis not here—*
> *Such thoughts should shake my soul, nor now*
> *Where glory decks the hero's bier,*
> *   Or binds his brow.*
>
> *The sword, the banner, and the field,*
> *Glory and Greece, around me see!*
> *The Spartan, borne upon his shield,*
> *   Was not more free . . .*
>
> *If thou regret'st thy youth, why live?*
> *The land of honourable death*
> *Is here:—up to the field, and give*
> *   Away thy breath!*

Seek out—less often sought than found—
A soldier's grave, for thee the best;
Then look around, and choose thy ground,
And take thy rest.

Suddenly the British gun brig *Alacrity* appeared. Her officers came ashore and went to Byron to demand compensation for an Ionian Greek caïque under British protection which had been captured by the rebel Greeks.

"Come to dinner," Byron said, "and we'll discuss it. I want the Greeks to remain on good terms with the European powers —particularly the British."

That night he went out of his way to be charming. He bustled about, actually setting the table himself and drawing corks, and he even apologized for having no tablecloth. Tita, in full livery with silver epaulets, ushered in his guests and announced them, and Loukas, with a new, handsomely chased dagger in his girdle, waited on them. After dinner Byron invited his guests to compete with him at pistol-shooting. They all fired at Maraschino bottles at twelve paces. Time and again Byron shattered the neck of a bottle no wider than the ring on his finger, though his hand shook as if he had ague. After each shot the Newfoundland dog, Lion, retrieved the bottle and laid it at the foot of the staircase.

After they had gone, Byron gave Mavrocordatos the two hundred pounds the officers had demanded so that he could pay it to them. Colonel Stanhope was very upset. "You've been bullied, Your Excellency," he declared. "That's the sum of it."

Byron flew into a rage. "Law, justice and equity have nothing to do with politics!" he shouted. Colonel Stanhope bowed stiffly and left the room. It was late that night before Byron went to him. "Give me that honest right hand," he said, and Stanhope and he shook hands solemnly.

Mavrocordatos had made Byron commander of the expedition to Lepanto. He would have authority not only over his own Suliotes but over the troops of several other commanders —three thousand men in all. Then Byron assigned his own Suliotes to Pietro.

At the end of January the Turkish squadron was still in the gulf, but there was no sign of the Greek ships. They had promised to stay when their crews had been paid, but they had gone home. By then, too, Byron had discovered that though he had undertaken to maintain only five hundred Suliotes he was providing food for twelve hundred—they expected their families, and their livestock, to be maintained as well. He began at last to realize that the scheming Greeks were trying to use him as a source of money for their individual ends, and not looking to him as one who would enable them to triumph over the Turks.

The Archbishop and the primates of the church in Anatolica, the town which had heroically repulsed the Turkish army in the summer, invited Byron and his friends to visit them.

On the first Sunday in February Byron set out with Mavrocordatos, Pietro Gamba, Loukas, and a few others, in a flat-bottomed boat suitable for the shallow lagoon waters. It took them three hours to reach the head of the lagoon. As Byron landed the Greeks fired salvos from their muskets. The bullets whistled above their heads, and then suddenly a cannonball passed within three yards of the boat. As they walked along the streets they were followed by a crowd of people, shouting, playing music and still firing off muskets. Women in their best clothes waved from the balconies, and children shrilled and blew whistles.

Byron stayed less than an hour with his hosts, then rose to go.

"You *must* stay until tomorrow," the Archbishop pressed

him, and Mavrocordatos urged him to accept.

"No, no," Byron said irritably. "I must go back."

"But a squall is coming up."

"It doesn't matter."

He set off with Pietro and Loukas. Before they had been gone half an hour a storm broke. For two hours they were soaked to the skin.

That night, back in Missolonghi, Pietro was so ill he could hardly stagger to his bed. Next morning he had a high fever, and neither he nor Loukas could get up. Byron was very upset about Loukas. He ordered him to be carried to his own bed. Then he sat beside it, watching him anxiously as the fever rose, mopping his brow and begging him to get well. When he could sit up no longer he stretched out on a mattress on the floor.

It was more than a week before Loukas was better. Then, at last, Byron went to see Pietro. He had recovered from the fever and the severe attack of colic which followed it, and was up and about.

Byron was amusing himself with a new toy. He had found an extremely pretty nine-year-old Turkish girl called Hatadje, who, along with her mother, had been living with Dr. Millingen. Her mother had begged Millingen to shelter them from the cruelty of the Greeks. All her own relations, including two of her sons, had been murdered, and she did not know how to get in touch with her husband. As soon as Byron saw the pretty little creature he decided to adopt her and send her to Ada as a companion. "Ada is the same age," he said to Pietro, "and she'll need a companion. I won't ask the child to change her religion." When he told Hatadje's mother of his plan she seized his hand and kissed it, crying, "Allah is great!" Byron at once ordered more expensive dresses to be made for them than Dr. Millingen had provided, and sent Hatadje a necklace of sequins. Dr. Millingen sent them to visit him twice a week, and Byron took the little girl on his knees, stroking her hair and caressing her. Now that Loukas was better, he had more time for her.

At last Major Parry, the firemaster, arrived with the ordnance stores. He had been warned of the Turkish blockade by an English officer who had slipped through it at night in a small boat, and had made for Dragomestre instead of Missolonghi. Once there the arms had been shipped to Missolonghi by canal. He was a fat, fussy little man, but Byron found him full of energy.

The Suliotes were giving Byron a good deal of trouble. They proudly refused to act as porters, and he had to hire local Greeks to carry the arms to cover. Then the Greeks themselves downed tools soon after, declaring it was a public holiday. Byron could not leave the cases of valuable supplies on the beach being soaked by heavy rain. He ran down to the shore and began to drag them up the beach himself. Then at last the Greeks, shamed by his action, resumed work. At least, Byron congratulated himself, they had the vital weapons of war. But as they unpacked them they found serious gaps in the supplies. Worst of all, the Congreve rockets were missing.

Then Parry came to him. "My lord," he began nervously.

"Tita! Bring brandy and water!" Byron shouted. Parry looked curiously at him as he sat on his mattress, in his blue surtout coat, his loose trousers and his foraging cap. Parry's eyes strayed to Loukas, standing close at hand, his pretty face surly, his arms akimbo.

"My lord," Parry blurted out, "I must ask you to lend me some money."

Byron jumped up, and, to Parry's surprise, twirled round on his heel. It was an ungainly sight. "Is that all? I was afraid it was something else," he cried. "Tell me everything you want, and I'll help you as much as I can."

They talked for three hours. Byron unburdened himself,

telling Parry angrily how much he had been harassed and disappointed since he had arrived in Greece. "I don't know what will happen, or whether we'll win or lose. But I'll see the thing out."

Parry was concerned about him, watching him cracking his knuckles and scowling as he talked. He was very pale, and Parry thought he looked weak. He seemed to need to tell someone, anyone, that he felt he had been betrayed by the very people he had come to help. To Parry he seemed forlorn and forsaken—a miserable, lonely man who had taken on more than he could cope with.

Now that the time to strike had come, troubles were coming fast. Fifteen hundred men had already gone to Lepanto to prepare for the arrival of Byron's Suliotes and the artillery. Then Pietro found that the Suliotes had padded out their rolls with fabricated names so that their chiefs could draw the pay of non-existent soldiers. Now Pietro would start out with only three hundred men for a vanguard, and Byron would follow soon after with the rest of the artillery. Then, some ugly rumours were being spread—that Mavrocordatos was planning to invade the Morea peninsula with ten thousand men and sell the country to the English, and that Byron was really a Turk who planned to ruin the country with Mavrocordatos's help. Then the Suliote chieftains sent in their demands—excessive, as usual. Out of four hundred Suliotes, they insisted, there must be a hundred and fifty officers. Byron lost his temper and declared he would have no more to do with such people. He leaned more and more on Parry, the indefatigable, though he was bad-tempered, domineering and obstinate.

Byron was feeling ill. He had not been able to ride every day because of constant rain, and he was losing his temper frequently, stamping and shouting, and sometimes even threatening to shoot anyone who annoyed him. Pietro was very concerned.

Then at seven o'clock on the evening of February 15, Pietro

had a shock. He went to Byron's room on business and found him lying on his sofa.

"Come in," Byron called out. "I'm not asleep. I'm not well."

"I'll come back later," Pietro said.

He returned at eight o'clock. Byron said that he felt better. He got up and went downstairs with Pietro to Colonel Stanhope's apartment. Parry was there as well as Stanhope, and Tita was in attendance.

"I want to discuss Stanhope's idea for publishing a newspaper in several languages—mostly Italian," Byron said. "We could call it *The Greek Chronicle*."

After a while Pietro and Stanhope left. Then Byron said, "I'm very thirsty. Tita, get me some cider."

Tita brought him a glass of cider. Parry noticed that his face was flushed, and he tried to stop him taking it. "I don't think you should drink that, feeling as you do," he said. "At least add some brandy to it."

"Oh, I've often drunk cider. It does me no harm." Byron flung his head back and drained the glass. Parry remembered that he had seen Byron drink five very strong brandies that day already, but he said nothing more.

As soon as Byron had finished the cider he said, "My God, I feel very strange."

His face had changed. He staggered to his feet, but he could not walk. Parry ran forward, and Byron fell into his arms. His face was terribly distorted, and his mouth was drawn to one side.

"Brandy!" Parry called to Tita.

Tita ran to get it, and they made Byron swallow a little. Within a minute his teeth were clenched, and he was unconscious and in strong convulsions. Parry laid him on the sofa, and Tita and he held him down. Then Parry sent Tita for Dr. Bruno and Dr. Millingen. They came very quickly. Byron was foaming at the mouth and gnashing his teeth, and rolling his eyes. The doctors looked at each other.

268

"Epilepsy?" Dr. Bruno asked.

"Epilepsy," Dr. Millingen agreed.

At last Byron opened his eyes. "Isn't this Sunday?" he muttered.

"Yes, my lord," Dr. Bruno said.

"I should have thought it very odd if it weren't," Byron said more clearly.

Gradually Byron came to himself. He sent for Colonel Stanhope. Stanhope came in. Byron, he thought, looked normal, but he seemed pale and haggard and extremely weak. He was asking the doctors again and again, very calmly, whether he was in danger of death. "Let me know if I am likely to die," he said. "I am not afraid. I didn't lose my senses when I lost my speech." But the doctors would not reply. Now he said to Stanhope, "I want to give you instructions in case I don't recover."

"Not now," Dr. Bruno said firmly. "We're going to take you upstairs to your own bed." They carried him upstairs.

Byron had not been there half an hour before an alarm was sounded. Pietro ran in, buckling on his saber.

"The Suliotes are going to attack the arsenal and seize the cannons and powder," he panted. "Parry and I are going there now." He ran out.

Then two drunken German soldiers burst into Byron's bedroom. "We've come to defend you!" they shouted. Tita and Fletcher came running in after them and pushed them out the door. "It's a false alarm, my lord," Tita said. "These fellows saw some armed soldiers changing quarters. They thought they were marching on the arsenal. It's all nothing."

Next day Byron was still weak and very pale. He got up at noon, still shaky. Immediately afterwards Dr. Bruno arrived.

"You must be bled, my lord."

"I won't have a vein opened. No. No matter what you say."

"My lord, it will be dangerous if you do not allow it."

Dr. Bruno would not give way, and at last Byron yielded.

"But you are not to open a vein."

"I'll apply eight leeches to your temples."

The leeches were applied. As they drew blood Byron kept calling out for them to be removed. But it was a long time before Bruno took them away. Then the blood could not be stanched. The leeches had gone too near the temporal artery. Dr. Bruno hastily applied styptics, but they did no good. Then he tried caustics, without result. He called in Dr. Millingen. Still the blood flowed.

Parry came in, just in time to see Byron slump over, fainting from loss of blood. He shouted at Dr. Millingen, who was still applying caustics in vain. Parry tore strips from his shirt and ordered Fletcher to burn them under Byron's nostrils. He himself rubbed Byron's lips and temples with brandy. At last Byron came to, and they went on trying to stop the flow of blood. Byron called out, "Oh, God! There's nothing but pain in this world." Then, realizing what had happened, he laughed and said, "Why, I've fainted at the sight of my own blood like a fine lady!"

It was eleven o'clock that night before the flow of blood was completely stopped.

Byron got up next day, but he did not go out. He was writing in his journal when a soldier came in to report that a Turkish warship had gone aground six or seven miles from Missolonghi. She and her twenty-two guns would make a splendid prize if they could be taken. Byron at once offered to pay all expenses, declaring that he would be at the attack. The doctors shook their heads, but he insisted that he would be well enough.

Early on February 18 everything was ready for the attack on the stranded vessel. Byron was still eager to go, but now Dr. Bruno expressly forbade it.

"You are too weak, and I don't like the inflammation in your eyes," he said decisively.

270

It was too late, it turned out, in any case. Three Turkish brigs had sailed up from Patras and had tried to get the ship off the sound. They had failed, and then had taken off her guns, her crew and most of her cargo. Then they set her alight. Parry was still waiting for darkness to make his raid on her. There was to be no triumph.

Byron felt disgruntled. He would have been glad to be able to report a success to the Greek Committee in London. He sent for Hatadje to amuse him. He had already changed his mind about her future. Ada's mother, he had decided, would never welcome the little infidel with her chatter of Allah and of Ada's father. So he had written a postscript to one of Pietro's letters to Teresa, saying that he had found a little Turkish girl whom he would send to her by and by. "She is as beautiful as the sun, and very lively," he wrote. "You can educate her."

But now he made up his mind that he would not send her to Teresa after all. He had spoiled her, and she had become very pert and forward. It was a case of Allegra all over again. Now he positively disliked her. He would give her mother some money, and Millingen could have them both back, or find someone else to look after them.

Next day an even more serious incident inflamed the town, which was already in a high state of tension.

The Suliotes had started pilfering from the arsenal, and a guard was posted, with orders to let no strangers inside. That morning a Suliote called Yiotes, a muscular warrior with a reputation for courage, went with the little son of the dead Greek hero Marco Botzaris to look at the weapons and ammunition in store. The German sentry refused to let him pass. Yiotes began to force his way in. The sentry pushed him back. In a moment they were fighting. Suddenly the officer of the day, Lieutenant Sass, a Swede, came running up. He shouted orders for the Suliote to be taken to the guardroom. Yiotes at once tried to escape. Sass drew his saber. Yiotes drew his dagger and his pistol. They rushed at each other, swearing. Sass struck Yiotes with the flat of his sword. Yiotes closed again and was wounded in the neck. Then Yiotes lost his head, slashed at Sass with his dagger and nearly severed his arm. Then he shot him in the head, and bolted. The little boy had already gone.

As Yiotes fled soldiers came running up. They carried Sass upstairs. Within the hour he was dead. He had been the best of the foreign officers, brave yet gentle. His death was a terrible blow to the morale of the artillery corps. Rumours were spreading that a foreigner had killed Yiotes the hero, and there was danger that the Suliotes would attack the arsenal and sack the town.

Weak as he was, Byron decided to take command. He ordered cannons to be drawn up and pointed towards the gate, in case the rioters attacked. He gave orders that no one was to be allowed to approach his house until he had held an inquiry into the incident. A crowd of Suliotes gathered outside the walls, screaming that they would attack the house and murder all the foreigners in it. All the English and the other foreigners waited with Byron, and his own personal Suliote bodyguard stood to inside the walls.

Then, suddenly, it was all over. The Suliotes outside stopped shouting and walked away.

"Why?" Byron asked.

"Perhaps because of the cannons and the guard," Colonel Stanhope said. "Or perhaps because they have heard that Yiotes has not been killed after all."

Byron's calm courage, while he was still weak from his illness and his terrible bleeding, in the face of the mutinous, savage Suliotes had impressed everyone. Colonel Stanhope, above all, felt that he had been misjudging him. He was a strange man, he thought. No sooner did he decide that he was avaricious than he was nobly generous; no sooner that he was ill-tempered and unworthy than he became unshakably cool and calm in the face of danger; no sooner that he was a coward than he behaved like a hero. He would never understand him.

*　*　*

CHAPTER
⚜ 22 ⚜

Everything seemed to have gone wrong. He had not recovered from his illness, as the doctors had promised. He suffered from palpitations and attacks of faintness, and often saw flashes before his eyes. He lived in terror of another fit, sure that it would leave him either paralyzed or an idiot, like Swift. As soon as he felt any symptoms coming on he would send for a doctor at once. He was more and more depressed, too, by the realization that the Suliotes regarded him merely as a source of money to be extorted by any means. They had even decided to go on an expedition to Arta instead of Lepanto, simply because there was more booty to be had there. He had given them a month's pay and told them they could go anywhere they liked, when they liked. The Greek primates, too, frequently came to see him, always with a new excuse but always to borrow money. He had given them three thousand dollars on condition that they saw that the Suliotes actually went off on their expedition. For himself, he had given up any idea of leading a military expedition. He was beginning to wonder, he said to Pietro, whether he had done anything but lose time and money, patience and health, with nothing to show for it all. He had even admitted to him that he was sorry he had ever come to Greece, and that he was angry with the Greek Committee in London for having published his letter from Genoa in which he had talked of going so that he had been unable to get out of it. It seemed the last straw when, after only fourteen days' work in the arsenal, six newly arrived foreign mechanics, frightened by the murder of Lieutenant Sass, asked to be sent home and demanded the money for their passages. Yet he had no choice, he felt, but to give it to them.

Colonel Stanhope left on the morning of February 21. There had been a moment when Byron thought of going to Athens with him, but it had been too much trouble to move, even from that unhealthy swamp. In a way he was glad to see Stanhope go. He had talked too much to him, as usual, about his foot, and about his marriage, and then, as usual, regretted it. Yet he was sorry, too. They had often differed; yet Stanhope, he believed, respected him.

That morning there was another meeting of the Suliotes—an ugly meeting, at which they refused to leave without their arrears. Prince Mavrocordatos wrung his hands and begged him to pay up. In the end Byron agreed to give them four thousand eight hundred dollars, on condition that they left for Arta in two days' time. He felt utterly defeated, but he said nothing of such feelings in his letters to England. He could not bring himself to reveal such disillusionment and despair to his English friends. He would have ceased to be a hero in their eyes, and that was too much to lose.

So the day had gone by. He was getting ready for bed and had taken off his shirt, when suddenly he felt the house move under him. He realized at once that it was an earthquake. Then he heard the sound of shots. The soldiers, he guessed, were discharging their muskets in hysteria. There was a sound of thudding feet, and he hurried to the stairs and began to run down them. Everyone in the house was scrambling to get out, running through doors or climbing out of windows.

Suddenly Byron remembered Loukas. He ran back up the stairs, shouting his name. There was no answer. He ran down again, still shouting, in panic. Still there was no reply. Then he realized that everyone was outside, and ran out of the open door, still shouting, "Loukas!" Suddenly he heard Parry call out, "He is here!" Loukas was waiting casually outside with the others. His relief was overwhelming. He went to put an arm about the boy's shoulders. Yet, he thought, Loukas had not shown any concern for *his* safety. Then he looked up to see Parry staring at them. He did not care for the expression on Parry's face.

Stanhope was gone, and the main body of the Suliotes had been dismissed. He was left with only his personal Suliote bodyguard, now fifty-six men—and Lion. He regarded Lion as his only friend, and talked more to him than to anyone else. "Lion," he would say, "*you're* no rogue," or "You're more faithful than men, Lion, I trust you more." Then Lion would spring up and bark, wagging his tail and licking his hand. Byron would laugh and exclaim, "Lion, I love you, you are my faithful dog." It was the nearest he came to happiness now.

He spent most of his time in the guardroom of his Suliotes, where they lounged about or played cards, their carbines propped against the wall. There was nowhere else to go when it was raining, and it rained steadily. He had taken to practical joking, too, to amuse himself. Once he put fifty of his Suliotes in a room above Parry's, and ordered them to wait until midnight and then stamp and shake the house, and roll barrels full of cannonballs across the floor. When midnight came and they began, he banged the doors and rushed downstairs. He roared with laughter when he found the fat little major on his knees begging God to spare him. Parry was very angry and threatened to leave his service if he ever played such a trick again.

His practical joke on Fletcher was even more successful. Fletcher, the lecherous, was always complaining that he could not find a woman. Byron ordered a young Suliote guardsman to be dressed as a Greek girl, and arranged for a Greek to offer "her" to Fletcher. Fletcher fell into the trap and asked "her" to sleep with him. He gave the "virgin"—for he was assured "she" was one—three dollars and promised "her" three more when "she" had slept with him. Then he took "her" up to the attic and began to make love, wooing "her" in his execrable Greek. Suddenly another disguised soldier ran upstairs, shouting and swearing that he was "her" brother, demanding his "sister," and threatening Fletcher. Sweating with terror, Fletcher was taken before Byron. Then Byron solemnly questioned Fletcher, the "girl," and her "brother." Fletcher denied everything and tried to blame everyone, including Pietro and Dr. Bruno. Within the hour a letter, supposedly written by Mavrocordatos, demanding justice for the insult to public morals, was waved in Fletcher's face. Fletcher produced some dollars to quiet the "brother."

Byron was busily composing a letter, supposed to come from the police, when Fletcher discovered the truth. No one knew who had told him. He lost his temper with Tita for not having told him of the plot and abused him. Tita thrashed him, and Byron dismissed him. Then, of course, he took him back.

Not even practical jokes were as amusing as they had once been. Byron was really only happy on those rare occasions when he could ride or march out in full dress with his military corps—and even that was beginning to pall in the face of growing troubles. He could hardly believe it when the Albanians in the Turkish garrison at Lepanto offered to surrender to him for twenty-five thousand dollars instead of the forty thousand they had originally asked, and the Suliotes refused to take on the siege of the city, even in its weakened state.

At least George Finlay—who had called on him at Metaxata on the island of Cephalonia in October—came towards the end of February, and he could talk to him as he could not to Parry. Yet he saw the shock in Finlay's eyes and knew the reasons for it—the confusion in his household; all the servants in uniform but the uniforms all different; everything in disorder; and the sight of him eating his scanty meals alone and at odd hours. In the face of Finlay's obvious distaste he took to wearing his uniform again. He talked too much to Finlay, of course, and indiscreetly, as always. It was not all about private matters, however. He and Mavrocordatos had fallen in with Finlay's suggestion that they should take steps to mend the rift between the two factions in the Greek government— the party led by Prince Mavrocordatos and the soldiers led by Theodore Kolokotrones, leader of the so-called "military" party among the insurgents and Prince Mavrocordatos's principal rival for the leadership, and his henchman, Odysseus. Byron suggested they should meet Odysseus at Salona in a fortnight. He missed Trelawny most of all at such times. He would have driven away the pesterers and put his house in order. But Trelawny was with Odysseus.

It could not be concealed—Byron was far from well. The riding and the marching had done nothing for him. The attacks of vertigo came too often and made him feel drunk. Sometimes, too, a strange terror overtook him for no reason. He had to clasp both hands and hold them over his mouth to prevent himself from crying out or breaking down. At such times he flew into a rage at nothing at all—he was even rude to Prince Mavrocordatos. He was existing on the dregs of his strength, physical and mental. As for Teresa—the thought of her was only another burden. But he brought himself at last to write her a cheerful note, another postscript to one of her brother's letters. He told her nothing of any importance. To him she was simply something left over from his past life, something he would rather be rid of. It was Loukas he thought of when he needed love, and if it had not been for Pietro's coming to him to beg him to add those intolerable postscripts in English to his letters he would not have written to her at all. Still, he made it as pleasant as he could.

"My dearest T.—The Spring is come—I have seen a swallow today—and it was time, for we have had but a wet winter hitherto, even for Greece. We are all very well, which will I hope keep up your hopes and spirits. I do not write letters about politics to you, which would only be tiresome, and yet we have little else to write about, except some private anecdotes which I reserve for *viva voce* when we meet, to divert you, at the expense of Pietro and some others. I write to you in English without apologies, as you say you have become a great proficient in that language. To the English and Greeks I generally write in Italian, from a spirit of contradiction, I suppose, and to show that I am Italianized by my long stay in your climate." It was patronizing and not very loverlike— a different matter from his letters of their early days of love. It was an improvement on more recent ones, at any rate. He had lied about his health, of course. He could not bear any hysterical reactions—and she was capable of following him to Greece.

Meanwhile an invitation had come from the officials of the Greek government at Kranidi in the Morea, asking him to visit them in person, and suggesting that he accept the office of Governor General of the part of Greece still under Turkish domination. He replied that he must make his visit to Salona first. He felt sure that the offer was made only because they had got wind of the fact that he was to be one of the administrators of the English loan. The Greeks only wanted money, not him.

But it was impossible to go to Salona. The weather was appalling. The streets of Missolonghi were rivers of mud. He was coughing, and he could not go riding. The Suliotes, disappointed in the loot at Arta, were on the way back to Missolonghi; and Mavrocordatos had sent him a letter to say that there was no money left in the treasury, and that he must ask for another loan for the troops. It was beginning all over again.

Departure day for Salona came and went. The roads were

impassable, the rivers unfordable. The Greek primates presented Byron with an impressive document conferring on him the citizenship of Missolonghi—and then with another request for money. He was infuriated, but he gave it. He wrote to Kinnaird that the Greek cause had cost him thirty thousand Spanish dollars of his own money so far, not counting his personal expenses. Yet he asked him to send every penny he could. He ordered Parry to take on the task of refusing money, since he always gave way. That March there were applications for fifty thousand dollars in one day alone. His disillusionment was now complete—with the Greeks, with the quarrelsome foreigners, and with Missolonghi. The rain constantly pelting down, in the lagoon and in the muddy streets, seemed an expression of his feelings, and every day he felt more ill. He lived in constant fear that the fit would recur. He had lost the will to go on.

Next news came that the Turkish fleet was reported to be preparing to blockade the port once more, and that there was a plot to seize him, and shut him up, and murder the prince. The fear in Mavrocordatos's eyes brought home the reality of the danger. Byron grew suspicious and apprehensive, and behaved like a spoiled child. He even quarrelled with Pietro over money he had spent on the artillery corps. He was convinced that, whatever he might do at Salona, he would never unite the Greek leaders—the last hope left to him. He knew, too, that there was little hope of ever setting up an honest government in Greece. He blamed himself and abandoned all hope for the Greeks. He even began to wonder whether he should recommend the Greek loan to his friends in England. He was afraid that many honest English families would lose their money because of him, and that he would be hated for it. Only the bankers would profit, with their commissions.

Worse than anything else was the coldness and cruelty of Loukas. What should have been a comfort to him was his greatest pain. The boy took everything, and gave him nothing.

He brooded for days; and then expressed his feelings, as always, in verse.

> *I watched thee when the foe was at our side,*
> *Ready to strike at him—or thee and me,*
> *Were safety hopeless—rather than divide*
> *Aught with one loved save love and liberty.*
>
> *I watched thee on the breakers, when the rock*
> *Received our prow, and all was storm and fear,*
> *And bade thee cling to me through every shock;*
> *This arm would be thy bark, or breast thy bier.*
>
> *I watched thee when the fever glazed thine eyes,*
> *Yielding my couch, and stretched me on the ground*
> *When overworn with watching, ne'er to rise*
> *From thence if thou an early grave hadst found.*
>
> *The earthquake came, and rocked the quivering wall,*
> *And men and nature reeled as if with wine,*
> *Whom did I seek around the tottering hall?*
> *For thee. Whose safety first provide for? Thine.*
>
> *And when convulsive throes denied my breath*
> *The faintest utterance to my fading thought,*
> *To thee—to thee—e'en in the gasp of death*
> *My spirit turned, oh! oftener than it ought.*
>
> *Thus much and more; and yet thou lov'st me not,*
> *And never wilt! Love dwells not in our will.*
> *Nor can I blame thee, though it be my lot*
> *To strongly, wrongly, vainly, love thee still.*

When he had finished he reread his poem. He would, he decided, call it *Love and Death*. He felt very tired. Would he ever write another? At length he drew another piece of paper towards him and wrote, "These verses are addressed to no one in particular, and are a mere poetical scherzo." No one must ever know that such verses were written to Loukas. Let them be thought of as a mere *jeu d'esprit,* a jest.

And what, he asked himself, of Augusta—his "Goose"? His feelings for Loukas and for her were worlds apart. Loukas was everything to him now. But he knew in his heart that, given time, he would tire of him as he had tired of Robert Rushton, and of Nicolo Giraud, and of all the other pretty boys—even Edleston. He had given his cornelian to Elizabeth Pigot. It was his death which had reawakened that passion, and made him feel guilty and treacherous. But his love for Guss was deep-rooted, unshakable. Would he ever see her again? Of course he would. One day he would go back to England, and drive straight to Newmarket in his Napoleonic carriage. Then he would get to the root of all her damned crinkum crankum, and they would laugh together as they laughed with no one else, and life would be good once more. She had cost him a great deal of money already, and he would give her more—all she wanted. She would be grateful and love him again as she used to.

Now time was against them. The Turkish vessels had arrived and were blockading the port. The town was full of false alarms about landings of Turkish forces. Then a hundred and fifty soldiers of Karaiskakis, a chieftain who had set himself up at Anatolica, paddled across the lagoon to seek vengeance for Karaiskakis's nephew, who had been wounded in a quarrel with some Missolonghi boatmen. Suddenly all the shops were shut and the bazaars were empty. Soldiers paraded in the streets looking for the boatmen. Prince Mavrocordatos was growing more and more frightened and useless, doing nothing about it. Byron was bitter and contemptuous. He urged him, as calmly as he could, to display some courage and firmness.

Whenever the weather was fine enough he went for a ride. For the rest, he waited for something to happen.

Then, at last, on April 5 Byron grew tired of doing nothing. He sent an armed party to Vasilidi, the fortress at the edge of the lagoon, to dislodge the rebels. At the sight of them they abandoned the island and surrendered the two primates they had seized as hostages. Then the rebels were allowed to embark for Anatolica. Byron was elated. But when it was all over reaction set in, and once again he was filled with depression and despair. What would happen to the loan when news of civil war and conspiracy reached England? And Mavrocordatos was a broken reed.

He was very thin, almost skeletal, again. He was more irritable than ever. He still complained of vertigo and faintness, and the feeling of terror which overtook him at such times was coming more frequently. Dr. Millingen was watching him, disturbed at his childish behaviour, his hypochondria, and his obsession about palsy and epilepsy. Even a brief, rare letter from Augusta, bringing him a silhouette of Ada and good news of her health, did not raise his spirits. He seized on the fact that Augusta had been seriously ill at the time when he had had his convulsive fit, and took it as an evil omen.

On April 9 Byron was not feeling well, but he insisted on going out riding with Pietro. When they were three miles from the town a heavy rainstorm broke. They galloped on. An hour later they turned back. By the time they reached the walls of Missolonghi they were wet through and drenched with sweat. They generally dismounted at the walls and returned by boat. Byron dismounted, as usual.

"Please don't," Pietro begged. "You'll be ill if you sit in an open boat in that state for half an hour."

"A pretty soldier I'd make if I worried about such trifles," Byron scoffed, and got into the boat.

Two hours after they returned Pietro went in to see Byron. He could see at once that he was shivering. "I've got a high temperature," he said. "I think it's a fever. I'm in great pain, too—with shooting pains in my hips and my loins."

"You must lie down at once," Pietro insisted. He would not leave until Byron lay down on his bed.

At eight o'clock that evening Pietro went back to Byron's room. He was not in bed, but sitting on his sofa. He seemed restless. "I'm in very great pain," he said. "I don't mind dying, but I can't bear these agonies."

Next morning Byron said that he had slept well, but still complained of a headache and pains in his bones. However, he decided to go riding again, earlier than usual. He rode with Pietro through the olive groves for a long time with his Suliote bodyguard riding behind. He seemed in high spirits; but when they returned he scolded his groom for putting the saddle which was still wet from the previous day's drenching on his horse.

That evening George Finlay and Dr. Millingen called on Byron. Finlay had come to say good-bye, on his way to Athens. Byron was lying on the sofa. He seemed morose.

"I've been thinking all day about a prediction which was made to me when I was a boy by a famous Scottish fortune-teller," he said. "He warned me, 'Beware your thirty-seventh year.'"

"You are superstitious, then," Dr. Millingen said.

Byron did not reply to that. He said that he still had a fever and pain in his bones. He noticed that Millingen did not even offer to feel his pulse; but he did not suggest it.

It was late that night before Byron sent for his own doctor, Dr. Bruno. He told him that he had cold shivers and hot spells following each other, and that there were pains all over his body. "It's because I went out yesterday on a horse with a wet saddle," he said. "I've taken a hot bath and two ounces of castor oil."

"You should be bled. Your pulse is strong, but it is irregular."

"I will not be bled. Don't talk to me of it."

"Well, then, I'll give you six doses of fifteen grains each of antimony powder. Take one every hour."

That evening Byron sweated a little and slept fitfully. Next morning Dr. Bruno was sure he would soon be better. "The sweating has done him good," he said to Parry. But Parry was alarmed. He was sure that Byron was very ill. He went to see him and found that he was rambling. He decided to sit beside him and keep watch. After a while Byron fell asleep; and when he awoke he was lucid. Parry managed to obtain his consent to get a ship ready to take him and his servants to Zante until he was better. The moment Parry had his agreement he hurried away to put the preparations in hand.

Next morning Byron was worse. Dr. Bruno gave him a hot bath and pressed him again to consent to be bled. Byron refused. Then Bruno insisted that leeches should be applied to his temples. Byron refused again, this time very angrily. He complained of pains in his head and his rectum. "I had hemorrhoidal discharges when I was young," he said. That night, as he lay sleepless, Bruno gave him four grains of extract of henbane. He had nothing to eat or drink but some broth with the yolk of an egg beaten up in it.

The following morning Byron seemed better, and he got out of bed, but still complained of pains in his head and his bones. He was depressed and very irritable. He refused all food except a little broth and a spoonful or two of arrowroot. Parry's ship was ready to take him to Zante, but now a sirocco had blown up and had reached hurricane strength. The rain was coming down in torrents, and no vessel could leave the port. Dr. Bruno dosed Byron with castor oil and Epsom salts, and gave him a hot footbath. He slept fitfully during the night, but woke still complaining of pains. For the first time Dr. Millingen was called in as a consultant. He agreed with Dr. Bruno that bleeding was necessary, but, faced with Byron's fury, said that it might be postponed.

Next day Byron was very weak and still complaining of pains in his head. He said he wanted to go out riding or sailing, but the doctors would not hear of it. He went back to bed. No one was allowed to see him except the two doctors, Pietro, Tita, Fletcher and Parry. Parry was certain that the doctors were keeping him away as much as they could, on the excuse that Byron was asleep or resting, because he encouraged him to resist bleeding—for now the doctors were urging it vigorously on him. When he was allowed to see him Parry noted that Byron's mind was wandering more often, and that he was often actually delirious.

Fletcher too was worried. Whenever he found Byron in one of his lucid intervals he begged him to let him send to Zante for the English doctor, Dr. Thomas, who was based there. The two doctors were insisting that Byron would be well in a few days if only he would allow himself to be bled.

"They don't understand my illness, Fletcher," Byron said.

"Then, my lord, have other advice, I beseech you."

That day, when Dr. Bruno brought Dr. Millingen to him again, in the hope that the two together might persuade him to be bled, Byron lost his temper. "I know quite well that the lancet has killed more people than the lance. Leave me alone!" he cried.

He would go no further than to agree to take pills for the flatulence he was suffering from, and he was more restless than ever.

It was the fifth day since his soaking on horseback.

* * *

CHAPTER
❧ 23 ❧

Day after day Byron continued feverish, and in pain, and with intermittent bouts of delirium. Day after day the two doctors, Bruno and Millingen, badgered him to allow them to bleed him.

In a lucid interval Byron begged Dr. Millingen, "Would you inquire in the town for an old and ugly witch for me?"

"You are joking, Your Excellency."

"No. I want to see whether this sudden loss of my health is due to the evil eye. She may be able to undo the spell."

Dr. Millingen left, shaking his head. However, he went at once to make inquiries in the town. To his surprise he was given the name of a witch at once—an old and ugly one, too. He was prepared to give it to Byron. But Byron never mentioned the subject again, and so he said nothing to him.

The sirocco was still blowing. It was impossible either to take Byron to Zante or to bring Dr. Thomas to him.

One night Byron sat up in bed and spoke to Parry about his family, his aims for Greece, his plans for the campaign— and death. "I believe in an eternal life," he said. "I look forward to it." Then he added, "But I don't want to die yet, and if they bleed me they will kill me. Don't let them do it, Parry."

At long last the doctors threatened Byron. "Perhaps you don't care about your life," Dr. Millingen exclaimed, "but this illness may end in insanity."

Byron looked at Dr. Millingen with hatred. He scowled so fiercely that the doctor flinched. Then, suddenly, he flung his arm out towards him and cried, "Come, then. You're a damned set of butchers. Take as much blood as you want."

The doctors opened a vein. Byron called out to them again and again to close it, but they did not stop until they had drawn out sixteen ounces of blood. Two hours later they drew out another sixteen ounces of blood.

So it went on, day after day, the doctors insisting on bleeding Byron despite his protests. On the ninth day of his illness they brought in two other physicians for consultation—Dr. Loukas Vaya, the trusted physician of Ali Pasha, the pasha at Jannina, who had entertained Byron in 1809 and made sexual advances to him, and Dr. Enrico Treiber, the German doctor attached to the artillery corps. The doctors pretended that Prince Mavrocordatos had sent them to visit him. They suggested only a simple draft of cream of tartar, boracic powder and sugar, and Dr. Millingen agreed with them. But Dr. Bruno would have none of it. "What we need," he insisted, "is immediate bleeding—*immediate and drastic*. If I am not allowed to open a vein the patient will certainly die. And *I* am his doctor, after all."

While the doctors were talking alone Byron became weak and faint. Fletcher summoned Dr. Bruno, and the four doctors went to Byron. They decided to apply two blisters. As they were about to apply the first Byron asked whether both might be put on the same leg. Dr. Millingen glanced at him, understanding what was troubling him.

"I'll put them above the knees, on the inside of the thighs," he said.

"Do that. For as long as I live I will not allow anyone to see my lame foot."

Almost at once Byron went into delirium. His hands were rigid and contorted, and he flung himself about, struggling to get out of bed. The four doctors were hard put to it to keep him down. They called Fletcher and Tita, and gave orders that he must be controlled. Sometimes Byron recognized them, and sometimes he did not, struggling and shouting that Tita was an enemy.

Throughout the night Byron's delirium continued at intervals. Sometimes he lay silent and motionless, and sometimes he struggled and shouted. At such times he seemed to imagine he was in battle. "I'll fight, I'll fight!" he yelled. "They won't kill me!"

Next day was Easter Sunday. The townspeople of Missolonghi were firing off muskets in the streets, as was their custom. Parry went to see Byron and found him still delirious.

Prince Mavrocordatos arranged for Parry to march with the Suliotes and the artillery brigade some way outside the town, so that the inhabitants would follow them; and the town guards patrolled the streets, announcing that Byron was dangerously ill and asking everyone to make as little noise as possible near his quarters.

Dr. Bruno went to confer with the other three doctors. Once again he argued that Byron was getting worse and that only bleeding would save him. When he had finished speaking there was a long silence. Then the other three doctors exchanged glances and nodded. Dr. Bruno at once went to Byron and applied twelve leeches to his temple. He did not remove them until they had drawn thirty-two ounces of blood. Byron lay back, exhausted and depleted. But, his doctors congratulated themselves, his breathing was easier and his pulse quieter.

"Now you will see that you will get better," Dr. Bruno said.

"Yes, I feel better," Byron answered.

At noon Pietro came to Byron's bedside. He was alarmed to see how much worse he seemed. Byron asked for letters, and Pietro said that none had come. He did not tell him of the letter from Archbishop Ignatius of Arta, informing him that the Sultan, in full divan, had proclaimed him an enemy of Turkey. Byron demanded he bring him another one, which had arrived days before, written to Mavrocordatos, saying that the loan had been concluded and that Byron was to be the head of the commission for handling it. Pietro brought it and handed it to him. It was written half in French, half in Greek. Byron read the French easily, then found himself in difficulties over the Greek. Pietro offered to get it translated, but he struggled on until he had succeeded. He sighed and said, "I wish Hobhouse was here." Pietro was encouraged to think Byron was a little better—or at least felt so.

By midafternoon, however, there was no longer any question of hiding it from Byron that he was in danger of death. The servants were standing weeping in the room, and the doctors no longer tried to conceal their panic. Byron called Dr. Millingen to him. "You won't save me, I can see that," he said. "I must die. I feel it. Well, I came to Greece to end my wearisome existence, and I have devoted my wealth and my abilities to her cause. Now she can have my life. But I make one request to you. *Do not let my body be hacked or sent to England.* Lay me in the first corner you find here, without pomp or nonsense. Let my bones moulder here, in Greece."

At about half-past three in the afternoon Dr. Bruno and Dr. Millingen called in Dr. Vaya and Dr. Treiber again, but they were still in violent disagreement as to how to treat Byron. By four o'clock Byron was quite sure that he was dying. Dr. Millingen, Fletcher and Tita were all at his bedside. Soon Dr. Millingen and Fletcher, both in tears, left the room. Tita was in tears, too, but he could not leave as Byron was grasping his hand. Byron looked at Tita and said, *"Oh, questa è una bella scena!* Here's a pretty scene!" Then he became delirious again and began to rave. He seemed to imagine that he was leading a charge against a breach in the walls of some enemy city, calling out now in Italian, now in English, "Forward! Forward! Courage! Follow my example! Don't be afraid!"

Parry came in. Everything was in confusion. The doctors, thoroughly alarmed, were still bickering. Dr. Treiber was hotly condemning the treatment Byron had received. Byron was screaming, *"Ah, Christi!"*, clenching his hands and gnashing his teeth. He seemed in great pain from a bandage about his forehead which the doctors had applied after removing the leeches. Dr. Treiber was advising a dose of cinchona bark, and he asked Parry to persuade Byron to take it. Byron was refusing everything his doctors asked. Parry persuaded him to sip the bark, but when Byron took hold of his hand, as he held the spoon Parry found that his fingers were as cold as ice. Byron could only swallow about four mouthfuls. Then Parry and Tita tried to rub some warmth into his hands and feet, and loosened the bandage round his head. Byron wept with relief, and Parry encouraged him to go on crying. "Thank God, my lord. Cry all you can, and then you'll sleep." Byron clutched his hand and fell asleep. Parry was sure he would not wake again.

Byron did wake again. Now he was delirious, and now calm and rational. Pietro was too upset to stay, but Parry remained with him. Then, at last, Byron seemed to be trying to express his last wishes. He named sums of money, and the people to whom they should be left. Parry was at a loss, for he knew nothing of Byron's family and friends. Byron cried out, "Why wasn't I told I was dying?" and "Why didn't I go home before I came here?"

Soon Parry went away. Half an hour later he came back, but Byron did not seem to know him, though he was still insisting that he had something important to say about a will. Now his fits of delirium were alternating with periods of stupor. He kept saying that he must reward Loukas for his service, but no one could understand exactly what he wanted.

Once Byron said to Fletcher, "The doctors have murdered me, and you are in the plot."

Fletcher wept bitterly, crying, "Oh, my lord, how can you think so?"

Then Byron said, "No, Fletcher, I didn't mean it. Come

here." Tears poured down his face, and he held Fletcher's hand. "I'm sorry I've done nothing for you in my will," he said, "but Mr. Hobhouse will look after you."

Then he grew anxious again. "I *must* do something for Loukas, Fletcher—and Tita."

"You must talk of more important things, my lord," Fletcher begged him.

"Millingen!" Byron shouted. "Get out of the room. If it weren't for you I wouldn't be dying. You made light of this illness all along."

"I cannot leave you like this," Dr. Millingen protested. He too was weeping.

"You've been with me too long," Byron replied bitterly. "Now, Fletcher, I am sure I am dying. You are to give Loukas the receipt for the three thousand dollars I've lent to the town of Missolonghi. Go and fetch it."

Fletcher went, and brought the receipt to him.

"Now bring me the bag of Maria Teresa dollars in my room."

Fletcher left the room again and returned with the bag.

"Now, bring Loukas."

In a few minutes Fletcher returned with Loukas.

"Give them to him. Say I hope they'll pay him the money, but, if they don't, at least he will have the dollars."

Fletcher did his best, stumbling over the Greek. Loukas clutched the bag and the piece of paper. For a moment he stood in the doorway, looking at his master without emotion. Then Fletcher pushed him outside.

"Where do you want to be buried, my lord?" Fletcher asked. "In England?"

"Yes, if they want that. It doesn't matter. Yes, in England. Now, Fletcher, it's nearly over. I must tell you everything without losing a moment."

"Shall I go and fetch pen and ink and paper?"

292

"Oh, my God, no. You'll lose too much time, and I've none to spare. Now pay attention. You'll be provided for."

"Thank you, my lord."

"Oh, my poor little Ada. If I could only have seen her! Give her my blessing, and give it to my dear sister Augusta and her children. Go to Lady Byron and tell her everything." He continued to speak, but Fletcher could only make out a word here and there. He went on mumbling for a long time. Once he raised his voice and said, "Fletcher, now if you do not execute every order I have given you I will torment you hereafter." Then delirium again overtook him. He muttered, "My wife . . . my child . . . Ada . . . my poor sister . . . go and tell my sister . . . go to Hobhouse . . . tell Hobhouse." Over and over he repeated, "Four thousand five hundred dollars."

When at last he came out of his delirium Byron seized Fletcher's hand and said, "Be sure, mind all I say, Fletcher." His voice faltered, and Fletcher could make out nothing of what he was saying. For over a quarter of an hour Byron spoke on and on. Then he said, "Now I have told you everything I want you to do."

"My lord," Fletcher said, "I am very sorry, but I have not understood one word. I hope you'll tell it to me all over again." But now Byron was in despair. With the tears again streaming down his cheeks, he said, "If you have not understood me, Fletcher, it is too late." His voice failed again. Then he said, "I'll try to make you understand me again. But I know it is too late now."

His strength was going fast. Yet the doctors gave him another purgative of senna and Epsom salts and castor oil. He could scarcely stand when, as a result, he struggled out of bed with Fletcher's help.

At about six o'clock that evening Fletcher heard him say, "I want to sleep now." He turned on his back and shut his eyes. Now the doctors had him at their mercy. They advanced on him with their lancets. The blood flowed from his veins all night.

Soon after Byron had gone into a coma, letters had arrived from Hobhouse and Kinnaird. The Greek Committee in London was delighted with his services, Hobhouse said, and he meant to come out himself as soon as Parliament was prorogued. In a second letter Hobhouse told him that, as Kinnaird would bear out, his financial affairs were going well and he would have a very handsome fortune. "And if you have health," Hobhouse wrote, "I do not see what earthly advantage you can wish for that you have not got. Your present endeavour is certainly the most glorious ever undertaken by man."

Byron did not move during the next twenty-four hours. Sometimes he seemed to be suffocating, and then there was a rattling in his throat. Fletcher would call Tita to help him raise his head, and his body would stiffen. Soon the rattling and the choking began to come every half hour.

The two men went on raising Byron's head whenever the attacks came, until six o'clock on Monday evening. Then Fletcher suddenly saw his master open his eyes, and shut them again at once. He showed no sign of pain, and he did not move at all.

"Oh, my God, I fear his lordship is gone!" Fletcher cried.

The doctors hurried over to Byron. They each took one of his wrists and felt his pulse.

"You are right," Dr. Bruno said. "He is dead."

THE END

294

❧ EPILOGUE ❧

Byron had died on April 19, 1824. The warning of the Scottish fortune-teller, "Beware your thirty-seventh year," had proved prophetic.

Dr. Millingen paid no attention to Byron's last request that his body should not be "hacked." He and Dr. Bruno decided to embalm it and send it back to England. So, at nine o'clock on the morning of the day following his death, they stripped the body about which he had been so secretive, and exposed his right foot. It was, Millingen wrote later, deformed, and his right leg was smaller and shorter than the left one. There was no doubt, he stated, that Byron had been born club-footed.

The autopsy revealed very hard bones in the cranium, such as might be expected in a man of eighty. It took both doctors to saw through it. The autopsy was crude and unsatisfactory, even for the time an amateurish effort, and to this day doctors are unable to establish the cause of Byron's death. Although the condition of the brain suggested syphilis, the clinical symptoms were entirely out of keeping with that diagnosis. Doctors believe, on the whole, that the immediate cause was uremic poisoning, with death hastened by the numerous bleedings and purgings with strong cathartics.

The body was embalmed, and Byron's heart, brain and intestines were put in separate containers. His body was then placed in a tin-lined coffin of rough wood. Then Pietro and Parry made an inventory of his papers and personal effects. The list included his last poem, to Loukas, fourteen stanzas of a seventeenth canto of *Don Juan*—and an unfinished letter to Augusta.

On April 22 a funeral ceremony was performed in the church of San Spiridione. The crude coffin was covered with a black mantle as a pall, and a helmet, a sword and a crown of laurel were laid on it. The citizens of Missolonghi asked for some part of Byron's remains to be left in Greece, and in response the lungs were left with the church of Saint Nicholas. Then the coffin was sealed. Holes were bored in the wood and tin, and it was then placed in a large cask containing a hundred and eighty gallons of spirits.

Before the end of the month Trelawny turned up in Missolonghi, and was shown the body by Fletcher.

On May 2 Byron's body sailed from Greece in the *Florida*, to a salute of thirty-seven cannons. (Byron himself had once written to Tom Moore about the eviscerated remains of Lord Guilford, "Conceive a man going one way, and his intestines another, and his immortal soul a third!—was there ever such a distribution?") In the *Florida*, too, went Colonel Stanhope, Dr. Bruno, Byron's servants, and his dogs. With his usual delicacy Pietro Gamba sailed for England in another ship, for fear of giving offense to Byron's family because of his known liaison with his sister.

The news of Byron's death reached Kinnaird by express on Friday, May 14. He went to inform Hobhouse, who was thrown into an agony of grief. Hobhouse then went to see Augusta Leigh, and found her also devastated, having just read a letter from Fletcher breaking the news of Byron's death. Hobhouse implored her to be discreet.

Captain George Byron, now the seventh Lord Byron, broke the news to Annabella. He reported that she was in a distressing state, and had said that she had no right to be considered by Lord Byron's friends, but that she "had her feelings."

Hobhouse was determined to get hold of the memoirs

which Byron had given to Moore and have them destroyed, so as to protect Byron's reputation. To his surprise he found Murray agreeable to their destruction, and prepared to surrender the manuscript to Annabella or Augusta. Moore struggled to prevent their destruction, but was overborne, largely because the editor of the *Quarterly Review*, who had read the manuscript for Murray, said the memoirs were fit only for a brothel and would doom Lord Byron to everlasting infamy if published. So the memoirs were torn up and reduced to ashes in the hearth of Murray's parlour at number 50 Albemarle Street, with representatives of Augusta and Annabella looking on.

On the night of June 29 the *Florida* arrived in the Thames estuary. The Dean of Westminster refused the request, sent through Murray, that Byron be buried in Westminster Abbey. When Hobhouse finally brought himself to look at Byron's face, as his body lay in state at number 20 Great George Street, Westminster, he hardly recognized it—the mouth was distorted and half-open, the teeth discoloured by the spirits, the eyelids sunken, the cheeks baggy, the forehead marked by the surgeon's knife, and the skin a dull parchment yellow. He could feel no grief. Augusta's reaction was the same.

Immense numbers of people came to see the body on July 9 and 10, but there were very few of birth or distinction. The great families were chary of having anything to do with one whose name was still associated with a hideous scandal.

On July 12 the funeral procession left London. Once again the great were noticeable by their absence. Lord Carlisle and Lord Aberdeen, both of whom had been abused by Byron in his *English Bards and Scotch Reviewers*, sent their carriages —empty. Only three carriages had mourners in them, and, unusually, there were no ladies. Augusta Leigh, though she was the chief mourner, did not join the cortege, but sent Colonel Leigh in her place. In the first carriage sat Colonel Leigh, a representative of the new Lord Byron, Hanson and Hobhouse.

In the other two travelled Douglas Kinnaird; Michael Bruce (the travelling companion of Lady Hester Stanhope, whom Byron had not seen since 1811); Hobhouse's two radical friends, Sir Francis Burdett, Member of Parliament for Westminster, and Edward Ellice, who had been Member of Parliament for Coventry; three poets, Tom Moore, Samuel Rogers and Thomas Campbell; Pietro Gamba and Dr. Bruno; and a solitary member of the great Carlisle clan. The twenty-one-year-old George Borrow watched the procession make its way up Tottenham Court Road, and recorded: "Immediately behind the hearse were three or four mourning coaches, full of people, some of whom, from the partial glimpse which I caught of them, appeared to be foreigners. Behind these came a very long train of splendid carriages, all of which, without one exception, were empty." Mary Shelley, too, watched the procession as it climbed Highgate Hill; and it passed Lady Caroline Lamb, who, after a long illness, was taking her first drive with her husband in an open carriage close by Brocket Hall. William Lamb inquired whose funeral it was and was told, but he did not tell his wife.

It was not until four days after it had set out that the cortege reached Nottingham. There, at The Blackamoor's Head, those who wished to view the body were allowed to do so, twenty at a time. At about eleven o'clock the next day the procession started off again for the church at Hucknall Torkard, with eight horsemen, including two constables and two bailiffs, at its head. Then came the State Horse, its rider carrying a velvet cushion on which was laid Byron's coronet. The hearse, with its twelve large black plumes and drawn by six black horses with plumes on their heads, followed. Behind it came a coach-and-six bearing the urn holding the organs, and then a coach containing six mourners. Representatives from Missolonghi followed; then the Mayor of Nottingham, two Aldermen, the Sheriff, the Town Clerk, and other members of the Town Council. The procession was about a quarter of a mile long, and at its end came forty gentlemen on horseback, riding two and two.

The funeral party did not arrive at the church at Hucknall Torkard until half-past three. At four minutes to four the coffin and urn were borne down the steps of the vault. At ten minutes past four the service was over. The mourners stood for a few minutes gazing into the vault, and then dispersed. Fletcher broke down completely, and Tita was so overcome that he had to hold on to the back of a pew so as not to fall. Hobhouse, he wrote in his diary, was stunned. Then the two large stone slabs of the vault were replaced.

Byron's last journey was over. His bones had come back to rest with his mother's, and with those of his ancestors. Would that strange man have found the whole affair amusing? Once he had written:

> . . . *a deal of fun,*
> *Like mourning coaches when the funeral's done.*

By November Medwin had published his *Journal of the Conversations of Lord Byron, Noted During a Residence with His Lordship at Pisa in the Years 1821 and 1822,* in two volumes, to the titillation of the general public and the distress of the Pisa circle—only the first of volumes to be published, in due course, by Tom Moore, Dr. Millingen, Lady Blessington, Colonel Leicester Stanhope, Edward Blaquière, John Cam Hobhouse (by then Lord Broughton), James Hamilton Browne, Pietro Gamba, Teresa Guiccioli, Leigh Hunt, R. C. Dallas, William Parry, and, with his characteristically vivid mixture of truth and lies, Trelawny.

Annabella never remarried. She continued to exercise a strong influence over Augusta despite the eight years' difference in their ages, and claimed to have extracted a confession from her as to the fact of incest with Byron before (but not after) her marriage to him. Byron had left Augusta more than a hundred thousand pounds, partly at once, partly in reversion, for nearly two-thirds of it was Annabella's for life. He had entirely excluded the seventh Lord Byron, who believed the money should go with the title, and he had made no specific bequest to Ada in addition to the sixteen thousand pounds legally settled on her before her birth. Annabella had still nothing more than her marriage settlement of sixty thousand pounds—a source of lasting bitterness to her. To the end of Byron's life she had cherished the illusion that he would one day return to beg her forgiveness on his knees at her feet.

Between the demands of her spendthrift husband, and of her disastrously weak children, and, it seems possible, of blackmailers, all that Augusta had disappeared so rapidly that by 1826 she was borrowing from Annabella. By then, she claimed, Colonel Leigh was ill-treating her and threatening to abandon her. She was widowed in 1850, and the only loving child of the seven she had borne—her youngest daughter, Emily—implored Annabella for help once again, since her mother was facing ruin. Annabella proposed a last meeting— "unless," in her words, "summoned to your deathbed"—and on April 8 Augusta was met by Annabella's liveried footman at a railway station and taken to the White Hart Hotel at Reigate. There they had their last meeting. Annabella never saw Augusta again, though after the interview she wrote, "I saw Death in her face at once." When, soon afterwards, Augusta fell mortally ill, Annabella wrote to Emily asking her to whisper the words *Dearest Augusta* in her ear. Poor, sentimental Augusta wept to hear them, remembering their days of friendship. A few days later, on October 12, 1851, she died of heart disease and dropsy, at a little after three o'clock in the morning, with her hands in Emily's. She was sixty-seven. Annabella herself lived on for another nine years, and died on May 16, 1860, the day before her sixty-eighth birthday.

Teresa Guiccioli, who had been left by Byron penniless, homeless, and humiliated in the eyes of the world, returned to her husband in 1826. She left him five months later and never again went back to him. The Pope, after inquiries, ordered that she should receive an increased allowance. Her brother Pietro never returned to Italy. After Byron's funeral he went back to Greece to die of typhoid fever in Metana in 1827 at the age of twenty-six, and was buried there. Her father, Count Ruggero, was sentenced to twenty years of exile and imprisonment in Ferrara, and served nearly six of them. He did not return home until 1831. Then he took command of the National Guard of Ravenna, and saw active service at its head against the Austrians at Rimini. He died at his estate in Filetto in 1846.

In 1825 Teresa had a tempestuous affair with Henry Edward Fox, Lady Holland's son—another handsome and charming man with a limp. She visited England eight years after Byron's death with her brother Vincenzo, and was the recipient of much kindness from Lady Blessington. She spent three hours with Augusta in St. James's Palace talking of Byron, but they never saw each other again. When Lady Blessington asked to see Byron's letters to her from Greece, with a view to publication, Teresa, embarrassed by their lack of ardour, refused. She made pilgrimages to Harrow and to Newstead Abbey, where she collected souvenirs—a rose, an acorn, a piece of silk from Byron's bed curtains, and a twig from the silver birch on which he had carved his and Augusta's names—to be added to her other treasures, which she kept in a mahogany casket. She paid other visits to England in 1834, 1835, 1837, 1839 and 1859.

On December 15, 1847, at the age of forty-seven, Teresa married Hilaire Etienne Victor Rouillé, Marquis de Boissy, aged forty-nine and one of the richest men in France, who had been courting her for several years. She continued to regard herself as primarily Byron's mistress, exposing herself to ridicule by her habit of standing before a full-length portrait of him and exclaiming, "*Qu'il était beau! Mon Dieu, qui'il était beau!*" De Boissy, however, was the most complaisant of husbands, and showed equal pride in the connection. When, it was said, a French duke asked him tactfully whether the lady to whom he had become engaged was any relation of the Countess Guiccioli whose name had been linked with Lord Byron's, de Boissy replied proudly, *"Comment, donc, mais c'est elle-même, c'est elle!"* Teresa later took to automatic writing, and maintained that she was in frequent communication with Byron's spirit. When the Marquis de Boissy died in 1866, she said that she was also in communication with him. "They are together now," she claimed, "and are the best of friends."

Teresa tried to doctor Byron's letters, erasing coarse or compromising words, or cutting out with her embroidery scissors passages which displeased her. Yet, ridiculous or not, she was the only one of Byron's loves who never faltered in her devotion to him—and that despite the revelation of the selfish, flippant and often cruel way in which he had written to his friends of her, which she had to endure with the publication of his letters and journals by Moore. In the end, too, she said that *all* her papers were to be published after her death—"Whatever the consequences may be to my reputation is unimportant, so long as none of the documents are lost, which can reveal in its true light the great and kind heart of Lord Byron."

Teresa lived for seven years after the death of her second husband, spending most of her time at the pleasant villa he had bought for her at Settimello near Florence; and her tomb lies in the chapel there.

An ironical postscript to the story is that when Lady Blessington took refuge in Paris with D'Orsay in 1848—her fortune gambled away by that self-centered dandy, her fine house and beautiful possessions sold by auction, her heart broken—it was Teresa who now, as the Marquise de Boissy, was able to ask her to evening parties and offer to lend her her carriage. But "the most gorgeous Lady Blessington" was tired of life and did not respond. She was dead by 1849. D'Orsay himself died three years later.

Claire Clairmont moved on from Austria to Russia and Italy as a governess, full of self-pity. Shelley had left her twelve thousand pounds, which she would receive on the death of his father, Sir Timothy Shelley. To her disappointment, the supposedly frail Sir Timothy, destined in their eyes for an early grave, lived on and on. After the death in 1826 of Shelley's elder son, Charles, by his first wife, the baronetcy and entailed fortune would descend on Sir Timothy's death to Mary's Percy Florence. If *he* were to die and the entail be diverted, Claire would lose her twelve thousand pounds. With astounding tactlessness, even for her, Claire wrote letters to Mary which hardly concealed the selfish reason for her solicitude for the health and safety of her beloved child. For a time, in the eighteen-thirties, she lived in London and saw Trelawny, but was firm in refusing to live with him, either in wedlock or out of it. She became a Roman Catholic, and, with time, an extremely quarrelsome and untruthful old woman. In the end she settled in Florence and died, at the age of eighty-one, in March 1879.

Lady Caroline Lamb became too much even for the patient William Lamb, and the inevitable separation at last came about. Her mind gave way, and she passed the last few years of her life in seclusion, either in London or at Brocket Hall, always guarded. Alone, crippled in body and in mind, she died in 1828 of dropsy, at only forty-three, six months before William Lamb became Viscount Melbourne. Their handicapped son, Augustus, lived to twenty-nine, sometimes leading a vegetable existence, sometimes breaking out into terrible rages. Then, on November 26, 1836, he died, after a brief and startling bout of sanity, in his father's presence.

Trelawny went back to his adventures with Odysseus, and married his third wife, the chieftain's twelve- or thirteen-year-old half sister, Tersitza. In June 1825 two British philhellenes,

Whitcombe and Fenlow, were bribed by Prince Mavrocordatos to assassinate him. Miraculously, Trelawny survived, though he suffered for three weeks with a shattered mouth and a locked jaw, unable to take more sustenance than water and yolks of egg. With immense courage he eventually forced his jaw open wide enough to enable him to eat a piece of wild boar's meat, and from then on made a slow recovery. Odysseus, a traitor to the Greeks, ended strangled at the foot of a tower. Trelawny went to Athens with Tersitza, and from there to the Ionian Islands, claiming British protection. Tersitza bore him a daughter, Zela, but disobeyed his orders not to wear anything but Greek dress and went to a party wearing a Parisian gown. Trelawny at once cut off her hair, in public. Tersitza refused to have anything more to do with him, and when she bore her next child sent the baby to him. It died, and Trelawny put its body in a box and returned it to her. By the age of seventeen Tersitza had succeeded in divorcing him.

By November 1828 Trelawny was back in England, and was seeing Mary Shelley. Disfigured by smallpox, she was living quietly with Percy Florence at Hastings, on the income allowed her by Sir Timothy Shelley, and writing. She had almost abandoned her old radical leanings, and was trying to restore Shelley's reputation with the orthodox. By the end of the year Trelawny had settled in Florence, determined to write his own life as a tribute to Shelley. Mary refused him any help with details to do with Shelley. His *Adventures of a Younger Son* was published in the autumn of 1831, and he at once became a literary lion.

Suddenly, in 1832 at the age of forty, Trelawny disappeared to America. After being nearly drowned in Niagara Falls, he returned in December 1834 with an American Indian girl, whom he soon abandoned. His ambitions to become a Member of Parliament never bore fruit. By 1838 his friendship with Mary Shelley had come to an end, and by 1839 he had vanished again—this time to a near-idyllic romance with a married woman, Augusta Goring. Her husband divorced her, they married, and Trelawny went, with his fourth wife, to farm in Wales. The idyll lasted until 1857, when Trelawny, at sixty-five, reverted to his taste for underage women and suddenly brought a young mistress to live in his house. The marriage broke up, and in 1858 Trelawny returned to London, taking his mistress with him.

That year Trelawny's *Recollections of the Last Days of Shelley and Byron* was published, and he was once again a literary lion. By then he had decided to revenge himself on Byron for his uncharitable remarks about him in his letters and journals published by Moore. So his recollections were full of stories to Byron's disadvantage—the rich poet's meanness to Mary Shelley in her distress, his slothfulness about leaving the safety of the Ionian Islands for Greece, his poor judgment, his jealousy, and his snobbery. He maintained that Byron could not box well and was not even a good swimmer.

Trelawny's love and admiration for Shelley, at least, survived. On August 13, 1881, he died at the age of eighty-nine, still a confirmed atheist. He had long since organized his funeral arrangements, and his body was embalmed and sent to Germany to be cremated. The ashes were then taken to Rome, where they were buried in the grave he had bought in 1823 in the Protestant Cemetery, beside those of Shelley and his dead child, William, and close to that of Keats. The spot had impressed Shelley with its beauty, and he had written:

> *Go thou to Rome—at once the paradise,*
> *The grave, the city, and the wilderness . . .*
> *Pass, till the spirit of the spot shall lead*
> *Thy footsteps to a slope of green access*
> *Where like an infant's smile, over the dead*
> *A light of laughing flowers along the grass is spread.*

There the old sinner was laid, with some lines from Shelley carved at his request on his tombstone.

These are two friends whose lives were undivided
So let their memory be now they have glided
Under the grave: let not their bones be parted
For their two hearts in life were single-hearted.

It was not the truth. Trelawny died, as he had lived, an incorrigible weaver of romantic fiction.

Of the servants, Byron's gondolier, Tita Falcieri, went back to Greece with Pietro Gamba. He came out of that experience alive but destitute, and became the valet of the young Mr. Disraeli, often regaling him with tales of Lord Byron. He married Disraeli's mother's maid, and became a messenger in the India Office—his beard as magnificent as ever but white. He was still going strong in 1870, wearing a very English bowler hat and a great watch chain. Trelawny's black groom, Benjamin Lewis, died of smallpox within a few months of landing in England.

Fletcher was given a small annuity by Hanson and Hobhouse. It was obviously inadequate, so he and Lega Zambelli decided to set up a macaroni factory. Lega had been given only a year's pay and thirty pounds for his homeward passage. He had left behind him his unworthy but much loved mistress, Fanny Silvestrini, and their child, Aspasia. He had written to her frequently, but had no reply. By October 1824 he was very worried, begging her to come to London with the child in the spring. Then Pietro Gamba called on him. He had had a letter from Teresa, saying, "Lega goes on writing to Fanny, but does he not know yet, poor thing, that she has been dead three months? Poor Lega." She had died, ill and in debt. The packet of savings Lega had sent to her had arrived too late to save her.

The factory was set up, but in 1835 when the duty was taken off foreign macaroni, it failed. Fletcher tried to persuade Hobhouse to help him, but neither he nor Augusta seem to have come to the rescue. After that Fletcher became a shabby and pathetic figure, and even served a term in a debtor's prison. He too had suffered from serving Byron. In the next generation, however, the story had a happier ending. Fletcher's elder son, William, had been in love with Lega's daughter, Aspasia, who had joined her father in England, since she was twelve years old, and in 1838 they married. They appear to have been happy together, though Lega Zambelli regarded it as a great comedown for the daughter of an unfrocked priest to marry the son of a valet.

Medora Leigh's life was disastrous. She was selfish, deeply ungrateful and a liar. She became pregnant when she was fifteen by her brother-in-law, Henry Trevanion, by her account with the connivance of his wife Georgiana, her sister, whom he brutalized. Without Augusta's knowledge Annabella and the seventh Lord Byron helped all three to leave England, and Medora's child was born at Calais in February 1830. She returned to live with her mother at St. James's Palace, and the child died in France after three months. By 1831 Medora was pregnant again by Trevanion. This time Augusta was informed and told her husband. With the aid of a solicitor and a Bow Street officer, Colonel Leigh removed Medora from the Trevanion household and put her in the strict charge of a landlady. Medora escaped and fled to France with Trevanion. She lived with him in Normandy for two years—the child was apparently stillborn—then went into a convent in Brittany at Augusta's expense. Pregnant for the third time, she left the convent, and in 1834 a daughter, Marie, was born at Quimper.

Trevanion later rejoined Medora, and they lived together, this time with Medora acting as a servant to his new mistress and being mistreated. Eventually, with money supplied by Augusta's half sister, the Countess of Chichester, she escaped to Pontivy. Next, in distress, she was anxious to sell her reversionary interest in a deed executed by Augusta in 1839, by which she would receive three thousand pounds on the deaths of her mother and Annabella. Augusta had retained the original deed, giving Medora only a legally attested copy, specifically in order to prevent what she was now trying to do and to provide for her daughter, Marie. With Annabella's help, Medora sued her mother for possession of the deed, and by 1841 she had succeeded in getting hold of it.

Delighted to be able to make mischief for Augusta, Annabella took responsibility for Medora and her child, affecting great love for her, and travelled abroad with them, even introducing Medora to her daughter Ada, and allowing her to call her by Byron's old nickname, "Pip." (Augusta, with only eight hundred pounds a year, was struggling to keep her husband, herself, her son Henry, Emily, and her servants, while giving her eldest son George a hundred pounds a year and her son Frederick two hundred pounds a year, to say nothing of providing for the now penniless Georgiana Trevanion and her three growing daughters.) Medora's greed and her determination to bleed Annabella dry knew no bounds. She created appalling scenes, and even Annabella could not control her.

In the end Medora refused to surrender the deed, which Annabella made a condition of her help, and disappeared from England with Marie. Still calling herself Madame Aubin, the name she and Trevanion had used, she arrived at the village of St. Affrique (Aveyron), halfway between Nimes and Toulouse, in November 1845, about eighteen months later. On January 27, 1846, she gave birth to a son, and that day a thirty-eight-year-old French soldier of peasant stock appeared—Jean Louis Taillefer of the Eleventh Hussars. He hailed from the village of Lapeyre, a few miles away. The baby was registered as Jean-Marie Taillefer, and Medora went with the child and Marie to settle at Lapeyre. In a year or so the hussar, by then out of the army, returned to marry her. She used her correct name—and Six Mile Bottom appeared on the marriage certificate as *Lix Mille Jostan*. Medora continued to call herself Madame Aubin nonetheless, and boasted that she was the daughter of a *grand seigneur*, a poet, genius and hero. On

August 28, 1849, she died of smallpox at the age of thirty-five. In her will she bequeathed all she possessed to her husband and Marie, who was then fifteen, her son presumably having died in infancy, and declared that she forgave her mother and all the others who had cruelly persecuted her. Marie herself showed signs of a bad heredity of instability and immorality. Her efforts to enlist Annabella's interest were ignored, and she died unmarried in a French convent while still in her thirties.

Annabella's behaviour throughout the Medora affair was very spiteful towards Augusta. She stooped to any weapon she could find to wound her, actually lying on at least one occasion, and revealed to many of her friends confidences which Augusta had made to her under the seal of secrecy.

It is possible that Medora was not Byron's daughter after all. She showed certain physical resemblances to Colonel Leigh, the most noteworthy being her height. Both Byron and Augusta were comparatively short, but Colonel Leigh and Medora were tall. The Colonel himself seemed never to have any doubt that she was his child.

Ada, Byron's only legitimate daughter, also had a sad history and gave unhappy proof of an unsound heredity. After a sickly childhood, during which she suffered from various illnesses ranging from nervous disorders to cholera, she delighted her mother by capturing the rich, ambitious and very eligible William, eighth Lord King. She married him in 1835 at the age of nineteen. By 1838 Annabella had persuaded her cousin William Lamb, by then Viscount Melbourne and Prime Minister, to have him created Earl of Lovelace.

Ada was eccentric, impractical and extremely ambitious to achieve fame as a mathematician. She was also a pretty, highly intelligent and gifted woman who could be charming when she pleased. She seemed to have everything to live for—an adoring, if rather mean, husband; two sons and a daughter; and the prospect of a large fortune when her mother died. Yet by her early thirties she was deep in debt, because of her compulsive gambling on the horses, and suffered from chronic and distressing ill health. Like her father, she borrowed money from anyone who would lend it to her, including her banker and the family solicitors, always under the seal of secrecy.

When Lovelace, at last alerted to the situation on both counts, went to Annabella in distress, she blamed him roundly for the financial catastrophe, sanctimoniously refusing all help, and made light of her daughter's illness. (Her chief hobby might be said to have been her own ill health, and she indulged in frequent "deathbed" crises, which the family had to attend.) Unknown to them both, Ada was having a love affair with a young married man, John Crosse, also addicted to betting on the horses, which would lead to blackmail.

Worse was to come. Ada pawned the Lovelace jewels, a diamond parure, for a mere eight hundred pounds, and had a reproduction made in paste to conceal their absence. Annabella, if grudgingly, agreed to redeem them, pay the interest, pay for the reproduction, and conceal the transaction from Lovelace.

As Ada's death, from cancer of the womb, drew nearer, Annabella moved into the house, dismissed all the servants, including Ada's personal maid, and delivered sermons to her, directed to making her confess and repent of her sins. Astonishingly, as she lay dying in agony, Ada succeeded in having the newly redeemed jewels pawned once more by Crosse, who had come to see her.

This time Lovelace was told the truth. Worse, he had to endure Ada's deathbed confession about her affair with Crosse, and, after her death, pay that gentleman a stiff price for her love letters so that they could be destroyed.

Ada died on November 27, 1852, at the same age as her father, thirty-six. She had asked that her coffin should be laid with his in the Byron family vault, and that her memorial tablet should state that she was laid there at her own request.

Ada's body travelled to Nottingham by the Midland Railway—a very different journey from that of her father's. Once again the hearse journeyed from Nottingham to Hucknall Torkard, but the mourners came by special train. Lovelace, the seventh Lord Byron, and Colonel Wildman attended it, but Annabella was not present. Ada's coffin was laid, with some difficulty, beside her father's and touching it. Later Lord Lovelace put up a tablet to his wife:

In the Byron vault below
lie the remains of
Augusta Ada
only daughter of
George Gordon Noel
sixth Lord Byron
and wife of
William, Earl of Lovelace.

Born 10th December 1815
Died 27th November 1852

He had not carried out Ada's request that her memorial tablet should read she had been laid there at her own request.

Ada was not the only daughter of Lord Byron. It was not until 1938, one hundred and sixteen years after her death, that a small plaque was placed close to the entrance to the vault.

It reads—in the words drafted by Byron himself as he grieved for her at Pisa, intending them for a memorial to her in Harrow Church:

In memory of Allegra
daughter of George Gordon Lord Byron
who died at Bagnacavallo
in Italy, April 20th 1822
aged five years and three months.

I shall go to her but she shall not return to me.
2 Samuel XII.22.

BB January 22, 1938.

The child who, because she was illegitimate, had been refused more than an unmarked grave in an unconsecrated part
of the cemetery at Harrow-on-the-Hill, had at last been given
a place, however small, among her ancestors.

Byron's own memorial in the same church stands under a
handsome bas-relief of his head in profile with the words "The
Pilgrim of Eternity" beneath it. It reads:

In the vault beneath
where many of his ancestors and his mother are buried
lie the remains of

GEORGE GORDON NOEL BYRON

LORD BYRON OF ROCHDALE

IN THE COUNTY OF LANCASTER
the author of Childe Harold's Pilgrimage.

He was born in London on the 22nd January 1788.
He died at Missolonghi, in Western Greece
on the
19th April 1824
engaged in the glorious attempt to restore
that country to her ancient freedom and renown.

The words follow: "His sister, the Honourable Augusta
Mary Leigh, placed this tablet to his memory."

Augusta, whom Byron had called "the *one* whom I most
loved," had done that, at least, for him.

* * *